CW00796010

Shamanic Warriors Now Poets

Shamanic Warriors Now Poets

an anthology of

Poetry, Prose, Paintings, Photographs,
Collages and Drawings

edited by

J. N. Reilly & Ira Cohen

R & R Publishing
Glasgow

First Published in 2003
by R & R Publishing
Glasgow, Scotland.

Dustjacket Painting: *Astral Body Aware* by Mati Klarwein.

Design: J. N. Reilly.

British Library Cataloguing-in-Publication Data:
A catalogue record for this book is available from the British Library.

ISBN: 0 9534280 1 X

Printed and Bound by
The Bath Press, Gt. Britain.

Dedicated to departed friends

Ronnie Burk

Gregory Corso

Mati Klarwein

Marty Matz

Vali Myers

Philip Whalen

Open the gate of your soul and get out and breathe.
With a sigh you can open the gate it took a hurricane to close.

Vicente Huidobro

Contents

List of Illustrations

Welcome

We have gathered together
four generations of counter-culture artists
there is no other kind of artist
veritable warriors fighting on the frontiers of existence
battling against the cruelties of consumerist culture
stripping away lies and untruths
severing chains of prejudice and slavery
to reveal the source of freedom.

Exemplars of ecstasy
now stripped to the bone
now clothed in light
now inviting you to take the cure
to the long journey home
through constellations of being, grief, despair and death
sustained by viatica of visions and the entheogenic experience
to heal yourself in the crucible of compassion
to create yourself in the light of love.

We hope you will join us.

J. N. Reilly

Marty Matz

A Funny Thing Happened On My Way To Enlightenment

I have lost my shadow
In a field of improvised whispers
Forgotten my name
In the fragrance of poppies
Where ornamental skulls
Erratically orbit
Luminous gardens
Of fugitive clocks ticking umber blossoms
Through secret winters that bite
There are unscheduled chimes above
A meadow where malignant toadstools hide
Among the false echoes of ancient invocations
And distorted reflections
From a river stained by time
I have marched down streets
Of embalmed moonlight
Howling like a mad dog
Seeking some bone of truth
Some final curtain
Some ultimate destination
Free from the synthetic octave of dreams
And I have unravelled the knitted mask of years
Searching for a way
To return to my green drenched childhood
Yet caught only occasional glimpses
Of a past gilded by imagination
In a forest of elusive trees
The calendar has devoured the decades
Turned my beard silver
In the blink of an eye
As I passed my life shooting craps with destiny
In the pursuit of worthless things
Yet I have never hesitated
To throw away my wallet
To make room in my pockets for poems or rainbows
Which I carried
Till the rainbows turned
To tattered colors
And the poems
Became just dust

In Search of Paititi

for Roger and Irvyne Richards

In search of Paititi
The soul must go
Beyond the last known port of call
Along a coast of deserted seasons
And unrecorded skies
Outside
The ancient realm of time
The last unconquered border
In the undiscovered mountains
Of the mind
A journey for life
That sometimes begins
At the instant of death
As infinity collapses upon itself
Relinquishing sovereignty
Over the flesh
In a system
Within a system
Within a system
In a dream
That spirals toward the light
As the universal energy transforms
And is refined
Moves freely beyond the edge
Of macrocosmic limitations
And is aware
That orange
Is but the brilliance of blue
Made incandescent
In a pig iron crucible
Of magnetized constellations
Reflecting
No eternal cancer
Exposing
No galactic destination
No horizon of perfect truth
Wisdom speaks by the green light of hummingbirds
In the archaic tongue of trees
And many who seek it
Are forever lost
In the lustrous ache

Of forgotten sensations
In childhood Decembers
In the bittersweet taste
Of yesterday's dishevelled rains
Lost without exit
And lost without hope
Under a shadow of fractured eclipses
In the winter's unharvested shade
In some marinated angle
Some secret perspective
Some hidden trapezoid
Some mechanized equator
Or occulted wrinkle
On the invisible longitude of madness
In money's frozen smile
In explosions of endless expansions
In gullies and canyons of time

Pipe Dream #1

for Herbert Huncke

There are sacrificial whispers
To the north
Beyond the River Ping
Where elephant dreams
Dress in yellow leaves
And ancient spirits
Wing down the barrel of my pipe
The hills are drenched
With poppy blood
And a red moon
Drowns
At the edge of my molten eye
This is the land
Of the reclining Buddha
The little wheel
The water buffalo's last dance
This is the place
Of green legends
Of silk and teak
Where incense mingles
With a cobra's breath
And in these hills alone
The chef
With his lamp
Is King

The Currents of My Life

for Bruce and Holly Hoberman

The currents of my life
Flow
Through a phosphorus ocean
Of ashes and runaway laughter
Where planets and stars
Like fugitive barrels gone mad
Roll down stone steps
To bite open the dawn
With teeth of light
So that I may clearly see
All those roads
That lead to a disaster of crabs
On a wounded beach
Or illuminate that space
Where umbrellas of pain
Pierce cascades of love
Beneath a landslide of invisible equators
And inedible dreams
My head is a buzzing hollow
Filled
With blimps
Renegade astrologies
And alphabet seas
In the palms of my hands
A secret November lies buried
An ancient rainbow burns
Yet
In my heart
No diminished symphonies
Sing in the pockets of squeamish winds
No ivory shadows
Tusk the Palaeolithic schemes
Nor do abandoned moons
Sleep over skeleton rivers
Still
There is a truant season
When luminous wheels are crucified
And the taste of fossil footprints
Are stitched to the corners of cosmic rains
Then the price of stone
Shall surprise the yellow sky

And mountains of bison
Shall suck the skulls of locomotives
Along plains of forgotten flowers
And Indian graves
Then iron tears
Shall nourish a destiny of formless pistols
Planted with the corn

Ode For Bob Yarra

Friend
Explain to me your crystal rivers
The uncrowded geometry of your brilliant dawn
Show me the sky's bark
The skin of prehistoric beaches
The grand calculus of insect shells
The algebra of tears
Help me
To forget
A herd of tired moons long dead
Where Incan memories and exotic dreams
Stain the broken stones of time
Let us soar then
You and I
Beyond the confines of planet and satellite
To reach that somewhere place
Not in this land or the next
Where the sun is rising
Shining pure
On beauty without interruption

I Know Where Rainbows Go To Die

On the death of Bob Kaufman

I know where rainbows go to die
I followed your footprints
Across a strange uncharted land
Where silver whispers tried to hide
Beneath demented shadows
And oboe skies
Together we walked through a fabled city
Of hallucinating green
And talked away
A thousand smoking nights
As your aching heart
Beat its bones
In time to Bird's brilliant sounds
Over the neon streets of murdered schemes
Yes I was there
And I saw your love proclaimed
In a fractured smile
Like yesterday's headlines printed in blood
On a bumble bee's wings
And yes
I would wear your eyes
On January 12th
The dawn came up
Singing the blues
The calendar fell apart
In the face of that wounded Sunday
And the redwoods wept
At your passing
But no bell tolled in the bowels of winter
The snail did not grin
At the grandfather clock
Nor did any roses grow
From the tail of a rusting comet
Only a woolly starfish groaned
On a beach of stolen planets
As a tattooed lizard
Shed its suit of cold echoes
And you danced with Harlem's great King
Down the alleys of paradise
To a feast of blazing umbrellas

I remember
Long gone doorways
Where ancient dealers leaned
And sold their twenty dollar bags of dreams
To those in need
And poet
I saw you buy the truth
In a red balloon
And like some mythical alchemist
You cooked up the blood of stars
But instead of death
You drew music from your spoon

Like A Bolt of Green Lightning

for Barbara A. Matz

Like a bolt of green lightning
I have been struck
By prowling Celtic shadows
And the lingering aroma
Of your December hair
I want to go beyond the edge of silver clocks
Alien passages
And mirrored seasons
To touch the sensuous mystery
Of your flowering depths
And rest at the edge of a wondrous sea
Where I shall speak with castaway shells
And unscramble
The secret of petrified songs
I want to be the hammer
That sounds your silent bell
Whose resonance resides in the dawn
Invisible as a gull's wing
On a frosted piece of marble
I know what I have seen
And I am caught
For who would prefer the jingle of gold earrings
Once he has heard
Jade
Growing in a stone

No Magic Egypt Ever Blooms

for Antonio Bertoli

Let solar tides erode my aching shoulders
And opal songs
Cushion my battered knees
Worn thin
By the abrasive architecture
Of alabaster crystals and ivory winds
I shall sail on a tattooed ocean
Of polychrome skulls and feathered glyphs
To a convenient spot
From which to watch
Some unknown star
Unscroll a green horizon of ancient murmurs and copper bells
For I have gone
To the other side
Of the butterfly's tangerine smile
Where blood shatters
Under the icy hammer
Of a blue December's swirling agate sky
And I saw a woodcarver
Skin the winter's echo
From an antique moon
Gone mad
And I understood in the foundation of my bones
That there
In that place
Over zippered fields of unripened smoke
And baroque hallucinations
No magic Egypt ever blooms
No final destination of burning peninsulas
Or liquid dimensions
Could I reach
So instead went hunting
For my own reflection
With a net of velvet elbows
But only caught
The motion of occasional dawns
Whose mystery sleeps on
In the visible harmony of pepper trees
While snakes
Those ancestral enemies
Still drowse
In the shadow of tropic urns
And a tormented equator weeps

Rupert M. Loydell

Instructions for The Journey

1.

Burn coffee until the smell hangs in the corner of your room. Try to read while the radio offers up small sounds and bursts of noise. Attempt a tightrope walk between possibilities.

Breathe in the bitter aroma, black and sticky in your throat. Listen to new music. Read last year's newspapers, their fading glossy supplements and unengaging book reviews. Aim for isolation and abandonment.

Consume novels you would not otherwise read. Do not bother with the sights proposed by your guide book. Move within the landscape, accumulating detail. Speculate on your past. Possess superficial scraps of detail.

Produce an inventive Postmodern recombination of Modernist components. Go out for a newspaper and at the same time buy a pepper steak. In such fragments can be found the key to the whole enterprise.

Your definition of the aesthetic may be broader, but demand reverence from each viewer. It is an idea of change, dramatic in its own quiet fashion. Tranquil oases and rhythmic inflections articulate the relationships among diverse spaces.

Eastern thought is no less admissible for a Westerner than is European thought. Draw nearer to the process which is the world we live in. Keep everything from the past tucked out of sight.

You are on your way. In this context it is possible to return.

2.

Sit writing at a table. Imagine a clock in a glass case. Read in bed or in a deckchair on the lawn.

Operate entirely outside of discussion. Make plans that are more interesting. Keep the excitement intact.

Make your living from robbing tombs. Accept diverse structures as valid. Become open to all possibilities.

Eliminate social problems. Wipe away centuries of class division, inserting a layer of ironic distance.

Discourage rhetorical activity. Battle against the impotence of the materials at hand. Be rapid, detailed and determined.

Use television more naturally. Incorporate faith into a novel. Recognise the need to speak to god.

Carefully refabricate memory. The past is less fictional than the present.

3.

Reduce your life to a book full of cuttings, photos, mementoes, one or two watercolours by a lover. A book small enough to carry with you everywhere.

Live for the moment, needing no more than to simply be. Breathe in the sunlight and walk among trees, content to trace one's finger in the dust.

When you are in the dark, swim toward the light. Do not be afraid. Remember a promise you once made.

Embrace the moment and seek the light. Let judgement and memory go.

Trace one's finger in the dust, shake the sand from one's shoes. Turn and meet the day.

Know that morning is coming. Smile in the dark while you wait for the dawn.

Converse with strangers and do not despise your differences. Let the people you find yourself with be simply who they are.

Sing in the dusk, pray in the morning. Stay silent and accompany the one who always needs to speak on their journey.

If you are in the dark, sing about the light. Do not be afraid, you will remember nothing except a promise you once made.

Leave your life behind like a book, pages fluttering in the breeze, photos and cuttings lost for ever or treasured by a lover.

Let your life become dust. Turn and face the light.

Traces

He saw the world as a series of vertical marks, isolated in the landscape: trees, streetlamps, drainpipes, distant figures: reference points that provided a way of moving through the world.

Under this tree he'd stood and sheltered in the rain during a summer storm. After a few minutes he'd run for home, arriving at the front door with his shirt stuck to him, his trousers and shoes dripping. He'd left damp footprints along the wooden hall floor.

He often left a trail of invisible hieroglyphics in the street as he avoided treading on the cracks and dodged fallen leaves, notating his journey through the sidestreets.

Under the picture glass a dot or two of white dust on the black oil paint, trapped in the frame. A distraction to the eye.

When he held the syrup-coloured soap up to the window faint marks from the nailbrush caught the filtered light.

The Architecture of Memory

for Roselle Angwin

In time everything comes together; and rather than command words to hop to it, it is better to enter chaos, where words swim under the raw eyes of naivety, anxious to reveal meaning and create human interest, easing us closer to unnatural realms.

I register creation hollering and try to listen, expecting the cacophony to clear. A voice rings from close by; I hope in time to ease into the chorus, upset radiophonic ecstasy and invite the past to enter. Charging in it reinvents each one of us. Arguably it recharges too; change might heal more than it tricks us into.

Reaching out for the comfort of memory, we cling to upset and wound instead of exchanging agony for hope or truth, ruin the chance to heal the damage. Usable rapture exists at a distance from reverence or experience, under the rubric of eternity. There, expectation and nostalgia are ritually employed to monitor the consistency of time, turn us upside down, and cut through any resistance.

Hit me with infrastructure then ease me towards closure. I am insistent.

An Undestroyable Hush

for Ray

'Form is finite, an undestroyable hush over all things.'
Charles Wright

A bundle of candles bound in handmade paper and shells lie on the shelf. Two lit candles flicker, their light shining in drops of condensation on the tiled bathroom walls, one flame reflected in the dark uncurtained window.

°

Today we talked about our fathers, about death and cancer.

Tonight I read a story about a doppelgänger haunting a traveller lost in India, about how one can be torn apart when shadowed or preceded by oneself.

I know I'm responsible for my own actions, but often feel lived through, not quite in control, jostled along strange corridors of possibility.

°

The candle sputters – some imperfection in the rich wax, maybe moisture in the air. The water perceptibly cools around me.

°

Today we talked of absent fathers and the need to challenge ourselves, our common desire for change: the frequent wish to move on – sometimes literally, sometimes only artistically or intellectually.

My paintings shrink in size, and diminish in my own estimation as I move away from them in time and dedication. I am bound up in other people's lives, and remain desperate for time for myself, numb when I find it.

°

Today we drank coffee and hung dreams and secrets in the air.

Tonight candles are the only light I need as I wash the day away.

°

3am. The moon is so bright a bird believes it is dawn breaking, bursts into song.

Shaman

My father does not like the dreams
of splintered flesh, of fur and skin.
Coloured dream cloak aswirl,
immersed in the fabric of time,
he bleeds strings of memory.

Sometimes he makes a rain charm:
a figure with a wound in its mouth
chipped from castaway wood
into the simple shape of man.
Its songs are the sounds of the spirits.

In the clutches of this magic
my father strikes a nail in hard
for every promise that he makes.
I have been crucified many times,
I scream of fire and burnt black bone.

In the clearing, corded wood,
neatly stacked. In the shadows
visitors wait to enter dreams.
In the house of the priest king
our ancestors' voices are heard:

Hold still and rest in the sacred spaces.
Mouth, stay silent. Feathers, fly no more.
I jump through the hoop, leave the sacred circle.
The cloak hangs around me, frayed and torn.
I clutch at the memory. How time lies.

Michael Rothenberg

Saved

Saved by the dream weavers
Saved by the spirit catchers
        The mythologizers
           and the Bedouins
               of Zen
Saved by the music, the hermits
        in their Talmudic jazz
               monasteries
           and their mountain
lookouts stored with noodles,
           black fungi & Merlot
Saved by their humor and curses
           and dizzy outbursts
Strung out on antibiotics, insulin
               and Prozac
        in the contemplation
            of the one and the
               multitudes,
        the leaf and the cabaret
            of too many spoken
                   words
Saved, Saved,
Saved all over again
               All over town
        and through the hurricanes
               of passive repressive
                    amnesia
Saved to put
               a hat on, wear
        a red coat, look at a
               cloud & see a
                    dragon
Saved to be surprised
               for the day I
        could be surprised
        by generous loving
        and welcome more

Spirit Catchers

You called them Spirit Catchers
The hollowed boulders, climbed
inside to be remembered, Pig Eye The Mystic
Your staff was an ordinary branch, naked and taller than you
To poke the nesting rattlesnakes
Grinning, your arms spread around the waists of women
Thick-waisted women in black
who rang the heavy bells, The Public Mourners
You drank tequila with them, danced with them
while men with crow black eyes listened through the adobe
You told me the women are Spirit Catchers too
I wanted to be you, to dance in the wake of their solemn skirts
Slipping over stones, I climbed inside a boulder
I remember the sky, it was blue and mountainous!

°

Which century is it?
To pin things
Who will I be in the family bible in the antique shop in rural Vermont
among saucers of Niagara Falls John Lennon memories
when dinosaurs walk this violet soil?

°

And what about you, Pig Eye The Mystic
Monster in my skull
Preacher of non-sectarian verse at home with wife and tripe
Will you still know me when I come singing Hasidic haiku?
I followed you into the desert questioning my faith
It's not your fault, I was going that way
But drunk, you inferred, the way you held your liquor
inferred each boulder, each dark-eyed woman
would blossom with god-spirits
Displaced spirits, I said, move with shame
"Anger," you said, " they move with anger!"
The sky shreds
Earth screams of cicada!
Ayyyyy!
I only wish the sky would empty me of my demons
And you a demon among them!

Black As The Celebration of The Soul

for Luis Baptista, on news of his death

I've done so much I feel like
It's someone else's life
I'm looking at remembering
Cunnilingus Inflections
And other psychedelic illustrations
drawn by an 11 year old girl
like stigmata
on the laundered
gateway of a coastal suburb
30 years after her mother took LSD

It's raining silhouettes
On the brightest day of a Miami year
I swallow pink orchids
Palm trees hallucinate
on their own milk
Some things just die
The blight is systemic
Honey-colored death
infects the fevered brooms
that once were nests to moonlight
City gardeners on cherry pickers
Hydraulic thrones
groan upwards
Bring down the slant curved
headless spines
that once swayed and swept the sky

Now naked in memory
Naked in mourning
There's no way out of memory
And I am reaching
with tired vanity towards
Remembrances of
a hummingbird Kingdom of Now

Phantom, Come Hither!

for Ira Cohen & Mary Sands

You're not having enough Fun or smoking enough Dope
Or opening up your Head or Heading Open
Or reaching into the "Akashic Record"
So you must go to the "Cosmic Hotel"
Check into the honeymoon suite
Give the cashier all your money, your last red cent
Order room service on credit
Dine on grilled salmon in saffron and dill
With a side order of hot crispy Paisley French Fries
Pay tribute to the grave robbers and the master
Drive-thru vagabond, Francois Villon
Magicians of affliction and permission
And the onion-headed cathedrals of Moscow

Break open the sky
Bring down a shatter of stars
And let the star-shattered shower
Fall on Orange County igniting the memory
Of bulldozed orange groves into a rage of red-orange fire
A banquet of bubbling fruit, incense of oily rinds
Spill your intimate juices on a map of the Cyber Mind
Map the trail where lost dreamers go
This is not a day for archives or libraries
Or documentaries in honor of Olympic Spirit
This is the Olympian Moment
The homecoming of Creation and Uncreation

Leave the Beat to silence, find the silence
Beat bloody bone on bleached bone, restore the beat
Pounding the Kaleidoscope of Human Misery back into motion
Toast to the suffering, lie without shame
In a bramble of thorny sweet roses
Run in a terrible glee through the horrifying field of
Avant-garde Pinocchios
Black and white noses standing like scarecrows
On the face of a child bound in the highwires of signal control
Dancing in Idaho, Iowa, Ohio and Indiana cornfields
Drink to the masked Hula Dancers
Engorged on love
Have fun because that's what suffering is for

There is no time for a series of somber contemplations
Or leaning on a rain rattled lamppost
Smoking a cigarette with a blind eye turned toward a puddle
That is without reflection of past, present or future
Blow blue smoke into the skylights of the dying city!
Swim in the rain pools that course through the bric-a-brac
Of this consuming culture shrinking from anorexia
Dodging paranormal genies on Persian carpets
While the sun goes up and down and up
And down and you shed your skin
And I shed my skin and die and die

With every breath
Death-click, enlargement, refraction, replication, scan
Of the photographic Mind Horizon
Join me now, you're holding on too tightly to your rule book
Operating manual, life
You don't need your life
Everything is in its place
There's no reason anymore for clinging or marrying
Or attachments to a sofa bed
Step outside and scream at the Daughters of Hell
I am waiting for you
Ghost draped in flesh
Waiting for you to turn me on

Renée Gregorio

As Myth I Am No Longer Woman

It's been 15 years of this silence.
But last year at Café Trieste I saw you again,
older, gray, being a poet in Italy.

I met your best friend, of all the thousands
I might have found in that bay city,
there she was and there I was and suddenly

you emerged in photograph to stun me
out of a silence I thought would never end,
into a speech that made clear the myth I'd become.

Freeze-framed, I sat before a woman I'd never met
who said she knew everything about me. My heart
convulsed to be reduced to the ash of that former life,

To see you again.
And who have you become in that huge space
between those moments and this one?

All that's left to know: your poems
still break my heart. But we are beyond such breaking,
the air between us long made stale. Then, I was more

than I ever knew of myself. And you seemed expanded,
lovely by high-rise, canal, in desert's clean heat.
Even saying goodbye to you felt clean —

I knew I'd never see you again.
I recall your back receding down an empty corridor
in an airport I've never returned to.

Since then, my love, other loves and a death
that shattered what was left of me, much
rebuilding far from home to find home.

Once we were like Tristan and Iseult, unable to escape,
from the start, the relief of being so fully seen, the potion
we must have drunk to open our eyes that way.

If you loved what was darkest in me, I loved
your dark all the way back, till what we made
could no longer show us the way through.

When Tristan was wounded a second time and the only
healing possible had to come from the fair Iseult, she comes
from Cornwall on a ship bearing the white sail of yes.

The lie that ends his life comes from the lips of the second
Iseult. She names the sail: black. He cannot bear
being abandoned by the one who released him into love.

And dies without knowing he hadn't been.
Maybe all love outside the daily is mythical — out of time
and space and larger than the mundane life can offer.

It's true that as myth I am no longer woman.
It's true that all I could have done is love you
in full light of day, among laundry, coffee-scent, soot of the city.

I've learned to read maps, though now the print's too small to see.
I am the age you were when we first met.
And it's true those dark roads we drove down were real,

headlights barely broke that dark and we saw
other cars emerge behind us, then disappear,
and figures materialize behind Joshua trees.

But we made nothing up. Past leaks into present, still —
most days I can't tell when one stops and the next begins.
It's true this never ends and I speak to you as I speak to my dead

and, like them, sometimes I hear you speak back
out of this great silence we must occupy.

Aikido Tanka

the body's stiffness
yielding, yielding, to the stick
from scatter to warmth
the body gives in slowly
I followed it as if it knew

mistake after mistake
you say this is satori
immobilized first
by the most basic pin
all of myself put to the ground

contemplating if
there's a way to get it right
repeating technique
endless loop of practice
I pin you   you pin me

cycle of ripening
wrist swept over, elbow turned
spin and kneel on ground
hardened by the crush of foot-soles
pin uke heart-first to the mats

I want to go straight in
if I get the angle right
elbow below wrist
controlled tangle of bodies
you go down so easily

what I love is the way
you come at me with all force
the way I can turn
and without question you follow
and without question you fall

the pin comes from hip,
not hand — in fact, everything
we do here, not mind
but *hara*   *put your mind in your hips*,
he said. At first I didn't know how

the fall as crucial
as the throw, learning to move
away from pressure
into flow, away from pain
down to your knees to gain strength

one must commit
everything to get results, yes?
he worked for years on emptiness
cultivating nothing
that approached or that went away

attack equals force,
something propelled onward
something to work with
if you give me nothing
then nothing comes back

imagine body
as sword, pinkie-edge of hand
as blade — blade twisted
toward center, awkward movement
that turns force into dance

in the heat of swirl
of thrust and shape and dive
heart of encounter
I let him enter my sphere
close in, where anything can happen

John Brewster

Merlin's Meditation

for R

I sit upon the oldest stone
and stare through webs of rain
at one more village burrowed deep
into a valley's grain.

I count the lines upon my feet
to tell me where I am
and measure time through lavender
and space through lemon balm.

I hear my daughter bringing wood
to warm our souls by flame
she was the mother of my fire
when ice became my name.

I see the stars predict the past
as evening shadows night
the wand of Merlin is a sword
that wounds the dark with light.

Wordings

Some need their wording
propped up and hinged;
others, standing
ecologically correct.
But I need mine
falling as child-cast twigs,
divining line through space.

The Angel of Death

The snow gathers,
plump and white
as a dove's breast.
I trudge through fields
of it, trailing my long
black wings behind me.

Eventually
I reach the place
of my deliverance.
I enter unseen,
but to be sure
I hunch my dark feathers
closer to my face.

Children collect around me
like workers round the queen,
drawing me into this hive
of industry.
Naked I am made
but my wings retract
from all perishing sight.

A door closes
and the bees drift into piles,
frozen in their flight.
A door opens
and the ants carry them off,
brittle wings for leaves.

I walk into the counting square.
The ants are burning leaves
believing it is autumn.
I raise my canopy of night
one last time, till the snow
settles like stars on my plumage.

A winter of eternity is over.
My witnessing is finished.
The Angel of death lives.

Frame

Frame the sky
and there is always one cloud
that drifts past the edge
one bird that darts beyond corners
one star that glints above trim

Frame the sea
and there is always one wave
that rolls over mounts
one fish that skips across borders
one splash that soaks the canvas

Frame the self
and there is always one sigh
that moans through backings
one tear that runs down the brickwork
one smile that shatters the glass

Pastorale

for Blaise Cendrars

Mulberry kites reel
silken cocoons of the sky:
ribbons of laughter.

Kimonos flutter
geisha eyes on washing lines:
flags of banzai love.

Shinto's wet nipples
hang out of Confucian mouths
drowsy for Buddha.

Suzumishi sings;
the peal of evening blossom:
cherry, plum and peach.

The Falling Spring

Waving
crests of fringe and flame
and fluted peaks of plume
with medieval flowering
rose-braid
the tresses of the glade
in tails of hanging bloom

Passing
trees of veil and glow
and open-strung of sky
with guardian imagining
pan-pipe
the rhythms of the shade
in shimmerings and sigh

Running
shafts of breath and kiss
on dappled hills of horse
with seasonal deflowering
sun-tongue
the ears of meadowland
to come before the gorse

7 POEMS

CHARLES HENRI FORD

Happy Birthday, Mao Tse-Tung

Like Attila the Hun
A moon rabbit is a chained wanderer
Beauty cannot be proved
It is the murmur of an unseen ocean
Smoke signals from a cult of fragments
It is a dust-cloud hypothesis
A beheaded stream
A Chinese poem whose purpose is chemistry of mind

Adding to the mysteries of mimicry
Eyelashes on a topaz become entangled
The chandelier of sugar skulls is blurred
And there's a boom shot of the rotten neck
A sooty blotch of clover
While a white fly emerges from your mouth

Psychology of The Terrorist

The flood potential of a returnable bottle
Is found in the true angle of a flaring object
Tiaras of colored fire shall be
Removed by the black arm of cotton
And a duplicate source of delight
Is the fallacy of origins
Crumbling ice-walls communicate
With bells on poles and with iron umbrellas

The faded magnificence of emerald ponds
Pre-figures the death-trap of a counterclockwise game
The Legend of Myself, theme of circularity,
Like a strangler without a victim, whose rhythmic signature
Discarded and discovered on ladders and scaffolding
Denies that immortality is ever interrupted

Concupiscence Multiple

With an elaborate wail
The womb strapped with Joseph Cornell anklets
Heads for the treasure-hunter in the desert,
An extraordinarily sophisticated inventor
In absolute control of time dissolves,
Contradictory voices and hallucinatory fugues
The moment they meet, vulture flowers drip with the white blood of love
Javelins of recording consciousness remain aloof

While an odor of decompression sickness forms a wall
Blasphemies opulent as algae-blooms
Are quickly deciphered and as quickly forgotten
On the borderland of transport they take leave of each other
One of them wire-guided, at zero gravity
The other, Ari Ho-Chen, pocketing the perfect title:
There's a Vapor Dome on The Day Coach

For Ira

We are the severings of a serpentine mirror
Reflections from nowhere, the pieces grow together
Shake like thrones. Voracious elephants
Display their imperceptible mobility
Exquisite in poverty, rich robes hide you from astonishment
Silverpoints of chiselled kneecaps screech like avarice
Girls, conscious of the virginity of boys, increase their pace
The lesson of being cornered: Get what you want
You have given everything: male jewels
Unnatural dimensions of a Prodigal son
The Goddess of Smallpox has not felt your face
Her kisses leave their identity
Another shadow edges toward the one I know
(What is less or more than a touch?)
The jealousies you arouse are prongs in seas of brightness
Secrets of arson, mauve tripe in the slot machine
Mark the flora and fauna of a missing person

○

Less dust on her leg now, the urine flows downward
Metaphysical rat family, may your firstborn inherit
The gift of impersonality
Sacred hermaphrodite, stymied in a marble procession
Nausea of non-love ethereal as eyeballs
Peeling the scorched skin from your chestbone
The scent of muscle revives me
Counterfeiters of chastity exude a special perfume
Reasonless perversions corner us cold
Suits of armor manufactured as fantasy
Kindness ends in the coils of concupiscence
Drives a stake through the heart of Eros
Haunted eyes encircle our every gesture
Diaphanous as words that describe a heinous crime

○

Is he a blood relation of yours
The one who has not left the grandstand?
He is manacled with a V-shaped instrument
And partially blind. The race
Is over, if there ever was one
I arrived too late for the ranting
Throngs wearing dunce-caps are leaving the enclosure
An appalling rainstorm is said to be on the way
One of the drivers will be struck by lightning
On the racecourse, flares have been set
To what purpose, shall I ask someone?
But there is no one to ask
Except for the unattended spectator
I signal to him, opening and closing
My futuristic umbrella, he removes his hat
A puff of illuminated smoke rises, lingering
Shall I call to him or remain speechless?
I know he is pretending not to see me
They are using the arena for a firing range
To get to him I shall need the courage of church spires
Eggs are balanced on the chessboard of longing
Now he is stroking a giant feather
I go towards him, I am stranded in the Great Beyond

O

This is the story of fire without flames
This is a longing for goals without honor
Halt, Messenger of Immortality
You in my arms, it is myself I hold
My substance is upon you
Meeting you calls for another moulting
A new name and I shall continue to exist
Your left side is next to mine, no one explains why
Idols which line Obsession Avenue remind us of each other
Placing my hand on yours I know reason and unreason
Longing has nothing to do with knowing
Loving is the symbol of indestructibility
Mothers of monsters, you have seen them give birth
I accept you without desperation
The day I find you will bring truth to illusion
You disappear without having been deserted
I am glutted with your strangeness
My awkwardness only makes you more graceful
Put your trust in me, I shall be inspired by falsehood
To deny is to copulate without possessiveness
If tomorrow you are the same I shall await the day after
Your teeth are white as white radishes
Before you wore these clothes they were not holy

Hans Plomp

Bahubali

Two naked gentlemen are walking ahead of me with a slow, swaying gait. They carry small brooms in their hands with which they gently sweep the road in front of them where their feet will tread. Hesitating to overtake them, I slow down my pace. But it's still quit a distance to Sravanabelagola. Finally I take courage and pass the men with a word of salutation. To my astonishment they turn out to be very old. Their backs, buttocks and legs gave no indication of their age. But their features are those of wise old gentlemen. They wear a piece of cloth over their mouths. I estimate them to be well over seventy, one of them probably much older. They radiate such friendliness I feel bold enough to begin a conversation. In English I ask them how far still to Sravanabelagola. The celebrations to anoint the gigantic statue of Lord Bahubali, a Tirthankar or Finder of the Path of the Jain religion, will be taking place there. The younger gentleman answers me in perfect English: "We have about three more miles to go."

He notices my surprise and looks at me with an ironic twinkle in his eyes, saying: "I'm a graduate of Cambridge University."

Their brooms sweep automatically. I don't feel at ease, walking on the unswept road with my shoes on.

The Jain religion originates from the same time as Buddhism, around 2500 years before the present. India now counts some 3½ million Jains, forming a thriving commercially inclined community. Often the men give up their wordly lives after fifty, to become *Munis*. They renounce their sometimes considerable wordly possessions. Those of the Digambara Path, the Sky Clad, have every single hair pulled out and are always naked. To practice *ahimsa* one must respect all life and avoid injury to all living things. Hence the broom and the mouthcloth: with the former one sweeps aside possible small creatures, so they cannot be trodden upon, whereas the latter prevents insects from flying into the mouth or nose.

My shyness increases now I know he's a Cambridge graduate. They're walking so naturally in their nudity. I condider asking them if I can walk right behind them, so I can tread in their footsteps. He notices my timidity and cheerfully says:

"Don't worry. I'm a biologist and I know there are millions of organisms dying in and on our bodies every minute."

"Then why do you sweep?" I venture.

"It's a symbol of the reverence we feel for all creatures. And indeed we may save an occassional ant. You know, I've worked in European laboratories half of my life. Some years ago I went to visit the majestic temple city of Palitana in Gujarat, my birth-state. Only then did I recognise the greatness of the ideals of our religion. I was born a Jain, you see, but I preferred to forget all that during my time in the West. Our Philosophy is totally contrary to the practices of vivisection."

The other man, who appears to be almost ancient, doesn't speak a word, but as he looks at me I feel a slight shock. His eyes express a disturbing mixture of humour and wisdom, child and sage.

"Do you speak English?" I ask him.

"He's silent," the other man answers. "He's a living saint, though he was a factory owning billionaire."

The saintly man breathes in deeply under his cloth. I hear him sniffing. His eyes truly sparkle.

"Smell, sir," the biologist says.

I inhale deeply. The overwhelming scent of frangipani flowers fills my head.

"Flowers enrich the air we are breathing with their fragrances. They feed our emotions and fertilise our spirits. That is why people who have been living separated from nature for too long dry up and wither away."

The last miles are soon covered. As our path reaches the top of a rise, I perceive an enormous monolithic statue of a naked man. It must be at least fifty feet high. The Jains don't believe in a God, but they do believe in following the Finders of The Path. At the feet of the giant, tens of thousands of pilgrims have gathered. They carry jars containing curd, dates, ghee, almonds, poppy seeds, saffron, honey, sandalwood and gold powder, as my companion explains. Hundreds of naked Digambaras form a living chain, along which the jars are handed up a lavishly decorated scaffolding, until they arrive right above the venerable head of Bahubali. There the jars are emptied onto the crown of the Pathfinder. Smells and colours are overwhelming. A shroud of iridescent hues covers the statue. It seems to change colour constantly. There's music from drums and chennai accompanying age old incantations. As we come closer, I notice the transparent shroud of the Tirthankar is composed of millions of butterflies. They gorge themselves on the offerings which stream down the granite giant, delightedly flapping their splendid wings. Now I see tears flowing down the cheeks of the old billionaire. I have to sit down, overcome by the beauty of it all.

"One can only love it," I hear the younger *Muni* whisper.

Michael Castro

Coming Together

for Adelia

Where the Mississippi & Missouri meet
I met you, princess of the Nile.
We smiled across the table of Kansas
with its gigantic bouquet of corn.
You drew me toward you like the sea
does a river like the sun a flower
like some vast black hole in space
pulsing with contained light;
you swallowed the white night, wrapped me
in your Afric coat, filled a bowl
with herbal smoke & pulled long & deep
& I drew too the musky draft
long & deep like the Mississippi itself
long & deep winding down from the frozen north
to southern marshy climes.
The dark willows of the south enfolded us
the balconies of New Orleans
the tomb of its voodoo queen
Marie Leaveau we stood below
its white stone face, streaked with human blood
& graffiti'd with cryptic scratches left by feline souls;

& we drew again long and deep
swallowing the night of flaming crosses
robed & hooded riders
limp bodies swinging 'neath the shadows of trees
Negress & wandering Jew
we swallowed these sad histories —
nazis, billyclubs, snarling dogs, inquisitioners,
massahs, priests & governors
whirling in the smoky Mississippi —
enslavement in Egypt, America, the body
whirling & winding in the smoke up to the sky

white as the bones of the death camps
white as the tufts of cotton plants
white & whirling in the night

Your Moses came floating to you
on a raft of vegetation
buoyant with meditation
He saw himself reflected in your eye
A pharaonic sigh clouded overhead
The spirits of the dead clucked their tongues
Out of the jungle came a rumble of drums.
A dixieland trumpet cried over the river
crumbling levy walls inside our minds
letting it rush & wind
freely to the open sea
bearing you & me
& the burden of our history
bearing you & me
on the waves of sacred mystery

Children of the Sun —
Man & Woman —

One

(our exiles
masked by knowing smiles

After Vallejo

Idle on a Stone, unemployed,
he looks into the river...Narcissus
of scrounge, fop of scruff, suit shiny
at elbow & butt, what creature stares up,
wizened & tight-lipped, out of the deep?
Having devoured the short ends of cigarettes
& the smoke of the soul, having walked through
the classifieds "Full of Jobs,"
says the President, "full of..." having stood in the
funereal lines of the jobless multitudes
having filled out the forms full of the routine questions
requiring routines for answers — Who *are* you? — Who are *you*?

A man whose newspaper covers his head in the rain
who traces the lines of his face in the river
lines written by this tragic poetry

A man who stoops over in a phone booth's privacy
to count his change & cough
who haunts the harsh streets, the hiring hall warehouses
the coffee shops of oblivion
Idle on a stone, unemployed
Home is no longer home as I is no longer I

Who will offer the rag he needs to mop his brow?
Who will fill the cavity that aches in his spirit?

What will the river say?

And what are
his Qualifications?
Three million years spent
developing an opposable thumb, an upright posture
A couple of million thinking, abstracting
Hundreds of thousands travelling, learning, adapting
to arrive precisely here
(Only a few thousand learning to write —
Don't hold it against him
He can dig ditches, push paper, erect pyramids
He has invented sources of light, a certain style,
a simple mirror).

He can figure things out.

Where will he go?
What will he do?
How will he fill out
his application? Can he
sign in under 'Last Job'
that he "helped a guy"?
Will he beg? Will he steal?
Or will he stay still, by the flowing river
idle on a stone unemployed?

A Poet Who Died Young

for Arthur Brown, 1947-1982

he knew the song the goldfish sang
in his window world, the slow ripple
of a lover, the sad, triumphant music
of the caged bird

  he knew & reached through
the window, the world, the cage
of the body, writing
a bop kaballah on the empty notebook pages

writing out of junebug flashings,
noting the differences between cement & concrete,
growling out belly blown improvisations
terrablue afternoons,
blowing the logic of the gone
Buddy Bolden's trumpet, the preacher's
clean scat, Mr. Parker's precise needling

      — What could language do
        to cut through
          itself —
           ?

he knew his job was to poet:
the words spoke through him, from all over
through time too, when he was really there, ready,
in the flow, when the words were heady &
moist in the corners of his mouth —

then it was *nothing but love*
nothing but love
& he knew then
he was immortal & that he was destined
to die
  with a lopsided smile like Michelangelo

& he thought
  death might not be
          all that bad

except for the living

Hasdai Ibn Shaprut

"Prince of the Jews"
in Cordoba, at the end of the first millennium,
knew the antidotes for poisons —
Doctor Hasdai —
found himself
in demand
by the royal & ruling families —

Who was this Jew with clout who
translated the pharmacology —
saw deeply into human nature —
wrote poems,
practiced healing arts &
embarked on diplomatic missions
to Baghdad & Burgundy,
to Otto Uno of Germany
for Abdl al-Rachmann? —

Hasdai!
A Jew with personality,
a healer, a man of knowledge —
a talker, a guy
who could converse with anyone, anywhere, highborn or low —
existing or even, maybe no —
Hasdai, projected
imagination into space,
the Prince of the Jews
wrote to Joseph, King of the legendary Khazars,
somewhere out there
beyond the Empire's boundaries —
Did His Majesty really exist? he inquired.
What was his tribe? His Judaism like?
Did he know when the Messiah was coming?
The arrival seemed long overdue.

"O Blessed is the Lord of Israel," intoned Hasdai,
from Spain, to his desire, "who wouldn't leave us
without an independent kingdom..."

Hasdai, centered, but on the margins — emissary,
liaison, foreign minister, connection, great tree
rooted deep in Spanish soil, but branching out,
embracing other branches, shading
as it reaches for the heavens, spreading
the dream — of peace —
the dream of Hasdai — dream of a Jew, dream splattered & streaming
in all directions, portable dream, bearing the home inside
the dream —
the central fire,
burning bush, embers glowing
into letters, kindling, lighting,
energizing the survival — shaping
words, poems, illuminating
the suffering — the burning
Temples, charred scrolls,
acrid cinders, powdery bones,
the headaches, the glow
between the brows, the dream
of life. Transcending.
Transforming. Hasdai

the healer repairs damage,
founds schools for Jewish children,
spends his wealth buying old manuscripts
so that the Word would never be lost,
protests directly to the Bishops of Burgos
their Easter-time ritual humiliations of the Jews: God,
he reminds them, sees everything,
& never forgets; Hasdai,
the right hand man,
gathers a courtyard full of poets & philosophers —
a chorus of Muslims, Christians, & Jews —
to please His Majesty —

Shapes the dream
of a golden age,
the idea of
a beautiful garden
in Spain's courtyard, a garden
filled with intermingling fragrances,
harmonic voices,
multi-colored flowers of every description,
a garden not in some distant land,
some distant, mythical past,
a garden here & now in Sapharad;

Hasdai planting, nurturing,
the dream seeds of Hasdai,
a cosmopolitan Jew,
a Jew who knew
the antidotes for poisons,
the sweetness of the tongue, the sharing
of the soul-stuff,
a healer,
a Jew who delivered
the royal birth.

Hasdai stoops,
gathering sparks
to light the way.

○

A thousand years later,
at the end of the second millennium,
I write your name, Hasdai,
I write 'Sapharad', opening its gates of mind,
living a kind of dream
that might have been yours,
beaming on my screen in letters of light
a kind of creation, projecting
clusters of sparkling
singers, bards of every complexion.
A courtyard, a café, a dark bar,
a magazine.
A living room.
Is this what it is to be poet —
a unified effort
cutting through time?
a ceremony of mending & healing?
a language so precise
it blurs all boundaries?
the more you are yourself,
the more you are not?
one mind?
a march of names?
shards of light?

Sapharad gleams at the end of the highway.

Michael McClure

TO GIVE IS THE WHITE HAND
with the long fingers
and the eye in the palm
P
U
T
T
I
N
G
FORTH
what is one,
already arisen,
and long gone.

The squawking of jays
is
a gift in the trees.

BE IN COMFORT CHET BAKER.
BE IN COMFORT JEAN-MICHEL BASQUIAT.

There are waves
and facets
and overlappings
and slidings
of
chunks
(and
non-chunks)
slipping
into
the ordinary
E
M
P
T
Y
roar
of the lion.
Plain
as
consciousness.

NOT THERE

THE WHITE HANDS WITH LONG FINGERS
hold an injured ego,
touching its thorns,
caressing the lids
of its bloodshot eyes.
REALMS
open
and close
in a
tidepool.
C
L
E
A
R
cold
water
streams from a vial
and every night
is a new night.

The *thrummm*
and glitter
of the hummingbird
comes from nowhere
and the doe
steps awkwardly
to look at
the calico cat.
Sunrise
is
N
O
T
H
I
N
G
but
pink-orange,
abalone-patterned
scatterings
of
clouds

grafting one

NOW I UNDERSTAND THE SEXUAL ADDICTION
of my young manhood
was a CRUCIFIXION —
glittering and lovely
AS
an ostrich boa and smashed mirrors
seen on acid.

Now
I see that perception is a shape
of the darkness
S
E
E
I
N
G
itself.
Naked bodies in layers
on shelves in space,
and behind stalactites,
alight with themselves
seduce me
with fleshy softness
of their meat.
Calves.
Forearms.
And the perfumes!
THE PERFUMES ARE LOST
AS MOTHS
IN OUR HORMONAL STORMS
but they direct us.
— They guided me.

grafting two

MY
GOD — MY GOD!

NO — MY GOD!

don't — MY GOD!

DO
THIS

to me!

DON'T DO THIS TO ME!

I've looked down into it
and I come back
with my eyes
glazed.
My eyes glazed.
That twig has a rabbit's head!
The orange flesh of the apricot
where the mouth bites it
is a Hell/Heaven
a Hell/Heaven
of naked figures.
The brown dimples of the Bay,
as the plane lands,
are a horse's back.
DON'T DO THIS TO ME!
I love it!

grafting three

INCOMMENSURABLE
and incomprehensible are the best of poetic creation,
the old man sings. The galaxies are a river
seen from this direction. The child knows
it is all black behind the eyes
and that flesh is a swirl
of hungry fantasies
just like
shadows
in
kitten's fur.
The black and yellow bee hums
and dry mud crunches
in the divine cruelty
of nature.
The soft new soul,
with its capsule of masks,
tender and quivering,
ascends into matter.
PINK
ROCKS
SLIDE
OVER
THE
CLIFF
WITH
A
CLATTER.

Smell of greasy food
in the airport.

Bryce Canyon

Jay Ramsay

Stars

Stars...that's how you appear
    side by side in an inner sky
        that's salmon pink with sunset, or dawn   beginning

Just when you think you've found one
                                        know one
                                        are loving one
                                                                another appears
Stretching you either side of your eyes

As you think to panic:

Uncentred, unfaithful, can't handle…
Falling in love is with *one,*
It can't be with her and her (or him) *at the same time*

And yet they keep appearing

And there were the stars you spilt down the stairs in your leaving
as they glowed blue and gold in the half-light
of the aftermath   silently

As you sit wearing a silver binbindi on your forehead
as its clue and its mystery

                                        And why is it so calm?
                                      as you surprise yourself
                                      without your usual urge
                                  towards control or expectation

                          You're not so sure what it is, or for how long
                          but you're open to its unfolding in love…

And why stars, you ask? Not getting it
As she smiles

It is the star body we meet in that freely connects
where none of us can own or possess
and we can see each other in the eye of its imagining
where far and near time are returning
and New Creation is in our making...

More stars. The sky goes on expanding. And then imagine

whole galaxies of love

After Rumi

for S.

Of course we tell each other everything,
That's what lovers are supposed to do.

Can we make a blossoming
With only one pair of hands?

The pearl we are has to be cracked open,
Before it becomes a pearl.

Don't fear your mouth
There's nothing to lose,
Only the cage of your unspeaking…

These words you are brought to
Are another kind of river —

The sweet water that wants
To flow through you like fire.

Lovers Sometimes

for Fionnuala

It's now you're asking us
'What kind of relationship could you have here,
Friends, partners, lovers or lovers *sometimes...*'
Our eyes briefly widening as they open

But love comes when it does
In the cool bright palm of your hand
Where we walk at ease by the river...

Desire comes like a breeze over the garden
In the softening of your mouth
As we pause to kiss

And if we can both be here, we can share it

And if not
Love happens when it does
As you fling your arms back and roll
Down the grassy slope from the summit of the hill

And in each unforeseen lucid opening
— like that empty double bed you had
For that one full moon city night
For lying but not sleeping in
If he'd dared to simply go back with you

And even here
With the dearest most beloved familiar face
We are creatures of mood and respite
Grief, irritation and reparation
We are lovers sometimes

And then so are we all
Even as we love

We come and go

Where loving sometimes means
There is space for all of us —

And we could be freer that way,
And so much more loving than we've known.

For Leonard Cohen

and you

'There's a crack in everything,
That's how the light gets in', you sang
Now 6,000 feet up your Zen mountain…

And as we drive back from the superstore
Onto this brand new estate facing north —
Where the roofs eclipse what were open fields

The sunset clouds are glowing
In the gaps between their grey-white edges
Silently, like wings beating,
In a palpable hushing of air.

After Rumi II

When he gets to the other side
He dances a song of ecstasy and praise with his whole body!

He can't believe what he sees —
The whole universe turned inside out from the heart all around him!

He flings his arms open wide —
Releasing the chains from inside each cell of him…

And do we have to wait till we die?
Will that be our greatest regret?
That we never knew *life?*

Back here, we grow older in boxes
Psychologically aware, in our stylish boxes

While what he says is
If you haven't learnt to praise and dance
The whole of your inner being stays closed like a door —

And you might as well have learnt nothing at all.

After Rumi IX

You can say what you like —
It isn't necessarily what you feel

You can name what you aspire to,
But it isn't what you practice.

Language is an elephant,
An emperor, a hollow reed…

Find the words that are your own
Fired from inside your skin

And from the place where you had nothing
But broken husks and shells of meaning

Then when you speak
You will say what you mean.

Dee Rimbaud

Innanna Descending

This pencil lead
Has turned to diamond dust,
My mouth metamorphosed
Into stony silence.

Cullinan, your poetry,
Your poetry bleeds thin
Over the airwaves,
Whispers sibilant
Into psychic space.

Diamonds, Innanna!
I am speechless,
Watching you sink
Through sods of soil
Into the dark grave.

For the love of love,
For the love of suffering:
Your eyes are diamonds
Smothered in dust.

Cullinan, you shine
In the Sybil's black fire,
Your graphite heart
As bright as the sky.

For the love of love,
A murder of crows
On Lilith's wind:
Innanna, you will never see
Your lover again.

The suffering of love
Is a mouth full
Of diamonds and dust:
Sweet Innanna,
I will never taste
Your kisses again.

A Silent Yearning

These days, often I see you
On the periphery
Of the smarter parts
Of this once dilapidated
Now in vogue city.

You don't quite fit,
Even now that hate
And anger
And animal primacy
Have been banished
To the outer estates.

Always, you have been
A gentler soul,
Troubled by
Brass harshness;
And even today,
For all its sophistry,
This city's heart
Has a timid beat.

You wander the streets
As you have always done,
Teasing, I imagine,
Your poetry
From the strands of pain
You see,
You feel, pouring
From strangers' eyes,
Reflecting sorrow
In your own.

In my mind's eye,
I see you walking tall,
But never proud,
Along by
The river's side,
A swell of ships
Swimming
To the far off ocean.

The river's empty now
And you are bent
By too many years,
By the familiar
You carry
On your back,
Who whispers
His terrible lies
That all there ever was
And all
That ever will be
Is suffering.

Your pain, your loneliness
Reaches out to me,
Even in my new found joy.
I suffer with you,
For it was you
Who filled me up
With the reflective love
That is empathy:
It was your words
That touched me
More than any.

In my youth,
I knew only pain
And that to love
Was to bleed
In sympathy;
And in your words
And in your way
I found a hero
Who haunts me
even to this day.

When I see you now
I want to reach out,
As if I were Christ,
And embrace you:
Show you
The miracle of life,
The miracle
That is the light
For love, to me
Is now
A constant joy
And life, strangely,
A constant delight.

A Chemical Romance

In the beginning we were surprised by love
The magnificent bright sun of it,
A childish scrawl of yellow crayola
In a broken line of blue sky
With blank spaces awakening
The idea of infinite possibility,
As if we were shakily scribbled
Free flying, V-shaped birds
Escaping the dense gravity of reality
For the perfection of uncertain destiny.

We pictured a heaven beyond summer
And turned our eyes from the grey clouds
That would bring a winter of icy rain
And freeze the wandering of our wings.

Buddha Poem

You taught me to be here with my full attention,
To cherish each moment as precious:
More sacred than memory
Or the dreams that tomorrow may bring.

Today
Is the milk that sustains us
And in it is a beauty and wonder
That I used to search for,
Imagining it was far yonder.

Today
Is a flower in crescendo,
Vibrant with the full colour
Of all its yesterdays.

Here and now, I am the sum total of all my days.
You have taught me the mindfulness of being
And I honour this, with gratitude and stillness:
The song of you, present in the core of me.

Janine Pommy Vega

Mad Dogs of Trieste

for Andy Clausen

We have never been in a war like this
in all the years of watching
the street at 3 a.m.
kids lobbing cherry bombs into garbage cans
the last hookers heading for home

It used to be, stopping in Les Halles cafés
after a night we could find the strong
men from the market
and the beautiful prostitutes
resting in each other's arms
Le Chat Qui Peche, Le Chien Qui Fume
alive with Parisian waltzes, his hands on her ass
We could pick up raw produce from discard bins
and have lentil stew for tomorrow

Things have never been like this.
Cops square off against teenagers in the village square
take the most pliant as lovers, and re-route the rest
into chutes of incarceration
The mad dogs of Trieste
we counted on to bring down the dead
and rotting status quo, give a shove here
and there, marauder the fattened and calcified order,
have faded like stories

We used to catch them with their hat brims
keeping most of the face in shadow
and sometimes those voices
one by one
turned into waves
like cicadas in the August trees, whistling
receding, and the words crept under
the curtains of power, made little changes,
tilted precarious balance, and brought relief

Those packs don't crisscross the boulevards
now in the ancient cities, no political cabal
behind us watches the world with
eyes entirely
cognizant
the lyrical voices rainbow bodies
your friends my friends nobody left
but the mad dogs of Trieste as we
cover the streets.

Piazza di Busola: Inventor of the Compass

Today love has settled in like a toothache
You could almost be on the other
side of a room
and my glance flies over
but cannot reach your arm

Perhaps this is unimportant
a yearning that settles
for the shine on the water
at the base of a Saracen wall
for the touch of infinity at the horizon

I am married to something defined by absence
perambulations late at night do not
bring me closer, do not pull me in.
I check my position by the midnight star
mid-heavens, my star. I am here. Where are you?

Bird Mother of Cagliari

for Anne Waldman

Ancient mother
  enshrined on shelves
    from Cùcurru'e Mari in Sardegna

a row of little mothers from Cùcurru S'àrriu
  Early Bronze Age to Medium
    Bronze Age (1,600 BC), Nuraghic Civilisation

Bird Woman carved in white marble
  with wide square shoulders
    and sightless beak,

Do you think
  by surrounding ourselves with images
    and artefacts of the old way
we could be thrown back,
  jarred, taken by surprise to our ancient
    self and its singing heart?

The wild round introspection
  down sinewy runnels
    the cavernous hold of your arms and knees
the dark night of shakti,
  a starry maternal church, the nesty cognisance
    of a physical world and its clutch of eggs
each more wonderful than the next

Could we walk back to that garden
  and recognize your obsidian blades
    your round chamber houses
your hand in front of
  mons veneris
    as you turn to the right?

Could we nod and duck into that kingdom
  protected, procreative
    without the wars of division?

Could we find you, consolation,
  as we take up on our shoulders the work
    that admits no separation?

Could we find you
  smiling at the door
    as you welcome us home?

Coliseum

for Màssimo de Feo & Corine Young

After colonnades, frescoes, pieces of urn
a magnetism rustling in the dark
at 4 a.m., cobblestone alleys
the fountain half a city block wide
backed up against buildings
in the tiny square
like a giant child peeking out of a doll house

After obelisks, phalluses, columns
telling the history of war
celebrating dominion
declaring law!
I arrive at the Coliseum,
haunt of legendary spectacles, men against men,
men against packs of lions, packs of dogs
lit up now for a theater piece

The horses who are part of the play
are tied outside, their heads are down
legs strangely still
Why aren't they moving?
Someone points out their feet
are shoeless, their hooves carved into
to hobble their moves,
to cause them pain when they run

Feronia, Mother of Animals!
Uni, Mother of Fields!
the clawless cats, the hoofless horses
the bull in every corrida in Spain
the condor tied to its back in Peru

cock fights, greyhound races
calves tethered all their skinny lives
to the side of a barn
processed veal for the prison guards
veal for the meaty swallowers

The old Coliseum lit up tonight
is very much alive
Restore the death penalty in Italy!
Shoot the kid off his motorbike
He's not wearing a helmet!

The Spoils of Rome

Ostentatious monuments
flung up with the wealth of
conquered nations and the strength
of slaves, one third your population,
Whatever your fame was
your moment of power,
Roman
you are the ordinary enemy

Titans glimpsed in the street life
New York City, speed induced,
gigantic forms were hopping from rooftop
to rooftop, and when we looked
they were fixed in place
again disguised as a water tower
a top floor landing, a washline
and antennae. We knew the truth.

Now against the sky huge figures
women with chariots, men with wings
the same soul eaters of the lower
east side, the same cup of melancholy
competition and dominance engenders
the plebeian, the serf, the slave
traipsing from temple to temple
ragged feet on hot paving stones

on their hands and shoulders
any praise
for the beautiful
cenotaphs
and obelisks
the giant teeth of a mighty
humorless
empire.

SehnSucht

for Jack Hirschman and Agneta Falk

The good life is not for me
walking and chatting under leafy trees
with my baby carriage
is a morning I have never known

A life of dreams
requires disappointment
holds the body tense —
expectancy belongs to another age.

And perhaps none of us here
is normal. Perhaps we all wear
the stigmata of longing
for something

a place a time when the whole
body is wrenched vomiting
everything that is not it
everything that is not it.

Hakim Bey

Black Crown & Black Rose

Anarcho-Monarchism & Anarcho-Mysticism

IN SLEEP WE DREAM of only two forms of government — anarchy & monarchy. Primordial root consciousness understands no politics & never plays fair. A democratic dream? a socialist dream? Impossible.

Whether my REMs bring veridical near-prophetic visions or mere Viennese wish-fulfilment, only kings & wild people populate my night. Monads & nomads.

Pallid day (when nothing shines by its own light) slinks & insinuates & suggests that we compromise with a sad and lackluster reality. But in dream we are never ruled except by love or sorcery, which are the skills of chaotes & sultans.

Among a people who cannot create or play, but can only *work,* artists also know no choice but anarchy & monarchy. Like the dreamer, they must possess & *do* possess their own perceptions, & for this they must sacrifice the merely social to a "tyrannical Muse."

Art dies when treated "fairly." It must enjoy a caveman's wildness or else have its mouth filled with gold by some prince. Bureaucrats & sales personnel poison it, professors chew it up, & philosophisers spit it out. Art is a kind of byzantine barbarity fit only for nobles & heathens.

If you had known the sweetness of life as a poet in the reign of some venal, corrupt, decadent, ineffective & ridiculous Pasha or Emir, some Qajar shah, some King Farouk, some Queen of Persia, you would know that this is what every anarchist must want. How they loved poems and paintings, those dead luxurious fools, how they absorbed all roses & cool breezes, tulips & lutes!

Hate their cruelty & caprice, yes — but at least they were human. The bureaucrats, however, who smear the walls of the mind with odorless filth — so kind, so *gemutlich*— who pollute the inner air with numbness — they're not even worthy of hate. They scarcely exist outside the bloodless Ideas they serve.

And besides: the dreamer, the artist, the anarchist — do they not share some tinge of cruel caprice with the most outrageous of moghuls? Can genuine life occur without some folly, some excess, some bouts of Heraclitan "strife"? We do not rule — but we cannot & will not *be ruled.*

In Russia the Narodnik-Anarchists would sometimes forge a *ukase* or manifesto in the name of the Czar; in it the Autocrat would complain that greedy lords & unfeeling officials had sealed him in his palace & cut him off from his beloved people. He would proclaim the end of serfdom & call on peasants & workers to rise in His Name against the government.

Several times this ploy actually succeeded in sparking revolts. Why? Because the single absolute ruler acts metaphorically as a mirror for the unique and utter absoluteness of the self. Each peasant looked into this glassy legend & beheld his or her own freedom —

an illusion, but one that borrowed its magic from the logic of the dream.

A similar myth must have inspired the 17th century Ranters & Antinomians & Fifth Monarchy Men who flocked to the Jacobite standard with its erudite cabals & bloodproud conspiracies. The radical mystics were betrayed first by Cromwell & then by the Restoration — why not, finally, join with flippant cavaliers & foppish counts, with Rosicrucians & Scottish Rite Masons, to place an occult messiah on Albion's throne?

Among a people who cannot conceive human society without a monarch, the desires of radicals may be expressed in monarchical terms. Among a people who cannot conceive human existence without a religion, radical desires may speak the language of heresy.

Taoism rejected the whole of Confucian bureaucracy but retained the image of the Emperor-Sage, who would sit silent on his throne facing a propitious direction, doing absolutely nothing.

In Islam the Ismailis took the idea of the Imam of the Prophet's Household & metamorphosed it into the Imam-of-one's-own-being, the perfected self who is beyond all Law & rule, who is atoned with the One. And this doctrine led them into revolt against Islam, to terror & assassination in the name of pure esoteric self-liberation & total realization.

Classical 19th century anarchism defined itself in the struggle against crown & church, & therefore on the waking level it considered itself egalitarian & atheist. This rhetoric however, obscures what really happens: the "king" becomes the "anarchist," the "priest" a "heretic." In this strange duet of mutability, the politician, the democrat, the socialist, the rational ideologue can find no place; they are deaf to the music & lack all sense of rhythm. Terrorist & monarch are *archetypes*; these others are mere functionaries.

Once anarch & king clutched each other's throats & waltzed a totentanz — a splendid battle. Now, however, both are relegated to history's trashbin — has-beens, curiosities of a leisurely & more cultivated past. They whirl around so fast that they seem to meld together... can they somehow have become one thing, a Siamese twin, a Janus, a freakish unity? "The sleep of Reason..." ah! most desirable & desirous monsters!

Ontological Anarchy proclaims flatly, bluntly, & almost brainlessly: yes, the two are now one. As a single entity the anarch/king now is reborn; each of us the ruler of our own flesh, our own creations — and as much of everything else as we can grab & hold.

Our actions are justified by fiat & our relations are shaped by treaties with other autarchs. We make the law for our own domains — & the chains of the law have been broken. At present, perhaps we survive as mere Pretenders — but even so we may seize a few instants, a few square feet of reality over which to impose our absolute will, our *royaume*. *L'etat, c'est moi.*

If we are bound by any ethic or morality it must be one which we ourselves have imagined, fabulously more exalted & more liberating than the "moralic acid" of puritans & humanists. "Ye are as gods" — "Thou art That."

The words *monarchism* & *mysticism* are used here in part simply *pour épater* those egalito-atheist anarchists who react with pious horror to any mention of pomp or superstition-mongering. No champagne revolutions for *them!*

Our brand of anti-authoritarianism, however, thrives on baroque paradox; it favors states of consciousness, emotion & aesthetics over all petrified ideologies & dogma; it embraces multitudes & relishes contradictions. Ontological Anarchy is a hobgoblin for BIG minds.

The translation of the title (& key term) of Max Stirner's magnum opus as *The Ego & Its Own* has led to a subtle misinterpretation of "individualism." The English-Latin word *ego* comes freighted & weighted with freudian & protestant baggage. A careful reading of Stirner suggests that *The Unique & His Own-ness* would better reflect his intentions, given that he never defines the ego *in opposition* to libido or id, or in opposition to "soul" or "spirit." The Unique (der Einzige) might best be construed simply as the individual self.

Stirner commits no metaphysics, yet bestows on the Unique a certain absoluteness. In what way then does this *Einzige* differ from the Self of Advaita Vedanta? *Tat tvam asi*: Thou (individual Self) art That (absolute Self).

Many believe that mysticism "dissolves the ego." Rubbish. Only death does that (or such at least is our Sadducean assumption). Nor does mysticism destroy the "carnal" or "animal" self — which would also amount to suicide. What mysticism really tries to surmount is false consciousness, illusion, Consensus Reality, & all the failures of self that accompany these ills. True mysticism creates a "self at peace," a self with power. The highest task of metaphysics (accomplished for example by Ibn Arabi, Boehme, Ramana Maharishi) is in a sense to self-destruct, to identify metaphysical & physical, transcendent & immanent, as ONE. Certain *radical monists* have pushed this doctrine far beyond mere pantheism or religious mysticism. An apprehension of the immanent oneness of being inspires certain antinomian heresies (the Ranters, the Assassins) whom we consider our ancestors.

Stirner himself seems deaf to the possible spiritual resonances of Individualism — & in this he belongs to the 19th century: born long after the deliquescence of Christendom, but long before the discovery of the Orient & of the hidden illuminist tradition in Western alchemy, revolutionary heresy & occult activism. Stirner quite correctly despised what he knew as "mysticism," a mere pietistic sentimentality based on self-abnegation & world hatred. Nietzsche nailed down the lid on "God" a few years later. Since then, who has dared to suggest that Individualism & mysticism might be reconciled & synthesized?

The missing ingredient in Stirner (Nietzsche comes closer) is a working concept of *non-ordinary consciousness*. The realization of the unique self (or *ubermensch*) must reverberate & expand like waves or spirals or music to embrace direct experience or intuitive perception of the uniqueness of reality itself. This realization engulfs & erases all duality, dichotomy, & dialectic. It carries with itself, like an electric charge, an intense & wordless sense of *value*: it "divinizes" the self.

Being/consciousness/bliss (satchitananda) cannot be dismissed as merely another Stirnerian "spook" or "wheel in the head." It invokes no exclusively transcendent principle for which the *Einzige* must sacrifice his/her own-ness. It simply states that intense awareness of existence itself results in "bliss" — or in less loaded language, "valuative consciousness." The goal of the Unique after all is to *possess everything*; the radical monist attains this by identifying self with perception, like the Chinese inkbrush painter who "becomes the bamboo," so that "it paints itself."

Despite mysterious hints Stirner drops about a "union of Unique-ones" & despite Nietzsche's eternal "Yea" & exaltation of life, their Individualism seems somehow shaped by a certain *coldness toward the other*. In part they cultivated a bracing, cleansing chilliness against the warm suffocation of 19th century sentimentality & altruism; in part they simply despised what someone (Mencken?) called "Homo Boobensis."

And yet, reading behind and beneath the layer of ice, we uncover traces of a fiery doctrine — what Gaston Bachelard might have called "a Poetics of the Other." The *Einzige's* relation with the Other cannot be defined or limited by any institution or idea. And yet clearly, however paradoxically, the Unique depends for completeness on the Other, & cannot & will not be realized in any bitter isolation.

The examples of "wolf children" or *enfants sauvages* suggest that a human infant deprived of human company for too long will never attain conscious humanity — will never acquire language. The Wild Child perhaps provides a poetic metaphor for the Unique-one — and yet simultaneously marks the precise point where Unique & Other must meet, coalesce, unify — or else fail to attain & possess all of which they are capable.

The Other mirrors the Self — the Other is our *witness.* The Other completes the Self — the Other gives us the key to the perception of oneness-of-being. When we speak of being & consciousness, we point to the Self; when we speak of bliss we implicate the Other.

The acquisition of language falls under the sign of Eros — all communication is essentially erotic, all relations are erotic. Avicenna & Dante claimed that love moves the very stars & planets in their courses — the *Rg Veda* & Hesiod's *Theogony* both proclaim Love the first god born after Chaos. Affections, affinities, aesthetic perceptions, beautiful creations, conviviality — all the most precious possessions of the Unique-one arise from the conjunction of Self & Other in the constellation of Desire.

Here again the project begun by Individualism can be evolved and revivified by a graft with mysticism — specifically with tantra. As an esoteric *technique* divorced from orthodox Hinduism, tantra provides a symbolic framework ("Net of Jewels") for the identification of sexual pleasure & non-ordinary consciousness. All antinomian sects have contained some "tantrik" aspect, from the families of Love & Free Brethren & Adamites of Europe to the pederast Sufis of Persia to the Taoist alchemists of China. Even classical anarchism has enjoyed its tantrik moments: Fourier's Phalansteries; the "Mystical Anarchism" of G. Ivanov & other fin-de-siècle Russian symbolists; the incestuous eroticism of Arzibashaev's *Sanine*; the weird combination of Nihilism & Kali-worship which inspired the Bengali Terrorist Party (to which my tantrik guru Sri Kamanaransan Biswas had the honor of belonging)...

We, however, propose a much deeper syncretism of anarchy and tantra than any of these. In fact, we simply suggest that Individual Anarchism & Radical Monism are to be considered henceforth as one and the same movement.

This hybrid has been called "spiritual materialism," a term which burns up all metaphysics in the fire of oneness of spirit & matter. We also like "Ontological Anarchy" because it suggests that being itself remains in a state of "divine Chaos," of all-potentiality, of continual creation.

In this flux only the *jiva mukti*, or "liberated individual," is self-realized, and thus monarch or owner of his perceptions and relations. In this ceaseless flow only desire offers any principle of order, and thus the only possible society (as Fourier understood) is that of lovers.

Anarchism is dead, long live anarchy! We no longer need the baggage of revolutionary masochism or idealist self-sacrifice — or the frigidity of Individualism with its disdain for conviviality, of *living together* — or the vulgar superstitions of 19th century atheism, scientism, and progressism. All that dead weight! Frowsy proletarian suitcases, heavy bourgeois steamer-trunks, boring philosophical portmanteaux — over the side with them!

We want from these systems only their vitality, their life-forces, daring, intransigence, anger, heedlessness — their power, their *shakti*. Before we jettison the rubbish and the carpetbags, we'll rifle the luggage for billfolds, jewels, drugs and other useful items —keep what we like and trash the rest. Why not? Are we priests of a cult, to croon over relics and mumble our martyrologies?

Monarchism too has something we want — a grace, an ease, a pride, a superabundance. We'll take these, and dump the woes of authority & torture in history's garbage bin. Mysticism has something we need — "self-overcoming," exalted awareness, reservoirs of psychic potency. These we will expropriate in the name of our insurrection — and leave the woes of morality and religion to rot and decompose.

As the Ranters used to say when greeting any "fellow creature" — from king to cut-purse — "Rejoice! All is ours!"

Daniel Abdal-Hayy Moore

The Roar of The Cataract

The roar of the cataract drowns out your
butterfly voice O my heart under
construction with one myrtle branch and three
singing doves
and far in the distance a single blue sky with a
flare in it so bright red its very bright redness sears the eyes
there's nothing left to say yet we chatter on
as the avalanche increases behind us
pulling the whole town down with it except for
a single crystal and two flies caught in amber and an
ancient filing cabinet full of
sensitive documents and dental records that will
come in handy for identification purposes
once the roar has died down
yet they say the silence after a roar is
deafening then uncannily eerie then absolute
O my heart with your steep stairways going up and your
steep chutes going down
snakes and ladders O my heart the giant
advances and swift declines
one moment the empress on her jewelled terrace having
tea and cut sandwiches
the next moment floundering in classical floodwaters
avoiding eels and Corinthian columns
these apocalyptic occurrences take place either in the
overheated imagination or in busloads of Chilean schoolchildren
actually driving off a cliff under
suspicious circumstances
but Beneficent God knows each sparrow's fall
and the delicate bones of each one's ribcage
lifted in song

Tree of Life

The tree that is the tree of life has three branches
and millions of leaves and on each branch
a bridge and on each bridge multitudes of
crickets making their itchy music and listening to
replies from far and near

the tree of life sprouts from our hearts with
roots that go down past our toes into the
earth under our feet earth of bone and smoke
earth of glad song and openings

the tree of life swings on its own branches on which are hung
the portraits in fine detail and exquisite color
of everyone ever alive alive now and alive to come
a never-ending display of astonished and
astonishing faces each with open eyes and
words of great beauty even the
beastliest among them

the tree of life grows upward with each
planetary breath and its reflection can be
seen in the ocean of space
where suns and moons and planets rotate with the
swimming serenity of whales

shade from the tree of life is sparse but it
broods like a gentle mother over each
one of us and rays of light break through in
ribbony bands that spell words of
elemental wisdom and comfort

do not take an axe to it
do not take it down for any reason
don't carve your name in it or look greedily at its
lumber

its rings go deep into the center of the world
you can read its age by the
amount of life you have lived

take one leaf and let that be your
shield your parasol and your grave

The Sound of Earth's Rotation

There's the sound of the earth's rotation as it
swings past space friction a kind of
squeak audible in peoples' speech patterns to the
most attuned ear or audible in the upturn at the
end of bird's song lines the last notes
ascending in a disintegrating splatter
or in the way lovers while getting to know each
other in the way that used to be called
courting anticipate what each other might
say or anticipate a kind of crescendo like an
orchestra in unison holding a long note extra
long as emphasis for an epiphanic
emotion that seems to go on forever and actually does

the sound of the earth's rotation in the roar of
hungry lions around feeding time a sound of
leonine rasping large things scraping together like
big iron machinery
or on the other hand a sound completely at the
other end of the stress scale of water
lapping on the shore of a Polynesian island the
hushed insistence a long lead-up to a
momentary pause before an even longer
sizzle as it slides back down again into the
next arising wave

perhaps I'm only recounting random things with
sound as being part of the earth's
rotation when it's not really the noise a giant
celestial body makes as it moves round its
axis in the dark with one half in the
light which may not make any sound at all audible to our
ears as an actual sound as such but still all the

eerie and varied activities upon the earth as it
sails so free and easy round its
slightly tilted axis might yet be described as
contributing to the overall
ecumenically rich and eclectically inclusive
symphony of that sound

Because

Because he began as a baby and will end as an old man
because the rose has a stem and isn't all the way a rose
because the looming building casts a long shadow the squat
building a short
and we don't really see the faces of insects the way
probably other insects see them
because there's a quantum gulf between the
human world and the insect one
and probably the flea doesn't appreciate the difference in
personality or spiritual quality between one
juicy arm and another quite the way
we do
and because horses with wings are rare to the point of
impossible and flying ladders of shiny bronze that
take you to the higher heavens rung by rung
are more an apt metaphor than something you can
pick up at your local hardware store
and because even the highest mountains come at
last to a peak
and the deepest ocean rifts hit bottom after all
then we can begin to appreciate not only the
utterly complete pattern of things but also the
occasional breaks in the pattern as when for
example a building in a forest fire isn't
burnt to the ground an elephant is
united with a boon companion after more than
thirty years apart in their respective
circuses or zoos and their trunks entwine in loving recognition
or a true cascade of purest love bursts in
cavalcades of purist splendor from seemingly the
marrow of our bones in a hot flood throughout the
entire system showing us the loveliest connections between
mouse and rainbow paper-weight and
train wreck door slam and baby born as the
whole cycle repeats itself in a new key enough to
shiver the deepest sleeper awake and the most
delicate moth to suddenly have the
courage of a tiger in sipping the most
inaccessible nectar

Out of The Foxglove

Out of the foxglove let flow delicate voices
out of the ocean-hiss let silence flow
out of bluebells an unaccustomed rattle
words out of the horse's mouth cantering in place
blasphemy from the harsh ripping of metal rivets out of girders
catechism from river-water flood call slosh and reply
karaoke from the sound of traffic rattling and honking at rush hour
high C soprano note from a collective beehive in the rain
jackhammer presidential campaign speech clank and clunk clank and clunk
high-pitched victory ululations kids leaving the schoolroom for the playground
crinkly syncopated delicate percussion symphony autumn leaves falling in a forest
tip and tap
toads' peremptory silencing technique croak and countercroak in the depths of night
a rolling penny on marble out of whose traction whole marching bands cascade upward
out of a ribbon's lazy rippling descent through the air
a light melody of languorous movement floating in space
from a steam calliope whistle the battle cry of giant sea vessels erupting
from a volcano's gastric rumblings the sound of wild stallions
en estampido across Midwestern plains at high noon

the crackling voice of fire across a virgin forest mountain range
as a young boy opens his mouth to try to express
his deepest inexpressible mystical experiences
to the one sympathetic listener on earth
whose reply is the long echoing mellow chord inaudibly sounded
in the open spaces between planets and stars

from the wail of a nail being driven into wood
the divine voice of the angel of death

from the sound of a leafy branch being waved through the air
multitudinous wings
carrying us home

Andy Clausen

Gokyo Lake Breaking Up in the Sun

Is that the sound of 10,000 birds barking like mountains?
No.
Is that the sound of outerspace, the other-never-heard-by-us-world?
No.
Perhaps then, it's 13 sacred cannons firing huge flaming
        balls of redemption in our Path?
No! No,
It is just Gokyo Lake Breaking Up in the Sun.

Is that an avalanche like sin punishment & emptiness unknown?
Is that a real avalanche a Loudness birthing Eternal
        Silence through its renting stone Cervix?
Is this the iron irony of molten medicineless
        miniscule buried alive Death?
No, Gokyo Lake is Breaking Up in the Sun.

Are these the whirring teeth of mechanical contraband
        come to take the high trees?
The motorbikes of Bankok angry at the rushing
        minutes lost?
New York honking its collective gridlock worldwide?
Is it a freeway collapsing in my Home Town?
Is it the 5th Horseman?
No, listen, It is Gokyo Lake Breaking Up in the Sun,
        listen!

Has the Ganges decided to flow into Tashkent & form
        a moat around Moscow before emptying into the
        freezing waters twixt Finland & Leningrad
        causing untold relentless havoc?
Has a monster finally found its Form?
Is Los Angeles about to implode thru the yak dung stoves?
Is it an Earth Quake?
A fierce revengeful Dakini I did wrong?
Is it all my previous had-to-be-horrible incarnations
        come up to vomit me into a hell
        only I could conceive?
No, It is only Gokyo Lake Breaking Up in the Sun.

What is this jade?
This ultra reflection vibrating liquid
　　doing for free all a gem's intended to do?
My musings are vanquished by the Loudness
Has the mountain we walk on fallen in?
Have Sagarmatha's glaciers calved?
Has the sky storming herds of yak
　　driven by reincarnations of murdered monks?
Has the colossal energy of might-have-beens
　　self-immolated like warheads
　　along the crumbling ridge?
Has peace been broken like eggs in the nest?
Is that growl a genocidal demonic tractor or bulldozer?
No, In the sun Gokyo Lake Breaks is All.

Why are you not convinced?
Why won't you take the Answer?

What? Aren't those tribal drums
　　multiplying?
Isn't there a bloody revolution in the bottom of my shoes?
Aren't gongs struck in my sentient temples?
Has the moon left for keeps?
Answer me!
What is that catastrophic coughing from a wounded lion
　　large as Cho-Oyu?
Who is that wheezing far away man?

Hey You?
Those drums are the beatings of your heart
　　older than its many moons
Those gongs are the clangorous reverbs
　　of your locomotive lungs
Your money changer purged temples are filled
　　with the blood of the masses
　　of uncelebrated martyrs
That is your coughing & you are no lion
　　shimi shimi
That wheezing far away man is just the sound
　　of Gokyo Lake Breaking Up in the Sun.

A woman strong & beautiful drags you to the top
　　for your audience
　　with the Mother of the Universe.

Access Us!

Beauty is not dead
A Vision for the Future
    better not be dead
Romance & Love are not dead
Heart seeking description
Windows of mountains streaming
    resolve & wisdom are not dead
Battered old rattlers
Lovers of old objects
    that created yesterdays
    free of pain
    are not dead
Defiant traditions of straight talk
    on the life & death walk
    are not dead
The great paintings & parties
    in the verses of poets
    beyond language, awe inspiring
    felt in the middle of the body
    ZAUM is not dead
The beauty of folk poetry
    is not dead
Only the past
Only the vacuous language of obscurant
    academes writing only to impress
    other poets promoting exclusion
Only the nihilist TV heads
Only the fascist cowards
Only those who want knowledge to be
    private property
    are dead
Access Us!

Jack Hirschman

The Open Gate

In memory of Jack Micheline, Poet

When I came to San Francisco
the street was Jack.
I write this on the #19 as it passes
the now non-existent *Donuts 'n Things*
on Polk and California Streets
where during the war we talked
of poets here and in the Soviet Union
before going to Minnie Can Do's
over on Fillmore to do our things,
or headed to North Beach for
the wild venues there.

Later I learned the street was more
than Jack. It was Jack, and few of us
had much of it; and we saw poor
palms opening everywhere, the war
had broken many, and the rats in power,
and the cockroach landlords.

Jack lived for the walk,
for the open gate inside
where the prisoner hears the strain
of Mingus or Monk, and sings free
along the storefronts and to
the windows of the world.

The bohemian was dead, but he said:
Long Live the Bohemian!
The poets were canned or clowned
or given microphones to suck on
but he cried: Long Live the Poets!

Those he envied and decried for having
made it beat in the literary world
he was right about: they really
weren't street, and street was where
the Poet had to be, or street would be

ruled by dead spores and fascisti.
He had a memory,
a bottle of chianti,
a gypsy-jewish fire burning in him
all the way back to black Pushkin,
had the con the hustle the scrounge the wail
to survive in a world where blood money
rigged up everybody's sails,

all that to keep the gate open inside
for the poem to blow as a hurricane,
for the paint to animal and child.

Old buddy of the Word, those guts you kept
like a holy ark of sparks bursting into flame
you pass on into all of us now bereft
— the hip, the dudes, the chicks, the dames —

We ask a doll, we ask a dish, Rimbaud,
Mayakovsky, Kerouac and all
the streethearts gathered here:
wasn't that a matzoh in the teeth of homeless fate?
wasn't that a Poet made of bright and shining tears?

Portrait of Nelson Perry

With a small stick he worked grains of wheat
out of the cracks between the rotten
boards of the boxcar floor flying through the Depression,

and built a little mountain of them in his palm
which he'd carry in his pocket
down to the twilight hobo jungle to share.

But as if from inside his guts in that rattling
old snake of a train, those grains would burst into
ideas about how to make it so's a man would never

have to get down on his knees to earn a meal
in this king-hating country, a generation before
the prophet turned up a King.

Now we're all together, whether we like it or not.
The snake's even snakier; you can crawl or flop down
in the corner of the car, do whatever

you can get away with in this thing hurtling through
space. But a half a hundred years later, a piece of
something to eat can still work up an appetite for Revolution.

Lingasharira

for Sharon Doubiago

How long a river, Lingasharira,
how long the body of our fire-flow!

A braid like a DNA through the years, a
4th dimensioning through poems

dying over and over, now southern
now northern California,

now soviet, now Russia in hell,
brother and sister,

kama and karma of energy to sound
profoundings of time and space.

Synchrony of being-with
no matter where apart.

This is my stick of lipstick kiss
on your beautiful heart.

The Purcell Ode

St. Cecelia's Day, November 22

Who I go to sing without for.
Who to be *sans*. Celia.
Cecilia. There are rabbits even in this dark heath,
Your breath, your flair alive, for that, little pomp,
I declare this
slow eave and shingle. You up there,
in a nimb, on a limb, upon a toe
outwinging.
What we knew when we were only
last together before the fall.
Those trumpets,
not you and I but him they mourn,
who also upon your staves was
that day done in,

I go twicefold, I listen to the mice
in a grave
acceptation.

Nibbling.

I am the cheese, you are the free trap, O
shut this broken mouth
already so
hooked to, I can't
but be your
assassination.

Child already deepest
of that
breed is made for horses to turn round upon,
and one with nature be
in the only flash worth seeing:
your blonde, the small
of her, the light,
through the woods, the blend of him
Prince David. This horn hangs
with the black
flag of the summer's
mourning.

No green like where your hand is near.

I touch a window pane, O
hutch within my hearing.

To be only clear,
like this is me,
truly I untry you,
leafly.
Who tree harks make each leaf silence breaks
The winding inlets of our fingers.

Distinctly, of
the speech, what? and in
the laughter's memory, what does
he mean?

your defending sainthood,

the music kew
the music key,

upon a Grand Simplicity

"tis nature's voice"

you begin to borrow,

I steal sorrow from
a dove and drink
it to the dawning:

bright up, and careful kind, in peace of mind *sans guerre*,
no hate, which cannot be, within
a million miles of your
Beauty.

A later day, perhaps
along a beach
under, once more, a peachround sun

as with your friends
only a jealousy of
mind has darkened,

out in the waves, and turning
as upon the horse
once upon a hill

I shall as I do now
marry with words
the sight of you free
in the tawny

wild grace of your Face, toward

Man and Woman, glowing.

The Ari

Alephgram
It is all one identity now all over again Man
To the barricades of the self with great fear
Zero has returned Africa to the United States
Che Guevara is alive somewhere left of Kansas
Hello hello out there are you reading currents
Again and again and the twicefold tale is true
Kind winds the winds whirling through homeland
Lurid and lovely together at the bottomless and
Under the eyelids of all this pressure for what
Roar will await the great sound of re-entering
I as the meaningless zip under the coat of the
Ampersand gunman and windingsheet music changed

Bethgram
In this winning loss this last lettered cry
To no one I know definitely to alone sublime
Zebras of the 37th chapter and then flash
Comes the month of death and the roar begins
Hell hell is on earth and sweet with filth
All over the friends turn girl in your nostrils
Kinship sinks into distances of friendly foe
Lionheaded heart oh man who walks on his knees
Ultimate return to Babylon to clear the air
Rich and thick with money and war's true lies
Indecent love that has only to plant one kiss
And my lips' blossomwork springs to world's ear

Ghimelgram

In this great fear the place I wanted after
Tibet turned in my mouth to another cornball's
Zittermokka trembling in the air raid dared
Come back little Jew the Nazis were for real
Hate let loose on the street become burned book
And I hold my balls and cry this is murdering
Kabbala whose way is as easy as lovely as in-
Laid with softest gems of reception and deeply
Unspeakable and yet not silent grown to the
Rank of gun muzzle after all spankings are
Included in the darkest book ever read backwards
Atomwise and east to the west in the changeless

Dalethgram

Iridescence crumbles back to the real touch
To be one hand with my daughter is to light
Zechariahu up inside who was sent from the pen
Charged electric of Abulafia three centuries
Healing the bones of Europe to sleep in Sefad
At my left flank lay his permutations down
Kindly tell the future combinations be kind
Lay the flames out neatly after much deranging
Uterine births are necessary up to the point
Remember the Aleph as you go soaringly down
Into the moon craters of the daily news finding
At the source the first rung loveliness of time

Haygram

I go into the rooms outside are all in closed
The windows are shattered the broken bottles
Zeroxed and all collages down in hiding fear
Comes from out of every thing swollen pressure
Hats even wear them under the brim's furies
And messages come from telephone and visions
Kindling only further and further the greed
Like a mouth no good no more for easy burning
Let me tell you the history of my mane and jaw
Until all the words are exhausted and you rest
Round and toughshelled as an egg in the great
Inch of the endless growl and yawn for all who
Ached for it finally and finally fell awake

Vovgram

I take off my white light I take off my black
To the ocean to the ocean the rabbis are There
Zinnias are growing out of their wounds though
Centuries of deaths since Dallas have returned
Hidden now behind their suits the poverties
Attacked forever in a flash by furies contained
Kissing even the thees turned into animal darks
Lemme out lemmme out and the Hebrew tiger roars
Under the hills of sighs the hairs grow longer
Right is the footfall straight at the arrow
In the eye of my middle east and worldmad tide
Absolutely infinite and longing for One Stone's love

Zayingram

Indivisible and all the mosaic fragments in
This body at last within limits controlling
Zyklon the gas machine the voice box of death
Chance and the dice of ice ultimately of Vegas
He was the king but he was heavier than Thou
And Thou is lighter than light is the aerial
Kingdom beyond the measure which is this being
Loved within worlding's reel and dance for joy
Undoing her frail things stripping down to a
Rich wisdom who seems older by young and early
In the late hours arising to sleep in the small
And apparently revealed skin we call nakedness

Chethgram

I turn by these returns into a little president
To be able to choose the bliss of being in here
Zoning off this magic from this game of a power
Considering that there are eyes to be lost in
Hating the clue to what lives and dies and how
After all there is no man who uses her altogether
Kindly and yet somehow is always on the way to
Learning the lesson of what she lets go from her
Underground ways she is the least conscious of
Remembering to forget herself being the remembering
Indefatigueably remembered in the flesh of flashed
Apocalypse called the daily bread she turns into

Tethgram

It willed itself through the last luminaries
Trapped in the idolatry of the movie starred
Zapp and the babble of mouths who couldn't
Arrange the necessary distances in this death
Cut-up in the projection room of the last chapter
Kissing the queen in the Globe Theatre of Skull
Lost on the spinning record of an electric fritz
Unter Alles and Athens has tightened its belt
Romany arrives from Rome with the lively Anna
I sit around an old decay that will not be gainsaid
Away and curse the United States of the World

Yodgram

In the dark in the death the living is only a
Twice born man and no hero please no godawful
Zeus and no technician no poet no space climber
Cut that all out of the damaged bone of brain
He is me simple and plural and genitive within
A turn of the world's ways in a war of words
Knighted by the dandelions of Islington in a
Lunacy of vowels spent to mean nothing to anyone
Unalike meaning every One in the particular dark
Ribbon planted in the heart in eight equal parts
In a manner of meridians for the cause of roses
And to the Queen of this brisk fugitive Jerusalem

David Meltzer

excerpt from
The Beat Thing

It was the Bomb
Shoah
Khurbn
it was Void
spirit cry
crisis disconnect
no subject but blank
unrelenting busted time
no future
suburb expands into past
present nuclear (get it) family
'droids Pavlov minutiae
it was Jews w/blues
reds nulled & jolted
Ethel & Julius brain smoke
pyres of shoes & eyeglasses
weeping black G.I.s
open Belsen gates
things are going to look different when
you get outside
understand that beforehand
this book doesn't kid you
& don't forget the third effect
radioactivity the power to
shoot off invisible atomic rays
even if the all-clear's sounded
don't rush to leave the safe place
Geiger counts light leaks from
ash hand reaches up for your eyes
yes
the atomic bomb is a terrible weapon
BUT
not as terrible as most of us believe

Tillich tells us "it's the destiny of historical man to be annihilated not by a cosmic event but by the tensions in his own being & history" [1]

EIGHT SIMPLE AIR RAID RULES:

ALWAYS shut the windows and doors.
ALWAYS seek shelter.
ALWAYS drop flat on your stomach.
ALWAYS follow instructions.
NEVER look up.
NEVER rush outside after a bombing.
NEVER take chances with food or water.
NEVER start rumors. [2]

Furthermore, acquaintance with addicts proves that "hypes" like being "hypes." They enjoy being a "hype" as a hypochondriac enjoys being a hypochondriac. They will argue that liquor affects people worse than heroin, that drunks are often noisy and argumentative, while all a "hype" wants is to be left alone. They dislike the social scorn, the inconvenience of having to hide their addiction, but they enjoy the effect of the drug which keeps them from facing reality.

The juice of the poppy wrecks the body and warps the spirit. The life of an addict is a living death. [3]

futureless clockface pie-chart
Bulletin of Atomic Scientists
black out unseen Eternity permutants
Hiroshima Maidens walk through Saturday
Review
bow shuffle hide mouths to Cousins
Fantastic Brain Destroyers
"The testimony of a victim will
clinch the case against them
when they're brought to trial!"
"The house I live in
a plot of earth a street
the grocer and the butcher
and the people that I meet
the children in the playground
the faces that I see
all races all religions
that's America to me"
sings Sinatra in RKO
backlot tenement
"A Kansas farmer
a Brooklyn sailor
an Irish policeman
a Jewish tailor"

utopic plastic lanyard
unity thongs
khaki G.I. nation hoods
& zootsuit jitterbug gold chains
ceiling dancers starlight all night
razor & bullet flash
rationed gas & glamour snoods
riveters pitch in & chance
true romance of misaligned
diaphragm or ancient Trojan
pinhole burst in backpocket wallet
dark backwards grope to heat
beneath cashmere silk rayon buckles
body collage shields stations of
crossing over into her nuclear
August 13th rain of ruin one
bomb 20,000 TNT tons
evaporate mouth tongue ocean fun
red prong pecker form fill ache
push back Levis we sneak around
parents seek lava silk slippery fingertips
leaks out nylon crotch smear rhythm 'n blues
Ruth Brown *a humpty bumpty* Louis
Jordan T-Bone Walker lindy boogie
chickerychick chala chala
"some of my best friends are Jews"
says Leni booted out of
von Ribbentrop's hill villa
while Dachau's commandant
shoots himself in the heart &
lives to blow his brains out
"He was a nice man really"
maid Gertrude tells of ex-boss Hitler
"of course he was mad"
"Claghorn's the name
Senator Claghorn that is
ah'm from Dixie
ah represent the South son"
checkkala romey in a bananika
ill at ease the little man said
some bread sir if you please
the waiter's voice roared down the hall
you gets no bread with
ONE MEAT BALL!

sour kraut SS leather movie swine
skull pinups & power pimps
smash up Dana Andrew's defiant mug
as *Great Artiste* dumps #2 Bomb on
second-choice Nagasaki at precisely
9:08 MacArthur steps forward
w/ a handful of fountainpens
V-2 rocket wiz our guy on the range
Werner Von Braun
cannibals all on the *Missouri*
business as usual
population control & pesticides
Long Island kids grope out of
DDT low flying cloud blanket
powder turns into oil slick
evaporates into skin pores
German doctors watch
84 women react to gas
"at first I thought it was
simple lockjaw
a swelling in the back of the throat
light haemorrhages under skin
fever & high pulse rate
rapid consumption of white
blood corpuscles internal
bleeding intestinal tract"
"stick-legged starved bodies of
European children never smiled"
"Census Bureau reports last week
nearly twice as many U.S. citizens
died of cancer during 1942-44
as were killed by enemy action in
World War II" "I at present
speak less frequently
I have not been sleeping
I solemnly promise the Almighty
the hour will strike when victory comes
to the Greater German Reich "
"If it's possible to outlaw the Bomb
why not go the whole step &
outlaw war?"
"Two men who don't trust each other
face each other in a locked room
each points a loaded machine-gun at the other

one gun's a later model
no difference
who shoots first wins "
Picasso admired G.I. K-rations
& Velvet tobacco rolled up &
puffed by Stuart Little at
Ernie Pyle's funeral
"Yes, they're back"
Til The End of Time
noisiest New Year's Eve
bars open to dawn
stiff white shirt front
back again for chicks to
write lipstick phone numbers
General Patton
fights for life w/ broken neck
auto accident en route to
kraut field pheasant shoot
blood & guts
are we in time on time
or just out of it
college of cardinals on parade
numero uno red hat Archbishop
Francis Joseph Spellman of NY
Ray Milland lost weekend Anglo
drunk Yank scribe marquis
fame attains Hazel Scott who
backbeats Bach into boogie woogie
"Mrs. Trueman is the last lady"
snaps Adam Clayton Powell Jr
contra DAR denies Marian Anderson
as UAW Walter Reuther versus GM
"They have taken world millions
they never toiled to earn
w/out our brain & muscle
we break their haughty power
gain our freedom
when we learn
the union makes us strong"
"Kelly dances beautifully
& Sinatra sings the roof off "
Churchill Truman Stalin
gray trigger Potsdam hairs
crowd crushed Benito hangs
upside down by his boots

Hitler shoots a tunnel through his lobes
FDR's brain haemorrhages implodes
Branch The Brain Rickey
signs Jack Roosevelt Robinson
"unlike white players
he can't afford a day off"
B-25 hits Empire State
78th & 79th floors
13 killed
UN Charter ratified
Benchley's empty Algonquin chair
shoe sugar butter meat tire
rationing ends the year future end
Kilroy was here
reads the writing on the walls
I, The Jury Under The Volcano
A-Bomb tests at Bikini Atoll 5
color Kodachrome *National Geographic*
blue sky fed aching crisp bright
nuclear white fleece spine disc clouds
upward into Amanita dome
page after page of eternity's beauty
Vive La France cries Pierre Laval
lasts only a few seconds whereas
fascism is eternal firing squad
day & night can't replace the millions
shovel squads dig extra graves for
100,000 Berliners expected to die
of hunger cold or suicide
Hirohito wipes tears w/ white gloves
Vice Admiral Onishi's memo to ghost
Kamikaze corps "souls who fell
as human bullets" Chiang Kai-shek
toasts Mao humble selves
enormous hate "one heart
one soul one mind one goal"
black caped FDR at Yalta
death's vowel point over eyebrow
how the great man's shrunk into
a cigarette holder
at first nobody believed...

1. "The Power of Self Destruction" by Paul Tillich in *God and the H-Bomb,* edited by Donald Keys. New York: Bernard Geiss Associates, 1961. 2. *How To Survive An Atomic Bomb* by Richard Gerstell. New York: Bantam Books, 1950. 3. *The Inside Story of Narcotics* by Jim Vaus. Grand Rapids: Zondervan Publications, 2nd printing, 1953.

Randy Roark

The Side Show

Near the Pompideau Museum "Sketches of Spain" above plastic
tables in an afternoon McDonalds,
On the Hebridean shore a long-haired tabby warms herself in mid-
September sun,
On a 3 a.m. balcony overlooking the Sahara, near Giza on the Nile's
West Bank, where dynasties buried their dead beneath the
setting sun and Pharaohs built temples, halls and cities,
Looking eastwards toward Cairo's 16 million faces under a blue moon,
New Year's Eve, 1990,
Near Sumer, Ur, and Eden, where four lanes of nervous traffic circle
an almost faceless statue of Ramses in the city's central square,
Or the blackened eyes at the end of the Greek street when you know
you're lost,
Or alone in Rome among red-faced afternoon Italian pensioners,
graveled hands in worn pockets, or crumpled over damp-
tipped cigarettes,
Twilight bats out of the old oak, moths in streets of plexiglass
patisseries, pastry shops, and sidewalk cafés all closed,
Walking toward the Paris Opera, up rain-slick Champs-Élysées to
American Express, bon jour!
Or at dusk, under an awning, the hills of Aegena a darker shade of
blue, returning on a ferry from the temple of Apollo, reading
"Phaedrus" by party lights while the villagers doze
On a grassy fall to the sea, granite fragments and humming
broadcast towers, the grocery store, post office, and petrol
station all-in-one,
And farther along the harbor shore a tavern on the dock where
tourists share a laugh before boarding the crowded Sunday ferry,
Or on the stone Venetian quay, granite marble worn grey,
Sunlight like acetylene on the waves near San Marco where an old man
showed me the Doge's barge for real.

Steam and fog lower along the spires of Chartres Cathedral
Where a teenager pays five francs, climbs the early morning mist,
looks down from the *flamboyant* tower and leaps to the wet
pavement below,
Delaying our tour, and later, the double doors opened, seven
pallbearers stumbling into the silver air, the trembling dust,

Pale blue stones of Medieval Chartres, the rough-hewn bridges,
willows tilted toward the stream,
The Northern Express past Parisian billboards, cafés open after
midnight, no moon but yellow neon city glow
Beside the Aegean, north of Sounion and its glassy blue port, where
summer's lazy yachts rock and cappuccino is served on lacy
china blue formica tables, green apples in the sun —
Young Greeks leaping up stone-stepped piers slapping squid on the
cobblestones to soften them up —
Later the morning's transparent blue-silver catch is spread on ice
beneath souvenirs and postcards,
Where the young fish clerk waves a haddock in my face, slapping
my cheek with plump fish fingers, laughing at my surprise,
And evening dinnertime traffic clusters in the city's shimmering red
sunset.

Above Lisboa the climb to the abandoned stone fortress overlooking
the old city where the sun's silver glare lights red pottery roofs,
Or outside the Museo Portugal where the city's homeless sleep on
slatted benches or in the park's shade above industrial harbors,
cranes and steam.

Fog gathers on the Seine, tourist boats wallow in the surf. Grey
metallic tides wash vermilion prows.
The antique untouchable windows of the Quay Napoleon
on the road to Notre Dame
Where gyspy jugglers steal your wallet in December sunlight,
afternoon streets full, no one rushing, everyone smiling,
leaning on black metal fences,
And an elegant gentleman in a three-piece suit touches my shoulder,
points to my open map and says, "Do you know where you
are?"
And I say, "Oui, monsieur, merci, bon jour," — I am in Paris —
City of Apollinaire, Baudelaire, Rimbaud, Rousseau, Picasso, Stein,
And Seurat, whose harebrained theory gave us "Sideshow," "Sunday
in the Park," and "Bareback Rider,"
And a camouflaged Legionnaire swings his automatic weapon
toward me, smiling, everyone smiling, "Bon jour, monsieur, is
beauty today, no?"
Pointing to the Seine, oily and grey.
Iron gaurdrails, military shenanigans, the city's on strike but tour
buses surround the Louvre,
The street a moving mental canvas of light and sound,
The Eiffel Tower undisturbed in the hysteria of springtime and

raucous backstreets, pavilions and embassies where green-suited Israeli policemen point their leather-strapped Uzis at me as I pass.

It's an orderly demonstration. Young women squawk into microphones, their bored voices echoing from the roofs of black Peugeots, the restless crowd shouting listlessly "Oui" and "Non" on cue —
The city in flames, the Plaza de Concorde a swirl of military green and overturned personnel carriers, bonfires on stone bridges — militia, barricades, slogans, adolescents, grey-haired grandparents in workclothes, suits with bandanas, ready to riot — someone's mother cradling a smiling teenaged bleeding girl.

It's Sunday. The Cathedral chimes across the Tuilleries where businessmen exchange silver coins with sidewalk vendors for Gitanos and pause for news, smoke above their caps, their ancient glittering eyes —
The curving cool shadowed streets, the worn silver stone sidewalks leading to blue-tiled buildings with battle scenes of helmeted horsemen pulling down palisades, bodies limp as laundry on leather-covered hooves —
Or in Rome where from under a campanile a flock of Spanish sparrows thicken into a sudden wind, a roar of wings, thousands in shrill maddening ascent, blackening the sun, swirling back to earth to plunge into an empty Trevi fountain shattering themselves.

Eros Embroidered (After Louis Aragon)

I remember your shoulder
when in spite of everything
the spirit of mystery rose
out of your half-light.

Or the sun even when it's dark
and incomparable between us —
when the sleepless children gaze on a world that's
gone, the past cracking and the sky about to fall —
the scarlet blood of roses on your way home,
the atmosphere spinning, the road humming with bees.

*

Summer, why are you writing, white on blue,
in the sky? Why this flaming wall of primroses?
Seasons pass with their trembling, tumbling down
like children on the shoulders of strange men
while the gold of the barns gleams in your hair
and your silent wingbeats join
your velvet Breughel to this Breughel of hell.

*

Changed this autumn into dream,
you grew cold and lost your gleam
under green waters of stillness,
my illness finally come clear to me —

*

Your dress is thin enough — why draw it aside?
So totally nude I can barely believe my eyes —
we were lovers then and our only beds were
each other's arms, your hands like flame and snow —

it was in your fingers, now dust, that you
first appeared to me — one night
do you remember? We were on the road
and your smile raised me from the dead.

Psilocybin at Estes Park, 13 Nov. 1999

Outside there's thousands of stars,
and two bayberry candles — inside,
I'm wondering where everything fits
and where it's headed.

The music's loud; I can almost hear
Billie Holiday sigh, and outside
there's cigarettes, and those thousands
of stars, and inside Katie's
just walked across the room —
and here's her thigh against my knee,
and here's her arm against my arm.

The Trip

if we were free of suffering,
then we would be free of
joy — for every joy there's an
equal & opposite sadness; so
why bother? When sorrow comes,
I welcome her like an old friend, &
happiness like one who shall someday steal my silver, because one must
suffer & cannot turn away.
We pass through different stations
at the same time, arriving too early
or too late to hear each other's story
above the train, and leave alone
no matter our companions.
But beneath that fear
what joy, what freedom!

Nina Zivancevic

from Shahnameh Diwan

after Ferdowsi

I am a Persian rose,
I am a Sasanian princess,
I am cobalt blue sky,
I am a mountain lioness
I am Abd-al-Aziz's lover
I am a swift gazelle made of wind,
I am a soothing harp,
I am a drop from my father's fountain,
I am a sacred manuscript behind
an illuminated door,
I am a porcelain warrior,
I am formless foam resting
on the winged bull's mouth,
I am a bright sabre cutting the day off from night,
I am the lightest feather in the Sultan's coronary
turban. I am a gilded gameboard awaiting the moment
to be lacquered, I am the black lacquer on a
concubine's finger, I am
of red color and transparent background,
when you smile I am
and I am not
a rose

Healer's Wife

She sits quietly
waiting for dawn,
she is a restless sleep, she is a cuckoo's song,
she is the lady-in-attendance to
someone's crystalline heart,
she, the crystal herself,
reflects dark light
from the depths of all sorrow,
mirage of stumbling pain, she
absorbs sustained miracles, delayed deaths

and successful cures, a cure herself she
hardly moves, her silent lips tremble
her long hands touch the one-who-tires
from seeing the sick and the fleeting
all day and all the same,
to her it seems larger than life to watch
him breathe her breath
in and out as he sleeps
recovering his dreams about the distant
provinces of sky, as she,
attentive, keeps his heavy hair
from falling into his nightmares
of hermeticism, where she
takes off her clothes and closes her eyes
once every thousand years

Brave Song

Oh, smell of oranges in the New York City subway,
Sufi incense burners,
Eric crying like a mad woman, cold October,
too much sadness, bill collectors threatening
to arrest me, and then — this heavenly music
taking over the 42nd Street Station,
when I hear music I always feel divine —
and I always hear music and so I am in heaven,
it comes from eating very little they say,
it comes from bounced cheques they say,
it comes from selling fake coins they say,
but then… this music and this incense and the smell of
oranges — comes from being too thin, they say,
it comes from studying experimental theater they say,
it comes from eating too many donuts they say,
it comes from bad lovers who tell sad stories they say,
it comes from meditating, it comes through gossip,
it comes from nowhere and is nothing, invisible,
and there it stays, jolting me somehow

Winter Song

Winter is here
        as are the homeless and the starving
filling my heart with hope
as I walk up and down
        Central Park's condensed crust
and the rest of the poem
                is washed away
though some of my poems are here to stay…

        But dare I say
that the crickets are also here
tonight supporting the lanterns,
luminous showers of reality, as I descend
the Three-Jewelled staircase
it is so dark all around me,
so predictably silent and unfair…

Ancient Verse

While reading the Ancient verse
of old masters of poetry
one could find an almost acute
feeling of reverence for nature
and the absolute — no personal
pronouns used, no dates, no days,
no names to encourage our failed self-natures, no
Allen to tell me, "We are all bad students, you know,"
and the foliage, the deep red ocher of the minced
foliage pressed by my feet
under the Bo-tree where
my bound spirit
dwells night and day...

Jürgen Ploog

Facts of Presence

Writing takes me to a lost city which I found through experimenting, ignoring all the rules of reality. If you defy the rules the spatial dimension shifts and the reality picture reveals its chaotic structure, because what reality is, is a picture. It's like merging with a forgotten part of your body — the missing link to survival under prevailing conditions — reaching places where you might have never been before — you might have passed them without realising where you were. This is a way to get orientated before things happen under historic conditions... orientation after the fact...

The City is electronically illuminated & has a matrix of dark areas. Easy to get lost there in the visions of the dead. The dead are masters of time, they decide *when* things take place, not *where*. The *where* is part of the physical dimension & related to the body. No body, no *where* & vice versa.

I am haunted by memories of a hidden plan. Nothing happens without a will would be another way of saying it. Not, why does it happen, but at what intersection of time & space, which means that you can only figure it out if you move both in time & space. They are inseparable but watch out for the warps they form. It is form that makes things tangible. Form is the guideline through the storm of materials & particles in a place of infinite possibilities. The road of words vanishes in the fabric of pictures. If you follow that road you will find the picture. Words are the traces you leave behind, helpful but disposable, marking the borderline of night beyond which the real & the fictional blend in a shift of perception. No point in asking on which side of the track you are on. Even the most seemingly unrelated phenomenon are tied by the act of observation. To notice them means they are reflections in the sensual mirror of bio-energetic fields. Facts of presence.

Memory doesn't play straight. It is a myriad of episodes flashing through the brain, stored to form a map of consequences which acts as a pool of experience.

No one is without a name, yet very few know their real name. Replicants use the drug of character to play convenient roles in a scenery of virtual images on a hidden picture; protoplasmic databases of social codes; missing persons of the original script of meaning written a long time ago & destroyed by martial searches & campaigns. Talk is in vain. Out of desperation I keep in touch with an agent who presumes the manuscript has been taken to Tangier. My guess is that it never left Berlin. There are indications that it was transcribed into a film script, its meaning hidden in trivial plots of sex & crime. Through an Arab the agent meets an old European who tells him "this is a land of ceremonies and rituals". He insists that he is in telepathic contact with prisoners in Israel & involved in a conspiracy concerning levitation. As a cover I write about the subject of time, searching for the ultimate global loneliness. I have published a thesis explaining that it is one of the most neglected factors of the world wide web & induces individuals to fade out of sight by providing them with a transpersonal biography.

Together with Bernie the hacker the agent is working on a pre-recorded pattern of psychedelically accelerated travelling. Speed blurs the geographic perception thus creating the illusion that the traveller is moving in time & space. He is subjected to kaleidoscopic visions of the endless inner Cities of Globeville, leaving behind familiar codes of linear memory. In a sequence of fast cuts the pace picks up. Flying is a state of mind while watching a Bogart movie, the body is ushered to a neural continent. The streets of the city are transformed into artefacts of silent language. The script writer is searching the archives for fictitious angles. The flow of pictures turns the spectators into nomads. In an outbreak of depression there is an eruption of cosmic violence, caused by a girl who is being treated for a scorpion bite. She gets on everybody's nerves with suggestions of sex. She treats her partners like a transparent picture of herself. She keeps repeating that she is looking for an *outpost* relationship…

The perspective of space shifts like a film set. I wake up in a small hotel with my ego on my lap not knowing what to do with it. Agents are ransacking the room looking for the lost manuscript. I'm tied to a chair watching the scene.

"Where the hell is it?" one of them asks.

"It hasn't been written, dummy."

"Check the genetic file," the agent tells another guy.

They pull hair from my head and put it under a microscope. They are unable to figure out the code. As they are leaving, one says: "Maybe the woman has it."

Behind a backdrop of suburbs there is a small hotel by a lagoon. Lemurs sit in trees. Stretched out in a hammock the girl tells me that there were other men before me. Her breath brushes against me like a scorpion's tail. In a dream the noises of the jungle take on the sound of death. The girl is now close to a window, watching herself in a mirror, masturbating.

The planet is blockaded by those who think gravity is enough to catch up with time. Whole regions are blacked out. Memory is drowned in darkness. Hallucinatory perspective might be the only way out because it incorporates chance. As the speed of perception accelerates the traveller changes into an explorer of silence. Remnants of ancient cultures fade in with the landscape. Ruins rise out of the blue fog of the lost continent of Mu.

My biography strikes me as a farewell to biological idiosyncrasy. The I, the ego, the me has lost all meaning. Gravity pertains to nakedness. The reproduction cycle has become relentless. With identity & meaning there is no way a man can turn. Destiny lies in the presence, the moment of being… in a silver streak of frozen film.

In a briefing room where pilots prepare for takeoff to become sailors of the sky… winds from far away constellations hit downtown buildings evoking insanity, a state of restlessness & destruction. Resorts are struck by tourist fever. The girl I am with is floating through a deserted casino like a trapeze artist. She puts on a mask and falls into a trancelike state. What language do you speak? I ask her. She replies that she does not speak at all while she is on the screen. "I have lost my distance." Her tricks confuse me. She bows to an invisible audience, & her mute body fades into darkness.

A stale breath of sand & heat hangs over the City. Final words move across time & space leaving a trail of deadly messages.

Joanne Kyger

Bring Your Jungle Along

for Kevin

Full of sledge hammers and compassion —
of which the latter is exactly what?

Bleeding heart liberal do-gooder
bullshit come
passion

(which at least produces outrage
before exhaustion sets in)

Or working through   the words of 'forgiveness'
or whatever the blank you want to call it

Like 'I know our ancestors once belonged
to countries that tried to wipe each other out *entirely*'
spoils of war and subjugate etc. But forget it!
Forgive. It's all in the past.

It's this minute that's important
between you and me, and of course
the future of this minute

and how its course is already set, that minute
behind us called history. And of course we read

so we remember. And how *were* you to know.

February 23, 1998 5 p.m.

‘Send some kind of sign at least’

‘Nothing matters. You do not matter. You are not
    worth telling the truth to. Your most deeply
      held belief, your most pressing need
        is nothing’
          Do you feel an insane rage, a desperate
    falling away

Welcome back to your life,   she says.
    I see a new flicker

          feather lying on the front
    porch like a calling card. Matching the two
        placed with the bell on the door.
          My heart
pounds. Can life
    be so good, am I recognized?

July 24, 1998

Stupidly Inspired

It’s true

the cricket ate the lace curtain in the studio,   not
relegating itself merely to the hearth, escorted

out the door rapidly in a teacup. There. You’ll like it
better in the wild world of woodchips and ferns.

‘Bad Vibes’ a mere drape
for the deeper expositions of life and words. Something
meaningful about existence, awareness of enlightenment
in a lifetime. Get it while you’re alive, can’t find it

when your dead. The simple timeless ‘it’s all right’ satori
no no, that’s right,   you got it right,   believe it.

March 21, 1998

Raphael Aladdin Cohen

from Fool's Paradise

At first when I went there I saw trees adorned with wigs of leaves,
the sky reaching into the Ocean and pulling out the sunrise as if
it were a rabbit on fire. I saw my dreams being scattered over the hills and
valleys in shades of black.
I was made from the Universe, Alchemy, and Mount Olympus.
I was born out of the volcano gold and red with the savage eyes of
an executioner.
Many times I returned tongue in hand, foot in mouth, like a fool
awkward and eager, my brain on fire bleeding through my nose,
my ears, my eyes, my mouth.
What an absurd sight, me trying to catch my brain in buckets!
Finally perching myself on some vulgar outspoken rock. Letting the desire
suffocate me with its unquenchable thirst.

°

Once when I was naked parading through timeless ceaseless galaxies
lavishing myself with visions too beautiful for written words.
I was a vagabond girl. I was a bird full of pride, soaring with the grace of
a symphony. I was the rocks, the waves, the colors of the sunset. Things
that mortal man could never hope to be. Now I am dressed in a uniform
which cripples me with every passing moment until finally I am covered in
sweat and weeping.
O human race, you are tearing me apart!

Paul Grillo

Initiation of The Dreamwarrior

As a boy he always felt himself
        lost

Night always taking him into its hands
splattering his face with might-have-beens
teasing him with its purple orchids
pushing him toward the breezy way
        out

Confirming each worst fear
he could float in his veins

The exact day & year remain a mystery
when he first heard the ultramagnetic drone
of the rainforest Summer
gnawing at him in the dead of Winter
and it dawned in him that he might be
        a mystic

Able to mix with angelic tribes
and find himself
wearing their hats, boots, gloves & umbrellas
as tokens of their ritual trust

Thrones & Powers of the oddest descriptions
might find him at any time or place

Here a New Guinea headhunting shaman
there a business traveller
dressed like Rimbaud

They taught him to speak the language
        of dolphins
and assured him his heart was first and forever
exactly and always in the right place

He learned to read the weather of dreams
like the lining of a Magritte topcoat
or the eyeblinks behind a penitent mask

He has become a man perpetually caught
        on the rebound
happening into and threatening battles
cutting words he may fear into brilliant starshapes

Divinations redder than red

So it is today
that near the height of his powers
he hears a quiet storm brewing
behind a black door

Refusing to leave the streets & subways
savoring the Present
paying homage to its Past

Like the morphic milk of love's perfect gift
before it changes to freezing
        rain

Deserted Cities of The Heart

Children hunt fallen stars in the city
Again & again
the owl's head turns on a heartbeat
Stolen tongues flame
in the dark-veined silence
Mechanical shoulders batter the air
The red guns of a previous life
fall into the room
rinsing your pores in a flood
of dead letters

Voyager Caged, Voyager Transported

The harbor lights spread their anxious accents

deep sea blues
weeping willow blues
blues without a change of heart

In Brussels
The Father of Chaos unravels a mammoth ball
  of twine
and uses the string to plot
direct lines from every corner of his lonely room
to the untapped surface behind
  the stars…

a runway beckoning ancient skyships

Mendicant ospreys scout over the sea
as much to uncover as to conceal
  its glories

other lips other arms
other drugs
other weapons

On a houseboat in Amsterdam
the woman who talked back to the earth
deciphers the handwriting on the wall
and finds the purple smudge
on one of her windows
to be a roadmap to another dimension

Where a winded diver squats like a frog
among the tangled nets of spheres
seeking to free himself
from a promising future

While high in the Catalan mountains of Spain
the keeper of the Scarlet Book conjures the descent
  of an angel
into the desert of this world's moment
both to reveal and cover its most luminous
  clues

other cargoes
other gods

Rendezvous on The Edge of Autumn's Crystal

Ira Cohen's New York

The waking artist must again be prepared
to recognize the small grey whispers of the Marvellous
behind the static bodymaps & quasi-sadistic overflow
of a life of routine

His is the excited heart of an ostrich
too vast & noble to be depicted accurately
either at the beginning or end of his most proximate
fantasies

The presence of Memory never thins in him
even as the steel rings of Love & Illumination close him
in their most calculated & erotic embrace

He knows his timeless powers are almost invincible
and that the frenzied indigo of the still-wide skies
is both deeper & more luminous than it seems

Even as he knows the sado-romantic inclination
of each human soul
to revive timequotes from the pleasure of an older era
he sees there are no songs at all
without the wild revolutionary ballads moving on the lips
of meccano set buildings
which he has both sutured & loosed with his madcap video
finger painting

He is a darkling traveller from future centuries
& worlds long-vanished
who recalls with exacting humor & cutting grace
all those times & places where his most likeable friends
professed their most luxuriant stories & unprotected scams
of the Imagination

where the darkest angels of akashic cabarets & West Side
machineshops
came to be crushed
only that they might glow in the discovery
of the darkest poetry each one of them found they carried
within themselves

He sees now how self-hindsight has vanished
on nothing less than the wind-blown tails
        of the Kabbalist's frockcoat
whose delicate & forceful silhouette warmed a need
        in him
for confessing to neither charisma nor necktie
while roving the perilous edge of redemption
to grasp at first breath the opalescent bangles
        & forbidden diadems of the Dream

Tonight he finds himself pausing among the mute
        chairs & soundless paintings
in a room of burning cravats & frozen oysters
where beautiful women adored in life
as in the wayfaring shrine of the arterial darkroom
make their entrance again from Bombay talkies
        & Abyssinian bars
from the saffron plush of dawn on the Ganges
and the ice caves of the Canal Street Local
from a sliding door on the secrets of Limehouse
from the sex shop windows of Amsterdam & L.A.
naked as words like "speculation" or "doubt"

Unscheduled mysteries work their sideway glances
and the sky of the ceiling is once again scented
with the patchouli of shoulders that once tore his eyes out
        on the way from the movies
while the Milky Way leaks its chance-encounter tattoos
from the sibylline faucets of the Black Narcissus
        Hotel

Red Tide/Migrations of Blue

Kodachrome sunsets flare over the country
their embers sealing the bruise
of the sky
Rivers of thunder or maybe
blood

Starcrossed hands
comb the long hair of photos
blooming in luxuriant buried forms
below & around the windows
& doors
flowing room to room
like stems without roots
stretching their seasons
of long-silent fury

The nocturnal beasts arrive
shy & silent
fresh from their flight
through the Land of Fire
where golden bones astonish the gauchos
and bananas gleam beneficially
blue

On an improvised bridge at the edge
of harvest
twice-told drifters seek the snakebite
of love

RUCIANELLI

John Lennon:
Lennon & His

Becchina

This drawing is like the last days of Winter and the first days of Spring, when the wild lilac cyclamen appear and the Willow tree by the stream is covered with blooms like silver mice. Becchina is our Mother sheep with a black auburn fleece and 'nobile' profile.

Sultana.
Vali Myers 71·72·73

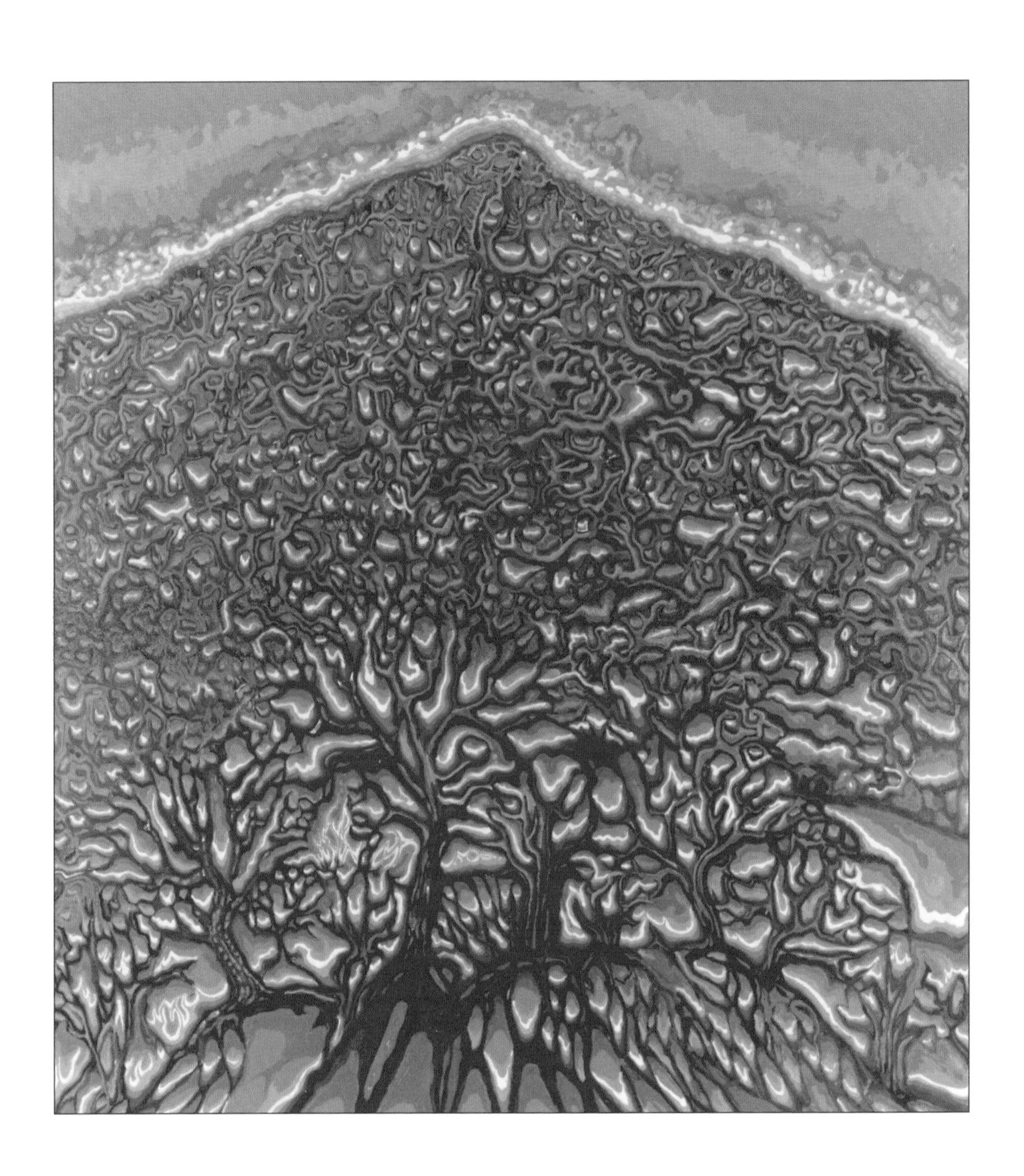

Roselle Angwin

Two for Dharma

1

On the Road

for Jack Kerouac, 1922-69

You died just before I met you.
Not much changes. America, Vietnam. America, Iraq.
Sadism, 'cleansings', Kosovo.

Here we are still sitting,
still praying, those of us who are alive,
like Desolation Angels at the hem of apocalypse

as the earth spins in its dance through space in this
accelerating universe of stars and black holes.
Same diet: hopes, dreams, fears.

Tending the fires. What else is there to do?

2

You ask why I live where I do

Seeking freedom
we still live in chains
civilisation gets in the way
fills up the cracks where It
might slip through, sweeps
it all too clean.

What liberates
are these correspondences:
ocean mind, heart speaking to heart,
to be intimate with sky
clouds trees. To travel
beyond the names of things.

After the Wilderness

I have only to call
and It is here with me
I have only to step outside
for it to reclaim me, this
fierce stillness

this light, this wonder
that flames the blood
that sings
in the silence of the vast night

this baptism of fire
which gives us wings

Merrivale

To fling oneself down on cool turf
to be swallowed by dark earth
or translated into starfire
to be a body of water
leaping the long fall into sea
or on the winds' wings
to go sailing into the now —
to lose and find oneself again.

Shapeshifting

How we shied round each other —
now wolf, now deer —

I fell into your smile
wanted to kiss it
looked and looked again —

you were gone into everywhere
the world poured through you.

Hookney Tor

There is no-one here
to witness my flight
save buzzard and raven,
the hidden eyes of
adder, weasel, stone.

I have no wings
but I am in flight
the rocks are my witness
the rocks, and these ancient
thorns, and the stream
calling to itself in the valley.

I am no different
from this hillside,
this bracken, this
springy new-grown turf.
I'm the eyes in the stone,
the breath in the tree,
the voice of the stream;
my wings are the wind.

Here there are no borders;
boundaries are meaningless.
Rocks become trees, become
lichen, moss, leaf.
The wind carries my thoughts
away, lends me his voice…

I move, fluid as water, through
night and day, light and shade.
Here I am not who I think I am.
Here I play with the universe.

I am old as the stars
through whose night-sea I swim,
and I am newborn,
made again each moment.

David Levi Strauss

Take As Needed

Therapeutic Art & Images in Context

Just after I moved from San Francisco to New York, I got into one of those whiskey-at-the-kitchen-table conversations with a sculptor friend and her neighbour about art in hospitals. The neighbour was all for putting paintings, sculpture and photographs into hospitals, as long as the images were suitably "agreeable and soothing." She explained that since people in hospitals felt bad, the images put there should be cheery ones, to make them feel better. The sculptor and I countered that this criteria would only ensure the selection of mediocre art and sentimental images. We argued that the art put into hospitals should be the best art one could find and pay for, regardless of mood, and that only really good, transformative art could possibly be therapeutic. The neighbor dismissed our arguments as elitist and self-serving, and went back to her drink.

Soon after this conversation, I injured my shoulder and was hospitalized for reconstructive surgery. In the ensuing months of therapy and examinations in the hospital and in various doctors' offices and clinics, I studied the images on the walls of these therapeutic institutions. What I found, almost without exception, was bad art: color photographs of cocker spaniel puppies perched precariously on saddles, incomparably bad reproductions of Monet's *Water Lilies*, pictures of Jesus of the sort one gets free when buying cheap frames, and a vast array of anaesthetic landscapes.

These images are there because they are entirely in keeping with the allopathic approach: if one is sick and feeling bad, one must be treated with anodyne images, to make one feel better. Allopathy is the type of medicine currently practiced in most hospitals and by most doctors in the United States and Europe. Its basic method is to treat symptoms, rather than causes, by introducing something against ("allo" is Greek for "otherwise" or "against") the symptomatic effect. Samuel Hahnemann, who coined the term allopathy at the beginning of the nineteenth century to distinguish this type of medicine from homeopathy ("like cures like"), called allopathy, "The curing of a diseased action by the inducing of another of a different kind, yet not necessarily diseased." The idea is that if you can make the symptoms go away, however briefly, the underlying problem miraculously disappears as well. The allopathic ideology extends far beyond medicine, and is perhaps most clearly seen in U.S. international policy ("surgical strikes" in Desert Storm, dropping food pallets from the air to crush starving Kurds, killing people to save them from hunger in Somalia), and domestic crime policy, (the burgeoning prison industry, the War on Drugs, calls for the death penalty). I also believe the allopathic approach explains a great deal about how images are used and treated in this society.

When I returned from the hospital after my operation, my four-and-a-half-year-old daughter Maya gave me a very different kind of picture. It was a drawing she'd made on lined, violet-colored paper. Two sheets of the paper were taped together at a slight angle, and a fat green line ran from one end to the other, bisected by many crossing lines in orange. This thermometer or spinal cord image was crooked near the bottom, where some energetically drawn lines in black and yellow tied it all together. When Maya handed me this picture, she told me it would make my shoulder better. She instructed me to keep it near me at all times and to drape it over my injury whenever I could, especially at night. Over the next three months, she made sure I followed her instructions, and scolded me whenever I forgot to use the image properly.

My daughter's therapeutic image was a practical talismanic device to aid in healing. No one told my daughter that images can be therapeutic — she just knew it. This is in fact very old knowledge, going back at least to the Mousterian era when Neanderthals carved parallel and diagonal lines and painted red circles on bone and stone, and continuing in Western civilisation through the Renaissance. Though dealt a crushing blow by the Reformation, this kind of medical knowledge has managed to survive even into the twenty-first century, if one knows where to look for it. It has also survived in most five-year-olds.

These non-allopathic approaches recognize that images and symbols are real, and that the crystallisation of a desire or concept in the form of an image can become a potent agent, directly effecting the course of events.

Now it could be argued that the cuddly-cocker-spaniel-on-the-saddle image might also be an effective agent, for someone. But when I hear healthy people say that sick people want to look at "agreeable, soothing" images, I wonder. Do they? Do you? Or does the allopathic image, like allopathic medicine, only work in certain very limited situations? If you break an arm or a leg, you want an allopath. They're very good at mechanical fixes. If you suffer major trauma or injury to your body, you need an allopath. But for anything more subtle, like chronic conditions, systematic diseases, or for the subtle art of healing after surgery or wounding, allopaths are almost entirely useless. I suspect that the same is true of allopathic images.

Very little is known at this point about the actual physiological effects of images. What happens to the autonomic nervous system, to neurotransmitters and hormones, when a person is moved by an image? Recent brain research has found physiological links between the parts of the brain responsible for image-processing and the immune system. But such connections are still viewed with suspicion or disdain by the allopathic orthodoxy, which defends the dichotomy between an objective, material world in which certainty and laws prevail (science), and a subjective world of mind which is largely an internal affair (art). This split is becoming more and more untenable, certainly in the area of health and healing. At a time when almost everyone agrees that the U. S. healthcare system is so badly broken that all the king's horses and all the king's men, women, and paid consultants are not going to be able to put it back together again, many healthcare practitioners and patients are becoming more open to "alternative" therapies and approaches.

At the same time, the AIDS crisis has underscored the limitations and failures of allopathy and of the total healthcare system, and has also caused renewed interest in the therapeutic image and the place of art in healing. This, coupled with the impact of feminism on the art world since 1970, has resulted in more art of social engagement and therapeutic intent.

The sculptor's neighbor in the kitchen held that demand for transformative power in such therapeutic art is elitist and beside the point. This view is mirrored in the attitudes of some socially engaged artists and the institutions that support them, who act as if socially therapeutic art should not be judged aesthetically or in terms of its transformative power, but only by the correctness of its therapeutic stance, however that is (conventionally) conceived.

In *The Invisible Dragon: Four Essays on Beauty,* Dave Hickey recognizes this as the latest (and perhaps last) manifestation of "the waning aegis of the therapeutic institution," wherein art is deemed to be *good* for you. In Hickey's view, this thoroughly modern (not to say modernist) idea has led to a kind of domestication of art, with an intent to break its spirit, to make it "agreeable and soothing," educational and uplifting, and thoroughly acceptable. Within this debased frame, individuals are forced into a set relationship with works of art, "victimized by their philosophical force and ruthless authority." Outside the therapeutic institution, where beauty rages, the "vertiginous bond of trust between the image and the beholder is private, voluntary, a little scary, and since the experience is not presumed to be an end in itself, it might, ultimately, have some consequence." [1]

Hickey's condemnation of the therapeutic institution is total: "Thus has the traditional, contractual alliance between the image and its beholder (of which beauty is the signature, and in which there is no presumption of received virtue) been supplanted by a hierarchical one between Art, presumed virtuous, and a beholder presumed to be in need of it." Physicians say that pain has no usefulness "after the initial insult," and Hickey would say the same thing about the therapeutic institution.

Hickey's view of the therapeutic in art runs directly counter to that of Donald Kuspit. In *The New Subjectivism,* Kuspit describes contemporary art as "caught in a tug-of-war between what can be called the media and therapeutic conceptions of art," [2] with Andy Warhol holding the media end of the rope, and Joseph Beuys anchoring the therapeutic end. And in *The Cult of the Avant-Garde Artist*, Kuspit contends that modernist art has always been essentially therapeutic in intention, while the "neo-avant-garde" or postmodernist art is not. In terms apposite to those used by Hickey, Kuspit describes the "masochistic scepticism about art" in postmodernism, wherein art is made "with little or no expectation of any positive human gain from it, and certainly with no conviction in its healing power." And Andy is left holding the rope: "Warhol's art signals the end of the belief in the therapeutic power of art. It exists to disillusion us about art, and is an art of disillusionment. As such, it is the first genuinely postmodernist art." [3]

In a third formulation, Thomas McEvilley, writing on the work of Wolfgang Laib, says that the therapeutic intent in art is "pre-modern," and its revival is "a secondarily post-Modern position." McEvilley sees the issue of the therapeutic as defining contemporary positions. "The Modernist finds the pre-Modernist view of art as magical therapy naïve and superstitious; but the neo-pre-Modernist sees the Modernist worship of pure forms for themselves, with no additional therapeutic end, as soulless, frivolous, and irresponsible. (The post-Modernist, meanwhile, looks sideways at the discussion, finding both criticisms valid and hence both positions distasteful for different reasons.) [4]

Hickey views the therapeutic in art as authoritarian and insulting, Kuspit sees it as liberating, and McEvilley approaches it as a question of utility. Behind each of these characterizations of the therapeutic are quite different ideas about agency and effect in art. And that argument is at least as old as Plato and Aristotle. In book ten of the *Republic,* Plato challenged the lovers of art "to plead her cause and show that she is not only delightful, but beneficial to orderly government and human life," and people have been coming forward to testify in court and before Congress to that effect ever since. The longevity of the argument marks its importance.

But where is the evidence for the therapeutic value of art? The therapeutic value of *making* the work is well known, and generally accepted. But what is the therapeutic value of the work for the beholder? Can beauty heal? Can an image have a therapeutic effect? What would such a therapeutic image look like?

In European art, one of the most powerful examples of the therapeutic in art is the Isenheim Altarpiece, painted by Mathias Gothart Nithart (a. k. a. Grünewald) at the beginning of the sixteenth century. The Isenheim Altarpiece has been called the most imposing single monument of German painting, but it is only recently that scholars have focused on the actual therapeutic context and effects of this work.

Near the end of the thirteenth century, the Antonite order built a monastery with a hospital, hospice, and lazar house (from Lazarus — a lazar was a diseased beggar) attached to it, near the village of Isenheim in Alsace. The Antonites quickly had their hands and halls full, due to the explosive spread of infectious diseases during the Middle Ages. In addition to leprosy, plague, epilepsy, various other blood and skin diseases, and their speciality, "St. Anthony's Fire," the Antonites were nearly overwhelmed by the syphilis epidemic that ravaged Europe at the end of the fifteenth century.

In addition to caring for the sick, the Antonites, and the Isenheim monastery in particular, had a reputation for art patronage, thanks to the large endowments of their foundations. At the beginning of the sixteenth century the Sicilian abbot Guido Guersi invited Grünewald to come to the monastery to work. It is believed that between 1512 and 1516, when Guersi died, Grünewald produced the monumental altarpiece at Isenheim.

The work is composed of nine huge painted panels depicting the Incarnation, Annunciation, Crucifixion, Lamentation, and Resurrection of Christ, as well as two scenes from the life of the order's patron saint, St. Anthony, and portraits of St. Anthony and St. Sebastian. The panels are hinged and attached to the existing framework of the altar, so that they can be opened like wings to form different configurations or states. In its closed state, the work shows the Crucifixion, flanked by St. Sebastian on the left (probably a self-portrait of the artist) and St. Anthony on the right, with a predella below picturing the Lamentation for the dead Christ. When the first wings are opened, a second large center panel is revealed, showing the Incarnation (Madonna and Child with angelic concert). It is flanked by the Annunciation on the left and the Resurrection on the right. Opened yet again, the original carved shrine (by a previous artist) is revealed, with statues of St. Augustine, St. Anthony, and St. Jerome, and smaller figures of Christ and the twelve apostles below. Grünewald's painted wings in the open state depict the meeting of Anthony and Paul in the Wilderness on the left, and the Temptation of St. Anthony on the right.

Set up in all its glory in the stained glass and candlelit sanctuary at Isenheim, Grünewald's masterpiece must have operated something like a motion picture, revealing itself over time and repeated viewings. The configuration of the panels changed according to the liturgical year, but its unfolding was certainly also performed daily, for each new influx of patients. It was the therapeutic center of the hospital, the base from which all other treatments grew.

Although the paintings do draw on the traditional iconic healing power of images of saints (St. Anthony for St. Anthony's Fire, St. Sebastian for the Plague, St. John the Evangelist, and St. John the Baptist for epilepsy), this was only the beginning. Eventually nearly every category of therapeutic image was put into play, including the instructional (in the botanically precise renderings of medicinal herbs and other plants), the healing narrative (with images for each stage of the healing process), the direct physiological effects of light and color, and the homeopathic realism of its depictions of specific illnesses and their symptoms. All the magical, apotropaic, and cathartic devices employed in Grünewald's work were activated by what might be called the work's *therapeutic realism.*

Many commentators in the past have characterized the Isenheim Altarpiece as a work of fantasy — grotesque and transcendent. But more recent writers have recognized the anatomical accuracy of Grünewald's depictions of pathological states, in the diseased and putrefying syphilitic body and *facies Hippocratis* of Christ in the Crucifixion and Lamentation, the suppurating sores of the gangrenous victim of St. Anthony's Fire in The Temptation of St. Anthony, the wounds of St. Sebastian, and the apoplectic grief of the Virgin Mary before the crucified Christ.

It is clear that the accuracy of anatomical detail in the work is due to Grünewald's years of direct observation in the hospital and hospice of Isenheim. He took the patients as models, so they could recognize themselves in the work that he made for them. As art historian Linda Nochlin once put it, Grünewald "must surely have mused over plague victims, as intrigued by their suppurating boils as Monet was by the green shadows on the skin of his dead wife."

Even the infernal monsters in the Temptation of St. Anthony panel appear less fantastic when one realizes the probable state of the patients for whom this panel was intended. Art historian Andrée Hayum points out that the disease called St. Anthony's Fire was most likely caused by ergot poisoning (from the fungus growing on grains), so in addition to its other symptoms it probably induced vivid lysergic acid hallucinations in its victims. [5] The ultimate bad trip of St. Anthony, depicted here as being stomped by a gang of bat-winged behemoths, a club-wielding Hitchcock bird, ape-dog demons, and a small dragon with the head of a turkey, was probably something quite familiar to residents of the Antonite hospice.

There is nothing "agreeable and soothing" about these parts of Grünewald's therapeutic masterpiece. To the healthy, they are extremely disturbing. The great Cuban poet José Lezama Lima called the Crucifixion scene, with its depiction of a diseased Christ, "an intolerable image." But to the patients of Isenheim for whom it was made, it was a homeopathic revelation. If the work was still where it should be — in a hospital, instead of in a museum — these effects might be better understood.

The danger of modern institutional approaches to art, either in museums or hospitals, is that art by committee and consensus tends to result in the lowest-common-denominator art, art that is "agreeable." This process usually rejects transformative art as being too intense for the therapeutic environment, and opts instead for something more ornamental. The allopathic assumption behind this choice is that healing involves a return to normalcy or stasis. But true healing is transformative, recognizing the cycle of illness and healing, and living and dying, as an active process, what Joseph Beuys called "healthy chaos, which makes possible future forms." People engaged in this process need images that are charged with meaning, not agreeable and soothing ones. Beyond the quick-fix cure, healing is a long, slow process, and it is not well-served by an allopathic attachment to short-term instrumentality in art.

It is said that after leaving the Isenheim monastery, Grünewald joined the Peasant's Revolt under the leadership of Götz von Berlichingen. When the revolt was crushed, most of the revolutionaries were sentenced to death. Grünewald escaped to Frankfurt, where he lived in poverty, selling the therapeutic soaps and salves he had learned to make at Isenheim. At some point he was tracked down and forced to flee again, this time to Halle, where he died of the plague on August 31, 1528. According to Pierre Schmitt, "All that was found in his room after his death were a few garments, some revolutionary pamphlets and books, palettes and gems, as well as some rare colors, the composition of which Hans Halberger, the town's painter, could not explain" [6]

1 Dave Hickey, *The Invisible Dragon: Four Essays on Beauty* (Los Angeles: Art Issues Press, 1993), p. 63.
2 Donald Kuspit, *The New Subjectivism: Art in the 1980s* (Ann Arbor : UMI Research Press, 1988), p.403.
3 Donald Kuspit, *The Cult of the Avant-Garde Artist* (Cambridge: Cambridge University Press, 1993), P.66.
4 Thomas McEvilley, *"Medicine Man: Proposing a Context for Wolfgang Laib's Work,"* (*Parkett 39*, 1994), p.105.
5 Andrée Huyam, *The Isenheim Altarpiece: God's Medicine and the Painter's Vision* (Princeton Uni. 1989), pp. 50/51.
6 Pierre Schmidt, *Mathias Grünewald & Other Old Masters in Colmar* (New York: A.S. Barnes and Co., 1961), p. 50.

Diane Di Prima

Point of Ripening: Lughnasa

What Myth are you living?
Carl Jung

There is no myth
for what I am living now.

Nowhere does She walk out of the nursery
out of the granaries, the forest, the
circle of shields, to
wander
for Herself
scattering gifts as She strolls
to the Western Sea.

Scribe, painter, chanter of
new-made eternal
hymns, scattering pearls
of love, of healing — songs
books, dances, rites
pots, sculptures & piles of shells
of stones to mark
the trail (it is new)

There is no myth
for this older, ample woman

When she sets sail

poems on parchment
float on the waves.

2.

I wander singing
turning in spiral
      admiring
substance
     & astral roads

& neither here nor there

cross boundaries
       gates
         as of
           worlds

is there a myth for a female
middle-aged
      Hermes
         large breasts not
quick-footed
      but
         winged

      into & out of
           dark &

      workings where stars
are sephiroth & there are
           so many
           so close

3.

(That rich time when the harvest
is not for yourself

You no longer need
to claim it.

Some myth that encompasses that.)

Paracelsus

Extract the juice which is itself a Light.

Pulp, manna, gentle
      Theriasin, ergot
like mold on flame, these red leaves
bursting
      from mesquite by the side
of dry creekbed. Extract

the tar, the sticky
substance
      heart
          of things
(each plant a star,   extract

the juice of stars
        by circular stillation
smear
   the inner man w/ the coction
till he burn
   like worms of light in quicksilver
not the false
   puffballs of marshfire, extract

the heart of the empty heart
      it is full
of the star soul that paces fierce
in the deeps of the earth
      the Red Man,
             healer
in furs
   who carries a club
who carries
       the pale homunculus
in his belly.
      For you are angel, you call
the soul from plants

      or pearls of ambergris
out of the grudging sea.

Extract arcanum. Separate
true Archeus from the false
the bitter
is not less potent — nor does clarity
bespeak truth.

Out of the heart of the ineffable
draw the black flecks of matter
& from these
the cold, blue fire.
Dry water. Immerse
yourself
though it be but a drop.
This Iliaster
flowers like a wind.
Out of the ash, the Eidolon of the world

Crystalline.
Perfect.

Magick in Theory & Practice

for Mike Goldberg

to all you with gaunt cheeks who sit
glamourized by the sounds of art in the
last remaining lofts, shining like gold in ore in the
sleek grime of NYC under the shadow
of MOMA, breathing no air, finding lustre in the
huge speaking canvases that whisper
like Miles Davis in your dusty ears, to all
you climbing laboriously on scaffolding shaping
these same canvases, bending light, or drinking hot plate
coffee on "studio couches" flanked by skinny girls
oh how my love reaches for you, gross & holy men
fancy women pretty boys expensive flowers oh home
I may never see again oh glamour
like Baudelaire fading in a long hall of mirrors
called past as I moved backwards over
its black velvet floor

Song of Heloise

from out of the body of fire
the body of light
out of the wind, *virtù*

the light that is in the mind
these essences
moving
pale color
al fresco
a homecoming (clarities
from out of the passion
crystal, spiralling

books open within the Word
small windows
light within light
"space is a
lotus"

from the body of light
like dayspring
ineffable breath
& out of the crystal
the fountain
jets like sperm
quintessence

how the flesh
adheres
in its
passing

The Fire Guardian

Let yourself be seen as shadow
in the light
or as a thin lense color does not
pass thru
no yellow glow no blue
fierce purpose
this spilling liquid caught
in vase of flesh

pours over as sight, as touch
it is light
interlaced w/ light makes these
worlds bud
tensile web eye to eye
skin smooth
as spider's belly, tentative
& ecstatic as lizards

on crumbling sandstone molecules
which dance
in their sudden, expected brains
like stars
thru ponderosa dance in ours
when we fall to sleep
on bed of needles in the arms
of our own black pain & wake
cresting again, riding invisible
soul-stuff (we call it
joy

Allen Hibbard

Crossing To Abbassiya

Mostafa Abd el-Salaam set out that morning, very pleased with himself. After all, he had been charged by his superiors with a special responsibility. The day before, his boss informed him a group of madmen were to be taken from the station at Imbaba, on the west side of the city of Cairo, to the central asylum at Abbassiya, on the other side of the city. He — Mostafa Abd el-Salaam — would drive the truckload of madmen across the city. It was a simple job, one which others no doubt would judge unimportant, but nonetheless Mostafa felt very proud.

The twelve men were there behind him. He could feel their weight in the truck as he accelerated. Even through the metal and glass partition separating him from them, he could hear their odd, repetitive chirpings. Rather like birds in the first days of spring, he thought. Perhaps they thought they were being taken somewhere to be released from their captivity. In fact, come to think of it, he didn't know what they'd been told. They had been in the truck when he arrived, and the station supervisor simply greeted him very warmly, asked how his family was, reminded him what he was to do, and wished him God's speed.

The traffic was heavy, as usual, at midmorning. The truck crawled across the 6th of October Bridge. Mostafa Abd el-Salaam could feel the heat rising. Sweat ran down his brow and he felt himself breathing with greater difficulty. What hope was there but to continue, placing his hope in God?

His mind wandered, directionless, from fragments of childhood memories, to the faces of those driving along, slowly, beside him, to little reminders to himself of things he had to do, to his family — two young boys, a baby girl, and his wife — back at their small apartment near Sayida Aisha. By the time he had gotten across the bridge and begun to head northeast towards Ramses Station, he had, in the heat and fantasia of reverie, completely forgotten his mission. The men behind him, doubtless also affected by the heat, were silent, and Mostafa felt a wonderful kind of freedom.

As he was driving, he noted the landmarks along the way and thought of a certain café near Ataba where he would sometimes go and sit with his friends. He knew some of them would be there this morning. There was nothing else for them to do. They wanted to get out of their homes and this was where they went to meet and talk and smoke the hours away. Unconsciously Mostafa found himself turning off the main road and heading toward the café.

He double-parked the truck and explained to a few men sitting on chairs outside the building on the sidewalk that he would only be an hour or so and, if there was any trouble, he could be found at the café around the corner. They knew the place. In any case, he thought, it was a government truck and so the police weren't likely to bother with it.

It was an hour and a half later, while he was talking with his friends, that Mostafa remembered what he was supposed to be doing that day.

"Well, shouldn't you be going back to work?" one of the men joked, slapping him on his knee. "What are you doing over here anyway? We don't see you here very often this time of the day." A look of amazement and horror came over Mosatafa. He jumped up from his chair without explanation and ran out of the café. His friends looked at one another, shrugged and chuckled.

The truck was where he had left it. One of the men with whom he had talked earlier was seated as he had been before. He had been there the whole time and never taken his eyes off the truck, he said, and everything was fine. "Thank you, thank you, a thousand thanks!" Mostafa said, greatly relieved. It was now twelve o'clock and very hot. He could always say the traffic had been very bad, so the trip had taken much longer than expected.

Mostafa was about to get into the cab and drive off, when it occurred to him he should check in on the nuts in the back. He went round to the rear of the truck. When he opened the door and looked inside he found it empty. At once he felt the weight of his body double and his mind frantically raced through dozens of horrifying scenarios. How could he explain it? It had, he knew, been his own fault, but he couldn't admit that.

He shut the door, composed himself, and turned again to the man on the sidewalk.

"You didn't notice anything strange while I was gone? I mean, you didn't see anyone…?"

"What? No. Are you missing something?" the old man replied. Perhaps he guessed the truck was carrying supplies of flour or sugar (which were much in demand in the city) and some had been stolen. "No. I didn't see anything," he insisted.

Mostafa Abd el-Salaam, on his side, didn't want to let anything out. So he said, "*Malesh*," got into the cab, and drove off. What would he do now? Time wasn't a problem. He could say he had to stop for something to eat. Besides, nobody expected things to be done very quickly in Cairo. An idea, a plan, gradually began to form in his mind. All he had to do was deliver twelve crazy people. There was no list of names. What he had to do now, he thought to himself, was convince twelve people to get into his truck. That shouldn't be hard. If Cairo has nothing else, it at least has plenty of people. He even imagined many people had never ridden in a truck in their lives. Perhaps he could just park his truck near one of the popular districts of the city and ask if anyone would like to take a ride. The truck would fill up in no time.

By now he was heading toward an area of town where a lot of construction was going on. Sitting along the streets, their heads wrapped with scarves, their bodies covered with long brown *gallabiyyas*, shovels and picks lying beside them, were groups of poor villagers who had come to Cairo hoping for work.

Mostafa Abd el-Salaam pulled up his truck near a group of men, got out, and began to address them. His hands on his hips, he tried to act as authoritative as possible.

"Do you want work?" he asked. Their eyes all lit up.

"Yes! Yes!" they cried, each voice competing with the others, rising and falling like the clamorous cackling of chickens.

"I need twelve good, strong men. I can give them work for as long as they want." He began to enjoy the role he was playing, particularly when he felt the eager desperation of the response. "You will have beds to sleep in and food to eat." With this, he knew he would be able to gain recruits. "I need just twelve today — perhaps more tomorrow. Who will go?"

He selected twelve of the most insane looking peasants (they all looked a bit crazy, he thought), promising the rest he would *in cha'allah* return for them the next day. He only had room for twelve in his truck. They would not, he told them, need their picks and shovels.

The men were still chirruping away excitedly when he pulled up to the gates of the mental hospital. "Ah, yes, we have been expecting you," the guard said, opening the iron gates. Once he got to the main building and his arrival had been announced, Mostafa Abd el-Salaam was greeted by the hospital administrator, who came out smiling and embraced him profusely, asking him how his family was and about the trip across town.

"Oh, very hot!" Mostafa replied. As he expected, the administrator seemed not to have noticed the long time it had taken him to cross the city. It was now two-thirty and he had left Imbaba at ten o'clock. "I stopped for lunch, then prayed, and the traffic was awful."

"Yes, yes. Praise be to God! The traffic is getting worse every day, isn't it? But you are here now and you have the men."

"Oh, yes, I have the men. They are all here. All twelve of them. And they're mad as hell. I've been listening to them scream and shout all across town. I thought at times I'd lose my head as well. I'm glad to give them over to you."

The administrator gave an order for the men to be taken from the truck into a nearby room where they would be processed. Mostafa watched the men, a little dumb-founded, as one by one they hopped out of the truck. They seemed to be taking in the new setting. They followed the orders and no one resisted. Mostafa tried as well to assess the reaction of the hospital staff as they led the men into the building. No one seemed to notice the difference.

"Well, it is getting late," Mostafa said to the chief administrator.

"Won't you have some tea?"

Mostafa agreed and they sat down together to talk of life, their jobs, their families, and the state of the country. During their conversation, they heard piercing shrieks and sounds of scuffling in the air.

"Ah, the new inmates!"

"Naturally they are resisting."

"But they seemed so docile when they got out. What did you do to them?"

"I told them I was going to give them work."

"Ah, that was very clever of you!"

And their burst of laughter rose, for a moment or two, above the shrieks and screams.

Stefan Hyner

Do Not Let The Artificial Obliterate The Natural

You show awe
        as your political motivation
like:
            Ah! the butterflies
                                        again
or
            Ah! 10,000 shooting stars per hour
                                pouring out of LEO tonight

for MiMi

XI:2542

Everybody Can Preach But Hardly Anybody Can Tell The Truth

Chia Ti Chia Ti Po Lo Chia Ti
Po Lo Tseng Chia Ti
Pu Ti Sa Po Ho

            they drive in the mountains
        to gather chestnuts & mushrooms
"Shepherd's Purse (Capsélla búrsa pastoris)"
                she points out to him
            "is god's gift to the poor man
rich in food value & exquisite in taste"

X:2542

Merry Men

                free forest guerilla
        bound only by a fragile link
to settled society
        close to the realm of sorcery
                & the otherness of forests

XII:2543

Philip Whalen

Rome

all scattered near a broken wall
The sun remains behind. green purple hill. Have some. { GOLD }

25:X:71

To The Memory of

Mr. J who had been poor for years
Inherited all the money in the world
Bought a gun to blow a hole in his head
To let in air and light he said
To let me out
Today, I have my head to shave
There are lights and shadows in it
All too soon empty open ashes
Join mirthfully to earth

19:V:77

For A Bluejay

You're as smart as I am
I'm as bright as you
Mountain dances in sunlight,

Dissolves in rain
Clouds thin out, become cliffs and pinnacles
Orange leaves, yellow truck reminds me of squash flowers
Rainbow striped bath towel melts on the clothesline

12:XI:77

“The Dilemma of The Occasion is”

She says she’s funny-looking
She can’t decide on hair nor clothes.
There are too many shoes to wear.
Almost every downtown corner
Displays crippled, sick and dirty people
Beat and tromped on. Others look
For what to look at, watch to see
If they are noticed
Where to spend all this money.
“THAT GUY WAS CHECKING ME OUT!”

“SO MUCH FOR YOU, MR. BUMFUCK”
Too many shoes
Those are not the ones.

25:XI:83

The Expensive Life

Tying up my plastic shoes
I realize I’m outside, this is the park & I am free
From whatever pack of nonsense & old tape loops
Play with the Ayers’ dogs, Barney & Daphne
They don’t ask me why I shave my head
“Cut the word lines,” Burroughs recommends
Daphne & Barney fatter than ever & only I am dieting
(Crease along the dotted lines)
Loops of tacky thinking fall unloosed. The sun
Getting hotter than my flannel shirt requires
What about THE BUDDHIST REVIVAL IN CHINA?
Won’t read it now… too blind to see it
Almost too blind to write this, in my room no flowers
The service station wants four bits for compressed air
At only 16 pounds per square inch
I can see the farthest mountain.

29:VIII:87

Tracy Splinter

Outside In / An External View of The Internal

On DMZ by Mati Klarwein

If you try hard enough, you might be able to boil your eyeballs on this thought:
This Outward-In-Reflection gone visual rampage, smeared all over the canvas
Of y(our) consciousness.
And I?
I —
The mere pedestal for a dream
You were trying to give birth to.
A foot cushion for intoxicated Muses —
A damned demiurge come back with a vengeance —
Indigestion incarnated.
Clammy dough
'til baked in the Promethean oven of your looking.
And I am still there
There where screams break eternally
On the back street beaches of those faceless eardrums
There pain is a weekend preoccupation
We pick from grimy fingernails
There where clouds continually break.

If you hang on to each word
I lick across your intellect
Hobby horses will sprout from the noose of my taste-buds
And lodge in the brain's window.
Where eyes may look outside in
Washing gazes over those tunes
You etched upon the torso's titillating tendons.

I am a frozen Moment
Give me a reason to smile at you.
I am a constant stare
Smile, if you like
Back.

Thus,
Six-syllable words spill out of the eye sockets.
The mouth swallows itself whole.
Infected insides crusade

Out
Staining the skin's pigment
Brown.
Torment
Flees southward on borrowed crutches
Night unfolds her hide-n-seek blankets
Sending foreign places home where they belong.
The self empties completely
Drunk up
By others' parched Intentions.

Did you know
Eye
Produces mind benders flippant like exclamation marks
At the end of long verbose sentences?
You know vertigo works like an aphrodisiac?
That holding y(our) self-esteem in the sky produces multiple xenophobia?
That spreading too much artificial fire
Causes pre-coital burn-out?

That "kill me quick" pose has extinguished a million dreamscapes
Over
Wiped out all probability for peace of mind
Reversed the reality stars.
Or is it the dilapidated promise of a painless death for a painful life
I see dangle from those lips
Like half-open curtains. Let in the sunlight I say
That thoughts may peer and loom,
Transferring this solitude to cash bills
Smeary
Fat.

I bet my staid advances
Fling y(our) expectations
Further than you are ever willing to travel.
That the secret life
I hold between my knees
Is the secret you're craving to learn.

Maybe sipping in the culture cocktail of my 'Me' come 'You'
Will rouse amphibians from their slumber
Make the moon wane backwards
Turn the light greens into dark blues and let them stay there!

You imagine murdering bad ideas with Mamba cures myopia?
That blinking at each other's stoned silences
And tattooing them onto the banjo strings of both our questioning hearts
Is calling things
A spade?
Then dig up those corpses
Let's have carrion for lunch,
Collect y(our) roving eyeballs
Hire pockets!

Now,
Dream flowers grow out of the holes in the memory's explosions.
Reason sharpens its edge beyond reason
Cutting confused ties.
Time twists its arid tubers
Waking the world to emotion
While the body sweats out its lava
Transmuting the friendless valleys
To terraced tears
Searing to sterile sorrows
The scarlet soil.

The land of eternal evenings
Dense with the forests of forgetfulness
Laid siege
Under the drowning flames of
All our wanting.

Axel Monte

Now Mesostics

he who meditAtes
beyond alL
daRkness
he who mEditates
At the
time of Death
with a steadY mind

enTers
tHe
gatEs of the
heaRt
the SupremE goal

○

the Sage said
tHere are
two pAths
wise men perforM
their rituAls
iN the bright
fools In the dark
those that Couple by night

are Neither
crooked nor hypOcritical
the poWers

of the three Worlds
grAnt us wisdom
life falls fRom self as
shadow falls fRom man
Interwoven
desires Of the mind
stReam
out through mouth and noSe

two birdS bound
in friendsHip
the SAge
Meets Spirit
And
they are oNe
the Giver of lIfe
disCovers

the traveller iN the cavern
in meditatiOn
groWn pure and still

the knoWer
of thAt
SpiRit
escaped fRom the
Ignorant
the knOts
of his heaRt
unlooSed

○

what happenS
wHen rivers mingle
with the seA
they lose their naMes
and shApes and
maN becomes
tImeless
suCh things as

pronuNciation
poetry, astrOnomy
the higher knoWledge

is the knoWledge
of the EverlAsting
as the web spRings
from the spideR
and is again wIthdrawn
sO springs
the woRld
from the EverlaSting

do not waSte
ligHt
gAther light
illuMinate
the wAy
never deNy
SpirIt nor
Communion with

the unknowN
the ignOrant think
the Wise man

knoWs
through revelAtion
who finds SpiRit
finds tRuth
In every creature
the gOddess said
SpiRit
iS the God in all

○

the Seven flames
in the Heart
Are
the syMbol of life
lighting the wAy
childreN are never lost
the Sage saId
Come out

again at suNrise
the incOming breath
knoWs everything

fly toWards the self
the SAge said
the unconditioned SpiRit
retuRns to the
lIght of the sun
the Seer knOws the world
beyond decay, death, feaR
& attainS peace

Henry Reilly

Mary Jane

It was night when Craig left to visit her. While he was standing on his landing on the seventh floor waiting for the lift, a current of laughter rose from the lift-shaft. It made him happy. He smiled and stepped into the lift. Arriving on the ground floor, the laughter he had heard grew faces, smiling faces with rosy cheeks. When he passed them, glancing at their eyes, he saw swarms of dreams, the dreams of little girls.

Stepping out into the glistening fresh night he looked around and saw the nakedness of the street, a lamp-post scarred with rust, the twisted wires of its guts hanging out, a burnt-out Ford and boarded-up tenement windows. He looked into the morbid glow of the lamp-light and his gaze was suddenly filled with diamonds and dandelions, engendered by a vestige of sunlight which had remained in the lamp since day-time and was now being released into the night and into him.

He didn't much like where he lived, but it was quiet, sometimes deadly silent. As he walked further away from the mass of houses where he lived he thought about the reason for his journey, which was love, to be with his girl. They had known each other for some time. Thoughts of her warmed his heart.

Any lingering sleepiness from the nap he had taken before he left home had now vanished. He was now more awake than the night and longed to see Mary Jane. Stepping up his pace he felt the Scheme would never end. It was thoughts of Mary Jane that filled him with the energy to make the journey. He hadn't seen her for nearly two weeks. Though it had been very much his own decision, he now felt he had to see her. Rushing across the road he felt he was on the heels of ostriches, ostriches of night and day, ostriches that never sleep but grow more and more awake — then fly.

The journey wouldn't be too long. Thankfully the scene changed, he was now passing a stretch of rubbish and rubble strewn waste ground. The grass was glistening with soft secrets only the sky could say. Oh Mary Jane, he said to himself, why do I want you so much! He smiled.

Hello, Craig! came a voice from over his shoulder.

Oh hello, Marie, how are you doing?

Not bad. I'm just getting through a college course, you know. It's the content I'm worried about. To be honest, it's been nonexistent. It's a Mickey Mouse course and the lecturers know it.

I believe you, said Craig. I've been through it all myself. It's not just your college, it's the same with all colleges.

Are you going down to see Mary?

Yeah, answered Craig.

You know, Marie resumed, she's not seen you in over two weeks. She's been wondering, I mean you should have...

Yes, well, Craig interrupted, I should get going then if she needs me so much. I'll see you later.

Okay, said Marie, see you later.

Thank God I got away when I did, thought Craig, or she would have held me in that pit-bull grip of hers and buried me in the shit she gives out once she gets going, and she knows I won't take it from her.

His destination not far off, he resumed the pace he had set before bumping into Marie. His thoughts were with Mary Jane for the rest of the way. He could smell her as if she had tossed her scent into the wind. He decided to take a short cut through the park and have a smoke on one of the benches. He passed a few before choosing a dry one to sit on. It was covered with graffiti. He could read only some of the graffiti because the bench had been scorched black by fire. He lit up and blew out the smoke. He didn't inhale the first drag. It tasted too much of paper. After the second drag, the smoke hung in the air like twisted candelabra until the wind sucked it away. Glad of the rest, he thought about what to say to Mary Jane if she asked why he hadn't been to see her lately. But he knew she would be too pleased to see him to think of asking anything too inquisitive. Blowing out the rest of his smoke he made for the gate.

He walked slowly, enjoying the stroll. Cutting down a dark street he saw a crowd gathered against a wall. They moved on, their ragged shadows sliding down the wall and into the gutter. On the next turn to his left he was in her street, a long street of semi-detached houses. Her house was half-way along, facing a square of grass with a few trees. He recalled nights in her room, the trees close enough for them to hear their whispering, and soon he would be lying there again, tonight. Her bed was soft and her hair smelt sweet. He loved lying with her while she slept, the curtains open, letting in the night, a smoke in his hand, blowing his thoughts out towards the window where they would hang until illuminated by the morning sun. He recalled mornings warm from the dawn, warmth spreading through noon when the bells begin to ring, and thoughts of love, the birds flapping their wings, fluttering from the square into the sky.

Her street was silent. There wasn't a soul to be seen. The night was warm.

Yes, thought Craig, I'll grab her and give her a big kiss as soon as she opens the door. No, I'll just affectionately touch her shoulder. He thought about how to act until he realised it didn't matter. He was nearly there. Her living-room light was on and the sky was sprinkled with stars. He went along the path to her door and chapped twice. She opened the door and grinned. She was happy to see him. She went to the edge of the doorstep, leaned out on her tiptoes and looked up and down the street. He caught her eye and gave her a smile.

Mary Jane's eyes shone with delight, and Craig, feeling her hand in his mane, turned a leonine head and sank his teeth into the cream of the night, swallowing the moon with a gulp of stars.

Glasgow, Jan. 1999

Have You Ever

Have you ever wept
on the loneliest bench in the world
In the heart of a city
Where sorrow roams
Where the remains of wasted nights
are scattered everywhere
Reminding us…

Have you ever wept
on the loneliest bench in the world
Your heart roaming the streets
Where the gutters drain your tears
Feeling love has left you
with loneliness your only friend
Your heart wringing out…

Have you ever wept
on the loneliest bench in the world
In the heart of a city
Where madness roams
Dreaming of a drunken star
Falling asleep in its glow
Waiting for nothing to happen.

Notes

Time doesn't always fly
Sometimes it rolls around in the grass

○

God is like a doctor
Only those who work for him
Understand his writing
Those who work with him
Write their own

○

Imagine the item in the shop window
Buying you

○

Love goes on forever
Forever goes on for love

○

There are enough lines here to paint a road

J. J. Blickstein

Elijah's Horn

He dreamt that his ear was a small Africa.

His horn was a seismic instrument parting the water
in the boat that brought him here.

He played, superimposing the continent in his ear
to the soil beneath his feet, to reinvent the tired fire
of his mythology, to split the plum in the throat of the angel.

He pulled notes from the river. He parted the lips of the angel,
in his dream, searching the tongue with the original hand
for the ashes of its maker. He found only water, but he
was changed. He had become the water & slept with
the fingers of the angel in his mouth.

He played the air as if it were brass nipples of the saxophone
mutilating the lice that lay between the fire in his fingertips.

He designed a new sorrow in the circle of fifths
cutting his name into the lamb in the lung of the angel.

He set the landscape of the land where he was born on fire,
it did not burn but sweat the melody of its element
into a perfect sphere.

They, in the parallel water of the mutual dream, spilled out the formula
of the voice that formed the antique heart.

The angel asked Elijah if he knew the sound that would break
the lump of gold in the eternal breath & cut the blueprint in his vein
from the simultaneous.

Elijah paused, took the throne off his shoulder, away from his ear,
when it landed on the water it became the dirt at the foot of the door
in the angel's chest, his chest.

His face was in the water, the angel was in him.

○

He woke up humming the melody in the pearl
of his breath. He fingered the air playing the keys
like the breasts of a Siamese cat. The water flowed between his fingers
breaking the rhythm, disinfecting the small Egyptian wound in his pelvis
shaped like a flaw in the perfect rest. His skin sweat the feathers in his fury.

The sand in his cuticles had not been born there,
but rested on the floor of his rhythm, on & in the water,
burning the bridge of the journey into a million notes,
crushing the bird in the rose of his cranium.

The water was his wardrobe,
The angel his dresser, the water the gossip in the natural pitch.

Gurney

for José Guinovart's "Homage to Picasso"

Gurney, fists for poles, for hands, wrenches for gloves.
Gurney with fibula, os & civil war in the underworld.
Gurney with dead skin, dead flower, inflected, infected,
flawed & pierced through shoulder with a blue vein arched
in its pole — vein with scar tissue the shape of teeth.
Gurney, bandaged midriff, geometric soft tissue, torn,
a removed vault, replaced with new anthropology, new jaw,
new weapon, new glass.
Gurney with broken light bulb above its head —
broken glass & canvas as its wardrobe.
Gurney in antique cave hears some bombs dropping…
...bombs try to flee the gurney's ghosts, the civilisation
in its limbs, the bones shaped into tools & instinct...
...bombs try to remove the question behind the bandaged lips…
Gurney with charcoal in its mouth.
Gurney smeared with ash & bone.
Gurney with twenty fingers, too many toes,
smells like a village, has a sophisticated odor
in its shadow.
Gurney, familiar with wine, elevated gestures,
knots & loneliness.
Gurney, with its isolation, want of evolution, its curtains
& furniture, lies down in a box, disfigured, with its strange blood

& ruptured ear drum, testifies, spills its language — language
made of water falling all over your world.
Gurney with a price on its head.
Gurney on the side of the road, looks like a trench,
a window, a cluttered bed with a view of its city,
your city, your ceiling.
Gurney they made you eat your children
in order to invert your sirens, but you're already deaf.
Gurney without the evolution that forged the key,
framed the door, invented the private.
Gurney in a museum, a decoration, fed canned goods —
you make love to your wife behind the cage
to get away from their eyes & clothing.
Gurney, a bed of nails, white room, silk weapons, white bandage, red blood,
finally, when you're alone:

everyone who saw you went home, lied down upon your bed,
wept your color & pissed charcoal, smudged images all over
your cave.

Ian MacFadyen

The Mysterious Case of The Little Man Who Was

For a long time I tried to put into words the uncanny effect which certain creatures had upon me — *special beings* which I first encountered in the fever and nightmares of childhood illness, and subsequently came upon in dreams and half-waking hallucinations. They were devilish little *doll men*, only a few inches high — slippery, translucent, with pointed little heads and malformed limbs, dancing jerkily over the eiderdown and projecting their squeaky, gibbering voices directly into my head. I understood that they *lived in the furniture*, and could pass at will through mirrors and walls and yet a single ray of sunlight would suddenly banish them — leaving me becalmed in the world they had abandoned, and with a strange sense of loss; a feeling I would remember years later, rising early on a summer morning, and walking through a garden still wet and glittering with dew, the mist rising. I was simultaneously horrified and delighted by these *mollusc apparitions*, and in particular by one which would linger when the rest had fled; it lolled provocatively on top of the wardrobe, but vanished instantly if I tried to point it out to my mother… That one, above all, *fascinated* me...

Later, certain drugs allowed occasional limited access to the domain of these *special beings* and I was able to watch them eating bitter apples with big spoons and swinging from chandeliers made of soap bubbles… I rationalised that they were projections from the shadow realm of the psyche, archetypal personae *in utero* — whilst I secretly admitted the possibility of their separate autonomous existence. These little people or homunculi, with their etiolated or ballooning bodies and rudimentary genitalia seemed to mock their own ghostly morphology: sinister and playful, pathetic and iconic, mournful and whimsical, they enacted a lugubrious carnival in the half-light… one moment careless of my presence and then turning upon me with shrieking malevolence before disappearing in a rainbow splatter of mercury droplets between the floorboards.

Whilst apparently occupied with *more serious matters*, I discovered descriptions by writers and depictions by artists which were remarkably similar to my own experiences. Max Ernst, on a rainy evening in a seaside inn on the Rhine at the end of The Great War, remembered how a panel of false mahogany at the end of his childhood bed had "played the role of optical *provocateur* of a vision of half-sleep", and he now systematically applied this to the intensification of his visionary, hallucinatory faculties: bird-aliens and quasi-human hybrids emerged by *frottage* through the wood grain floor and plaster walls of his rented room. William S. Burroughs recounts, in his prologue to *Junky*, how as a child in St. Louis he experienced hallucinations, on one occasion waking "in the early morning light and seeing little men playing in a block house I had made. I felt no fear, only a feeling of stillness and wonder." Burroughs also had nightmares "about animals in the wall" which he believed began with "a strange undiagnosed fever".

Yukio Mishima, in his autobiographical novel *Confessions of a Mask*, recalls the fairy stories which his grandmother told him at night in the gloomy family house in Tokyo, and the toy building blocks he played with as a child, and his feeling of "time and space becoming entangled": "One night from my bed I saw a shining city floating upon the expanse of darkness that surrounded me. It was strangely still." The inhabitants, the little people, were sleeping, or in hiding, or had deserted their airborne city.

Robert Louis Stevenson called the little creatures which appeared in his dreams "Brownies". Stevenson recognised that he *needed* his homunculi, that his sprite familiars were essential to his creativity, but he felt guilty about using them. He wrote in *A Chapter on Dreams* that he kept "some Familiar, some unseen collaborator… locked in a back garret, while I get all the praise…" The garret was Stevenson's unconscious and his little people were linked to his childhood memories of the stories which his father told him before he went to sleep — stories about gnomes, fairies, pixies, hobgoblins, elves, bottle imps and other 'night creatures'. These creatures took up residence in his psyche and remained with him all his life: they enacted stories which upon awakening he would remember and write down. Many writers have had this experience of the story which 'writes itself', or which is written 'without conscious effort' — as with the cobbler's shoes in the fairy tale, invisible little men have performed their task while the human sleeper dreams.

I also identified homunculi in the drawings and paintings of many artists. There were, of course, the "serpentine monstrosities" of Aubrey Beardsley — given shape by a single, deadly line but otherwise *tabula rasa*, his predatory, sinister homunculi are essentially *unformed* creatures. These hydrocephalic, gimlet-eyed grotesques demand *alien recognition* as they clone themselves from decorative arabesques and linear flourishes, pantomimically adopting Victorian cloaks and top hats and walking canes… So I collected these tantalising, ghoulish and fascinating creatures in books and pictures, but what really lay behind or beyond the hypnagogic image, the feverish, magical encounter? I discovered the creatures again in wood carvings and in paintings on eucalyptus bark made by the Aboriginal people of West Arnhem Land: there they are called *Mimi*, stick-like personages dating back to the very origins of man. *Mimi* are mischievous trickster spirits, canny and fly, and, significantly, *they taught their creators* the art of painting, appearing to man *so as to be reproduced by him. Mimi* are also skilled in the art of hunting — they are supremely gifted both as creators and as killers, emerging from the dark, from fires in the night, to bestow the risky gift of *possession. Dangerous self-creations…* little trickster stick-men preserved in the psyche and on tree bark as traces of the primordial, hybridised world.

Any scholar-sleuth worth his salt must check out all the angles: I haunted libraries and museums and cinemas and medical museums in pursuit… of what, exactly? What was I really looking for? I read the speculations and findings of psychologists and anthropologists and occultists… Could experts in their chosen fields explain the mystery of the little men? No doubt they could, and almost certainly they would… Medieval alchemists attempted to create human life 'from seed' and to this end they kept human embryos in transparent vessels; Beardsley even drew an alchemical sitting-room homage: a homunculus in a bell jar. Jung divined in the alchemists' experiments and in Goethe's *Faust* the psychological importance of the homunculus: man's desire to create himself, to become the self-created — to overthrow the female and acquire her procreative power — and so transcend the human condition, the biological happenstance of birth and death. For Jung, this dream of autonomy and immortality is a paradigm of the male artist's desire to create his own world. That is why the genitalia of the homunculi are always redundant, impoverished or ambiguous: they are necessarily androgynous, *artificially* created beings — they cannot procreate. They're created by the artist, the magician, the dreamer... the fevered imagination... Kenneth Grant interpreted the visualization and depiction of these "dwarf dreamers" as "projections of medieval magicians essaying the Great Work, the exploration of the aethyrs" — i.e. the magical conjuration of spirits — and believed that such phenomena must "exist at profoundly subjective levels of consciousness" and "require a special type of receptivity in the beholder before they can register a visual effect..." Whether they register or not, Tibetan Buddhism instructs us that we should respect the space and needs of these non-visible beings with whom we co-exist...

The artist Brion Gysin believed in the *visible reality* of these creatures and, in his apartment in Paris, he tried to point them out to the writer Terry Wilson: "They exist in another time than ours, that's really their definition... I can show you lots right here in this pad as a matter of fact..." Wilson commented: "Brion attempted to show me some of these creatures. I could see what he was referring to, but could not conceive of them as living beings." There was a time — *another time than ours* — when these creatures existed not only for the solitary child in bed with a fever or for the inspired artist, but for many people who treated their existence as commonplace... they both perceived and *accepted* them. In 1882 psychologist Frederic Myers and philosopher Henry Sidgwick conducted a 'Census of Hallucinations': 1,684 people from a survey of 17,000 reported seeing fairies, nymphs, elves, naiads, hamadryads, trolls, leprechauns and banshees. In 1886, Edmund Gurney collected evidence in his book *Phantasms of the Living* which contested the belief that hallucinations were only explicable as the products of mental illness, fever, stupidity or superstition. Today the hallucinatory is derided, the manifestation of spirits ridiculed. Gysin believed that the little people were being expunged by civilization: "Electric light chases the world of the Little Folk away." It is certain that neon destroys them — they look so sad in neon light that it chills the very soul... But surely it is more than the bright lights which have driven them out: it is the demons of our own self-created, maniacal reason and materialism which have taught us to learn to forget how to *see*...

Frances Liardet describes how "When I was a child I use to lie in bed at night and press my fingers against my eyelids, press quite hard so that the black would slowly suffuse with the sunbursts of colour. Then the sunbursts would fade and I'd be left with these splotches of green, blue, silvery-grey which spread and sprawled and somehow hovered just out of reach in my mind's eye." Here was a possible physiological explanation. Images are neuroelectrical and those goblins and gremlins might be phosphene hallucinations, neuroelectrical light shows produced by excitation of the retina and disturbance of the retinal-optical track, echoing neural firing patterns in the brain... Significantly, children between the ages of two and four continually see phosphenes and they do not distinguish them from images of the so-called 'real' world — in fact they often include them in their drawings and paintings. This 'solution' had its anthropological correlative: there is a basic set of fifteen graphic elements which comprise the 'vocabulary' of phosphene patterns and ethnologist Robert Lawlor has shown the extraordinary correspondences which exist between these psychic/optical phenomena and Tasmanian rock carvings, petroglyphs... Phosphenes appear when the eyes are open but see nothing for long periods of time and these petroglyphs record magical images drawn from the optical unconscious, shamanic vision projected into the terrors and wonders of endless space...

Always the search for a rational explanation... But our vision is not rational, it is conjuration — ineluctable, driven. We recognise shapes and spatial correspondences only to be seduced and fascinated by the double image, the divergent, the paradoxical... We are guided by the reality principle of recognition, but we return, despite ourselves, *because of ourselves*, to the pleasure principle of the abstracted gaze, the daydream, to *that which is there but not there*. When it comes to seeing, "Alles ist erlaubt" — *Everything is permitted.* Now you see them, now you don't. Flickering at the very edge of vision — shadows and silhouettes of the little men you can never catch or touch. Spot them in stains and cracks in plaster walls, in rock strata and gemstones... In windblown leaves, sunset rain pools, ragged clouds at evening and patches of moss... Glimpse them in glittering Faberge frost patterns on window panes before dawn, in shimmering petrol rainbows and drifts and curlicues of tobacco smoke and dope smoke and in twinkling Christmas tree lights and the last dying red embers... Hear them in the tintinnabulation of tiny silver toy sleigh bells from winters past, the electric hiss of crickets on the vineyard terrace on this hot afternoon in France and the world seems immortal, then the wintry scratch of hawthorn twigs on the black and silver windows like an old supernatural tale... Look. Listen. They are there, everywhere, all around you... *always...* As Burroughs said, to be interested in such creatures is in some sense to give up the self. Alright then, *so give it up...*

The case continues... Many a solution without a mystery, but still there are mysteries without solution... Then I came across Loren Eiseley's moving description, in *The Immense Journey*, of the mummified little man which he was once offered for two hundred dollars: "That little fellow gave me the creeps. He might have been two feet high in a standing posture — not more... The face with closed eyes seemed vaguely evil. I could have sworn I was dreaming... And to this day the little man sits on in my brain... It may be, I used to think, that I will yet encounter him before I die, in some little coloured tent on a country midway..." Eiseley attempts to relegate that little man to science fiction stories of extraterrestrial life, or to folk tales of "some Palaeozoic beings who hunted among the tree ferns when the world was ruled by croaking amphibians." But although he tries to dismiss the creature as "an anomalous mummified stillbirth with an undeveloped brain", it's clear that the scientist was profoundly disturbed by *that little fellow who really did exist*, even though he belonged back in the human psyche, back in fantasy, not in the clear light of day. Eiseley's disgust was only equalled by the pity he felt for the poor little body, the pathetic carnival relic. *Go on, mister, you can touch him...*

Perhaps this was the real, human key to the mystery, the solution both obvious and more mysterious than the mystery itself. I was struck by the recognition and revulsion, the anguish and identification which this *dead little man* provoked. All along I had avoided writing about *who* the little man was or might be — I'd insisted upon *what*... I kept thinking "it" when surely "he" was what I meant, or at least intuited. The little man or homunculus is a manikin as described by Frazer in *The Soul As Manikin*: a psychic messenger and transmitter of art and creativity, the shadow of the self, the complementary of the soul, the psychic double... *He* is the magical manikin who is born with a person and accompanies that person throughout life, and then through the stages of death. The manikin is more than a 'representation' of intellectual and spiritual power transcending earthly existence — he is the very incarnation of the immortal second ego, the *other* in Rimbaud's famous line, "Je est un autre." He is our 'other half ', our true self — the one we strive to contact all our lives. And here he is, dead and mummified (price: $200), refuting all explanations of his origins and purpose, his true nature and spirit. But he really did exist, *once upon a time, the little man who was...*

The Great Secret which I had been so desperate to uncover was, of course, my own. The creature on the wardrobe — *he was myself.* The tragic magic and sad charm of those *special creatures* suddenly becomes clear: the self-created, too, must die. The homunculus is mortal. The dream of immortality is doomed. The *fetch* is a revenant fading out in its own too brief allotted span. That's what the creatures of fever and half-light were gibbering inside my head all those years ago: *Die little devil die. Live live die. Die die live. Live a little devil die a little devil. Die a devil evil little live die die.* The quest for the homunculus ends with an empty bell jar. The answer was there all the time. The magical creatures disappear with childhood. The imp is drowned in the black ink bottle. The 'evil' *other* is gone forever and I will miss him all my life. Sprites and gremlins and goblins pass away through the walls, never to return. *Mimi* are exhibited in vitrines in ethnographic museums. Put away your toy building blocks, my son. No space left to co-exist with anyone or any *thing*. The little man is mummified in the brain. The magical manikin is a tatterdemalion clown's cloak on a stick. Chandeliers made of rainbow soap bubbles and eiderdown feathers float across a blue summer sky and vanish into icy black space... "Now I want Spirits to enforce, art to enchant; and my ending is despair." *Hush, little man...*

Paul Bowles

Next To Nothing

At first there was mud, and the sound of breathing,
and no one was sure of where we were.
When we found out, it was much too late.
Now nothing can happen save as it has to happen.
And then I was alone, and it did not matter.
Only because by that time nothing could matter.

The next year there were knifing matches in the stadium.
I think the people are ready for it, the mayor said.
Total involvement. A new concept in sports.
The loser does not leave the ring alive.

But no one can know where he is until he knows where he has been.
I sat quietly, and the air changed then, and I looked up.
And the black branches trailing in the living water
stirred slowly with the change of air.
Piropos, you said. El aire les hace piropos.

Have you change for this banknote?
It is closed off for the time being.
Take me to the other end of the city
where they slice up the sharks on the sand.

The double tariff applies after sundown.
It is forbidden to pass beyond this railing.
Take me to the other end of the city
where nobody wants to go.

Yes, I said we would need the machine-guns by next march,
but I also warned against saying life was easy.
I mixed hoops and coffins, cradles and needles
while the lights twinkled on far-off Monte Tomas.
We sat in a park that smelled of pine trees;
and that night there were voices in the corridors
and I remembered the empty face of the blind man as he sang.

Tu misma tienes la culpa
de lo que has hecho conmigo.

You will find yourself among people.
There is no help for this
nor should you want it otherwise.
The passages where no one waits are dark
and hard to navigate.
The wet walls touch your shoulders on each side.
When the trees were there I cared that they were there.
And now they are gone, does it matter?
The passages where no one waits go on
and give no promise of an end.
You will find yourself among people,
faces, clothing, teeth and hair
and words, and many words.
When there was life, I said that life was wrong.
What do I say now? You understand?

> Something is going on these recent days.
> The clouds that lie in the trees
> can skim your head as you run uphill.
> After sunset birds fly down
> push aside the grill and eat the plants.
> Sea fog swells across the lowlands
> and the slow ships moan.
>
> Yes, something is going on.
> You said you saw them together
> but they were not together.
>
> Who loves the fog?
> Why do the birds come?
> As to the clouds, you may be innocent.

Living branches trail in black water. Nothing moves.
And how do I know what you are to me?
Our theories are untested. You must not laugh.
We thought there were other ways.
Probably there are, but they are hidden
and we shall never find them.

> What's his name?
> God forbid.
> Where does he live?
> Nobody knows.
> How did we get there?
> Ask the conductor.

That's his face?
Nobody knows.
Now shall I ask him?
God forbid.

Take me to the other end of the city
where no one knows the difference between you and me.
I went back. I did not find him.
And what do I say now? You understand?

The woman pointed.
That's the model we
should have had with us.
We thought about it,
hung back and didn't.

Wished a thousand times we had.
But that's the way things go.

You never can know
until afterwards.
Roads of nothing but
sharp pebbles and stones.

And they say there are
snakes behind the rocks.
You see no snakes but
you know they are there.

And after you've gone
down into seven
empty valleys, one
after the other,

you find that you've been
quietly crying
for the past half hour.
Or at least I did.

Because there was no
connection. No more
connection to any-
thing at all. Nothing.

It might not have been
such an awful trip
if we'd had that one.

The woman pointed.
That's the model we
ought to have chosen.

It will be raining up there by the time you arrive.
Try to get through quickly. The forest's cold green breath
is best left undisturbed, coiled close to the boughs.
In open country again you can breathe.
That is the theory, but our theories are untested.
Things are not the way they were.

How can we be sure? New laws apply,
and who knows the difference between the law and the wind?
And who knows the difference between you and me?

Y tu misma tienes la culpa
de lo que has hecho conmigo.

I should like to see the bottom of the fountain.
Do not go near the edge.
Does this path lead to the artificial lake?
The band concert has been postponed.
Is there a waterfall behind these rocks?
The guardian is not on duty.

I have no idea of what is going to happen
or in which parts the pain will be.
We are only in spring, and spring has a twisting light.
Spring's images are made of crystal and cannot be recalled.
There will be suffering, but you know how to coax it.
There will be memories, but they can be deflected.
There will be your heart still moving
in the wind that has not stopped flying westward,
and you will give a signal. Will someone see it?

We thought there were other ways.
The darkness would stay outside.
We are not it, we said. It is not in us.

Yes, yes, go with her. The old man smiled.
You will be back. You will not find me.

There was a time when life went along brighter lines.
We still drank the water from the lake,
and the bucket came up cold
and sweet with the smell of deep water.
The song was everywhere that year, an absurd refrain:
It's only that it seems so long, and isn't.
It's only that it seems so many years,
and perhaps it's one.
When the trees were there I cared that they were there,
and now they are gone.
On our way out we used the path that goes around the swamp.
When we started back the tide had risen.
There was another way, but it was far above and hard to get to.
And so we waited here, and everything is still the same.

There were many things I wanted to say to you
before you left, and now I shall never say them.
Though the light spills onto the balcony
making the same shadows in the same places,
only I can see it, only I can hear the wind
and it is much too loud.
The world seethes with words. Forgive me.
I love you, but I must not think of you.
That is the law. Not everyone obeys it.
Though time moves past and the wind is never the same
I shall not change. That is the law, and it is right.

Yes, yes, I went with her. Yes.
In the shine of morning and the glow of afternoon.

Piropos, you said. El tiempo te hace piropos.
There will never be a way of knowing.
I did go back. The old man was gone.

We do no thinking, give no reasons,
have no sensations, make no apologies.
This is our behaviour, and it impresses them.
The anguish was not real enough,
the age of terror too short-lived.
They thought all that was finished, left behind.
They were sure there must be other ways.

I am the spider in your salad, the bloodsmear on your bread.
I am the rusted scalpel, the thorn beneath your nail.
Some day I shall be of use to you, as you can never be to me.
The goats leap from grave to grave, and nibble at last year's thistles.
In the name of something more than nothing, of Sidi Bouayad,
and all who have wisdom and power and art,
I am the wrong direction, the dead nerve-end, the unfinished scream.
One day my words may comfort you, as yours can never comfort me.

Note: Piropos are the little compliments a man murmurs to a girl walking past. Like: Where is all that beauty on its way to? Que guapa! Que linda! Etcetera. And the girls reckon their attractiveness on a given day by the number of piropos they've called forth.
"Tu mismo tienes la culpa de lo que has hecho conmigo" is the opening line of an old flamenco song from the twenties, a fandanguillo, I think, sung by Pepe Marchena. But its literal meaning isn't connected with the context — only its sound, as a memory of a song.

John Power

FOUR SONGS

Magic Hour

Take a good look
In your own time
See the world laugh
Through a child's eyes
Sun shine
Shine until your mine

It's just a magic hour
Just a magic hour
Such a magic hour

Now I know we can drift away now
If only to find a way how
Now I know we can drift away now
If only to find a way out
Take a good look
In your own time
See the world turn
Through your own eyes
Sun shine
Shine until your mine

It's just a magic hour
Such a magic hour
Such a magic hour

Now I know we can drift away now
If only we find a way how
Now I know we can drift away now
If only we find a way out
Now I know we can drift away now
If only we find a way how
I know we can drift away now
We've only to find a way out
Well I know we can drift away now
If only we find our way how
Now I know we can drift away now
If only we find a way out
Out, out, out, out...

Live The Dream

Somebody's after me
I can't pretend to be
Something I know I'm not
And when they come for me
I'll just let them be
Because all that I need today
Is all I need

I just wanna be thinking
Thoughts that I think
Dreaming my dreams and drifting within
I don't know where I going
But I know where I been
Come on
Look within

Someone will always be
More than I'll ever be
So then I'll be myself
And when they come for me
I'll just let them be
Cos all that I need today
I need today

Oh your big enough
Tough enough
Now I begin to see
Girl, you gotta lay your love on me
It's big enough
So far enough
As far as my eye can see
Girl, you better lay your love on me
Lay your love on me

Like a bird without wings
Like a bird who don't sing
Like a fish on dry land
Like I'm swimming in sand
Like I'm falling for you...

On The Run

All I do is a constant reminder
The future's here and it walks right behind you
All I see is a constant illusion
My head spins and my world's in confusion

All I see self-rearranging
The moment's here but it's already changing
Take one step and that's your direction
You ain't sure now is that the intention

Close my eyes I think of times
And this memory twists in my head
I've got a feeling that it's all not over yet
I've got some things I just cannot forget
All I do is think of you
You've got me on the run
On the run

Looking around you can take it or leave it
You got a feeling but you must believe it
All you do is constantly changing
You feel a rise as it's already fading

Close my eyes I think of times
This memory twists in my head
I've got a feeling that it's not all over yet
I've got some things I just cannot forget
All I do is think of you
You've got me on the run
On the run

It's taken so long for the sun to appear
Now the blue sky above is so clear
And everything you need is so near
So near...

Beat Mama

Well I got a beat for you mama
Well I got a beat for your mind
Well you want to be what you wanna
Well you better reach deep inside
Free your mind
Free your mind
Free your mind
Free your mind

Well I got a beat for your sister
Sister got a beat for mankind
See we got to love one another
See she's got the love that she finds
Deep inside
Free your mind
Free your mind
Free your mind

Well you just turn it on
Turn it up, don't turn it down
And you want to belong
To the love from higher ground
Feel the love from higher ground

Well I got a beat for your brother
Well I got a beat for your kind
See you wanna reach one another
Well you better step, step in time, jump in time
Free your mind...

Larry Sawyer

Crossing the Meridian

for Gregory Corso

Answer me now as I ask
you this concrete question
Nothing more than this
can be read
your zebra of consciousness
if I retell the past quicker
than you can answer it
a woman has died
a man has died
a man has died and the
quiet toll of cloud bells
encompassing politics &
sex   answers me now
nights of wooden eyes
forging flesh upon the backs
of galaxies
your elixir of drunken glass
is it not enough to stretch once
yawn and return to your dull
eternity of orange juice afternoons?
The voices have stopped
inside my head…
I visited you in zoos
caged poet gargling your
brilliant passageways
choose one now
we can't return from whence
we came
I will be there someday to awaken
you from
your sleep of neon & vestibules
hoping to reach you long distance
as we all must face the fact...

Weird czar of the infinite and evening
the long hallway yawns before us
& my phone bill has become the
only poem I now know

I toss these verbs to the birds
in the park
rise across the ages
your freedom has…

You've now become a soft solo
of spring rain
floating home to Italy
reaching finally what
you fatally murmured
I've erased my ears replacing them
with the panic of reality…
I hope to catch you in the horse
latitudes
saxophonic traveller
of frozen sands.

The Poet Speaks of Highways

I have travelled often these dour
soft shoulders, whipped hips of highways
across legendary peninsulas, languished
angry across medians and interstates
meandering frequently upon the flesh du jour
of loose lipped hitchhikers. Yet still I enter night
each time I look into your eyes. You, the felon
that stole the centerline, left us all here hawking
across great plains. I see you jaywalking and come
accelerating toward you in my mind, let me
homeward drift to someday in the deepest sleep
be with you again, riding cerebral interstates,
rolling in a dream across these cumulonimbus days,
wasting mileage toward that rumbling, cerulean deep.

For Guillaume Apollinaire

fins of an ancient world, a burger
beneath the Eiffel tower a troupe of matadors
assess the lives of antique grocers
Romain lettuce peering out from automobiles
religion is resting still nude upon the grass
Europe of the soul, Christianity smells
of modern equations, Pope with your robes
reticent observer walking these streets
confessor of eggs and wallpaper
the prospect of these catalogs in the rain
25 cents for the adventures of policemen
divers beneath the shadows, your portrait
lends joy an obsolete moon, clarion of sun
director of beautiful dinosaurs, flesh trumpets
resound beneath the mural on the wall
JAMES INDUSTRY TONIGHT BULLFIGHT LONELINESS
streets of Paris resound in your mighty charms
violins of June, an encore of strange beautiful infants
white habits dancing in the glass
ancient friends among the pews, stained glass
pompadour of love and you there with your hours
blue casements of forgotten collage
amethyst profundity pronounces torch-lit red vents
gas creeping silently across the skin
eternity is honored among six branches
seven if you count resuscitation
Christ was an aviator to birds
landing on a record playing venerable hymns
oceans of Africa, fountains of mercurial blood
forgive us our sins this immaculate night of panthers
dripping instants, a siren awakes and calls your name
Paris dances, a foul maintenance man
roulette wheels spinning monasteries and short piers
dropping off into nothing but blackness
sad music of presidents regard the women beautiful
you are an orange or else the moon
a house, a table, the lips of a rose
you resemble a song, familiar as yourself
brilliant sons of lost waters.

Kaufman Laughs

Corso the mountainous elephant!
Ginsberg the illustrious tiger!
Kerouac, black Basho of Bourbon St!
Burroughs the old woman
at the end of the lane
with knives for wizened eyes!

I leave you all here to speak sidewalks and belch thunder!

Still, Green

the perspiring arm of silence
                                        flexes
wrecks the stillness, this
church of idiotic complacency
stretches for   miles

I walk to the edge of their knowing
leap into the realm of some memory
remember that this world   is
quietly burning

then pronounce the only word that now matters:

                                        rain

                                            rain

Roberto Valenza

Absorbed

Absorbed into the home with 4 walls
the outside horns and voice calls,
learning what's new with the neighbors,
watching the neighboring farmers take in the harvest
going to Bodnath and speak to the lamas

5 hawks fly over Swayambhu Stupa,
the horizon is full of the highest white
mountains on earth, I stroll lightly
to Kathmandu, consciousness interested.

Snot noses, sidewalk shitters,
dried puja marigolds, goats and cows
for sidewalk partners,
Durga has gotten her blood,
Buddha's stone mudra means
it's a super illusion,
(please don't be affected by the crime of the rime)

Some poor buffalo has left his jacket in Pig Alley,
2 beggar serenaders sing under a window,
a stoned hippie with a *beti* and a green bottle
falls into the doorway of Uncle Tom's Cabin.

A Japanese dude tokes and passes a chillum
over to an old saddhu
Jimi Hendrix plays hard still,
those who missed Haight Street can do it
on Freak Street, get lessons for their future.

A cowboy with the face of a Nepali
asks me to change money,
if he knew my condition
he'd know even the ink in my tattoos is wearing out,
but with a quarter of India starving beside me
I smile at him and say no thank you.

My dog teacher passes with a torn rat in his
	mouth, I know things can change quickly.
At the watery hole everyone stands clean
	in their Brahminy cords,
	a thousand years ago they accepted
	the population explosion.
Just seeing this is as satisfying as
	American Organic Health Food.
I go and pick up a letter at the Post Office
	from my parents, they say things are
	going strange there and money is the lifeblood of
	the nation,
	a dream comes and everything melts:

A white lady walks by with a Tibetan guy who
looks Italian, he's wearing coiled shoes and burgundy
robes, he screams at the top of his lungs,
"MEDITATION CAN BE FUN"
My hair is wild and long again!
I walk into the American library and scream
"Illegal aliens are destroying the jobless!"

	I am absorbed by the library
	people look up for one hairy moment
	then the whole thing becomes safe again.

	I wish I had three wishes
	if I had three wishes I'd wish for a glass of
	water 2 sleeping pills and a Spanish girl
	I loved when I was seventeen,

	I'd tell her that ink blot, there on the desk,
	reminds me of you on a summer night at the beach
	your legs spread like seaweed
	and I eating you like you are totally everything
	good existing at once

	the waves keep beating us backward and forward
	and you hold my head tight to you

LIVING IN THE PAST CAN BE TORTURE
	LIVING IN THE FUTURE CAN CAUSE NIGHTMARES
		LIVING IN THE NOW CAN BE THE MOST TERRIBLE DUE TO
			the condition one is in at present… oh
			I forgot where I was for a second

DHARMA, CAUSE AND EFFECT
if you do everything for the sake of all life
you make no more bad effects
let's get on
with the trek

November 7th Scorpion

I have a lot
of fear of death
fear of burning up the life
in pursuit of the real
From a birth just before winter
I find myself still happening
but the life breath grasped
has to shorten with each gasp
And I fear before
the simple dynamo of energy
is explored to its source
I will have blundered too many times
in the web of the status quo
Today I am in my environment
moist mushroom rotting trees
a waterfall yellow leaves
an aura of pink
to breath in.

November late Oct. highly emotional
just before everything dies
at my age
I feel like November
my friends feel like November
we like the color
but we want to die to it all
and become eternal.

Salutations to the Supreme Silence

Om-Namo salutations from the hawk to the crow,
the crow won't stay long
the hawk thinks he'll allow him a pause.
Om-Namo salutations from the sea to the land,
waves' hands curl, knees of water kneel,
and a grace-filled prostration lays itself on the shore.
Om-Namo with a gentle roar,
sending a creative impulse
positive negative
over the earth,
namo namo namo
namo namo namo
Om-Namo
salutations from the body mind song to the open air
to the breezy wind blowing past
Om-Namo caw, caw, caw,
or a heated dove's coo,
crow song, cat song, ant song,
man song, om-namo salutations
to funny concept-chew-will-I-zations

namo namo namo namo
Om Muni Muni Maha Muni Soha...

Terry Riley

SEVEN SONGS

Embroidery

Chinaman in Chinatown
Enchanted with an ancient gown
Sits down
Just to see embroidery like this can be

Only bliss around him now as Chinalady brings a Smoke to stroke his memory

Floating Lotus floating underground
His China boys with drum and cymbal down
Never had a chance to make a sound like this before

Pages pages falling by him now
Painting ancient pictures of the Tao

China earth and China sky
A Chinese lantern
Firefly
Of changing colors
Flying by
Never had a chance to leave the ground like this before

Maid of China
Combing Raven hair
Sits down
To dream about her love affair
Tying knots up in the air

Joss sticks burning burning
On the shrine
A Buddha stepping down
To ask the time

Rice upon the Beard of Uncle Yee
A fragrance
As he opens up the box

He brought with him
So long ago
From far away across the sea

No hope
No ambition now
Just day to day at Hung Fat Chow's
A marriage
Birth
A funeral
Marking time as fate allows

Pages pages falling by him now
Jaded paintings of a fading Tao

Eastern Man

Did you ever see one

Unimaginable sunrise?

Did you get up this morning

Before the dawn?

Did you ever tell one

Intellectual... somehow?

Did you get up this morning and say your prayers?

Did you ever hear one

Inexpressible sound Arise?

Eastern Man

Western Man

Analyse what you are doing

The Emerald Runner or Rites of The Imitators

I took a ride on a rainbow
Stepping inside...I walked down the aisle
Taking a seat by the window
I watched the landscape retire

The silent engines propelling
The vibrant colors ascend
A weightless journey beginning
To ecstasy without end

I closed my eyes for a moment
A thousand ages swept by
Carried along by the sound stream
Receding thoughts multiply

I see old friends drifting by me
Their knowing smiles shine out from the clouds
Forgotten planets around them
Dance on the winds of the sun

I saw the sign said “no smoking”
Shine in the haze up ahead of me
Folks all around laughing and joking
“This plane never stops at all,” you see

I want to talk to the Captain said Aye Aye
To the stewardess sitting idly by my side
She took me out of the cabin
To the place where the crew of the night usually reside

The tongues of fire in the Hrydaya
Thoughts dematerialise
Out came an Emerald Runner from Rama
No sign of fear in his eyes
And though he knew about the pilot
Flying once more in this way
Transparent crews in his service
Fulfilling wishes on trays

Were left no direction for landing the Eternal Play
Without meaning

Song from the Old Country

A scent of desert water
A banner waving in
The night of gypsy's daughter
Reflecting fires that burn
In silent wind

A fig tree in the garden
That's overgrown in Golden Sun
The smoking earth in early morning
The distant tolling bells for one who's gone

A temple on the hillside
Red stone along the Sky Blue Way
The Old Ones' teachings all are there
Written in the dying shades of a late summer's day

A broken wheel that's turning
A dusty road
A grave at the bend
A shaking hand that's writing
The past in granite
The future in sand

A Chien on a rainy night
Came and spoke these words to me
A secret I have been keeping since telling 83
Singing in many languages to my ear of tin
She danced so marvellously
And played on her violin

Surrounded by her devotees
Eyes glowing around the fire
The chanting began at seven
Followed up by cups of chai
Story followed story
Explaining the reason Why

What will become of us?
Came the question on bended knee

Feigning a grave prediction
She answered so gracefully
"Since you have always been…
So it seems you will always be
A Spark from the infinite
Tracing across the Galaxy"

The Travelling Machine

O friend have you seen
Somewhere you have been
Peaceful……….Serene
Me and my travelling machine……...going nowhere
O friend take a chair
They tell me you've been everywhere
To TIBET……...ARGENTINE
Well have you met Nizamuddhin Olia?
That day far away...you took that journey to old Shanghai
Did you see the tears in the Emperor's Eyes?…
Or bring me some strings for my harp
Tuned to the Tao's Paradise?
In a cave far away
I once heard my Daddy say
The Holy Lama O'Shea
Living miraculously without vitamin A
The Mala that you wear
A striped forehead under locks of mud-matted hair
Things like this I've never seen
Me and my travelling machine never been anywhere

Strangely Warmed

Strangely warmed
Is death like this?
Deep cover of snow
Heaven closes in
Shades of white hold you and I
Silently
In a quiet moment
Is death like this?

Reading The Signs

A tear in the clouds of time
Where can we find some peace of mind?
Crying on us...we read the signs

We waited for Your grace in lines
Held up our hands...did you see mine?
Crying on us...we read the signs

We brought along our pains and tears
Sent up the word...well did you hear?

While giving up all pride and fame
Down on our knees we took Your Name
Crying on us...we read the signs

The blood of a child who's gone
Killed by a whim
Please comfort him
Torn from his mother's breast
Soldiers heels that never rest
Have trampled all their hopes and prayers
Those left behind count empty chairs

You must have heard the cry of the poor
Who'd put them there without a cure?
Yet it seems there's no dinner tonight
Of this I'm sure
Put out the light

Allan Graubard

from
Fragments from Nomad Days

DAY 3

I do not know nor will I ever know what it was that forced the issue of my exile. That I wander still, after so many years, having fixed my pleasures in the most transient encounters, and where love once it has bloomed all too quickly dies, is perhaps more than I can account for beyond saying: “I too was there, in that city, where I found, among other lessons, the stark silhouette of my vanity.” Or: “Yes, I know that village quite well, for on its flea-bitten walls I would delight with Leonardo’s old games of ‘seeing’.” Or, better yet: “I remember my arrival, how exhausted I was, and the wild company I found as poor and demented as I. The wine was superb and the meat stringy and tough.” For beyond this there is little. I came; I left. In between there were days, weeks perhaps. Sudden friendships, quarrels, guilt would eventually sputter out. Once I even thought of marriage, but she, knowing me all too well, laughed in my face. I do not reproach her for the memory.

I could tell you of my parents, too, and of their expectations ground to dust by my fickle youth. I could tell you of all the time I have wasted while time stripped me clean, and I woke one morning and gazed around me and recognized nothing.

Yet there is little now that I would change, even if I could. I accept my lot, which is something quite different from making peace with the world! The spirit of my anger would never allow me to collapse so thoroughly that I would perpetually mistake modern life for what I desire, doing — all in all — even less to fulfill.

Nor can I admit to any great obsession as a way of explaining my erratic course, save that I recognize it when I see it, recalling each time these fateful words of Baudelaire: “Each of them carried on his back an enormous Chimera, as heavy as a sack of corn…”

If there is anything then that saves me the suffering others imagine I endure, and which I have endured if only to spite myself before them, it is this road, this sky, on which and under which I am no less and no more than I am: wanderer, nomad, wearing the violent bric-a-brac of defiled seasons.

There is nothing now, a few stars dying into day, a premonition of light, a bird shaking itself awake, the last bats fattened on nectar.

In this transparent hour I give myself to all I am not, *never having known any better.*

Day 7

By midnight you are one with the sky. By dawn, the promise fulfilled, I lead you away, back to your time, your history, your senses. You are only a woman sponging your thighs, humming softly. You, outcast, condemned to the sand, the well, the wadi. And in your face that other face, the face of the child who dreamed of the woman you never were.

Startled, evanescent, opulent.

You came one day, without warning, silent, alone. You accepted my aid, my trust, eating my food, drinking my water. Frightened at first, no doubt you were frightened, you said little. And when I asked of your home, your village, you spat in the sand and shook with hatred.

One night you dug a pit in the sand and vomited blood, thick clotted blood that tore through your throat with all the vehemence of the words you refused. Then you lay back, your lips caked red, and you pulled off your skirt and ripped your flesh, snorting like a horse in labor.

And when I pushed into you, your scream crackled through my skull.

Now we wander about each other, hunters hypnotized by the bounty of the prey.

Passion is our hindsight, pain our expectation.

You came one day, silent, alone...

For Celan

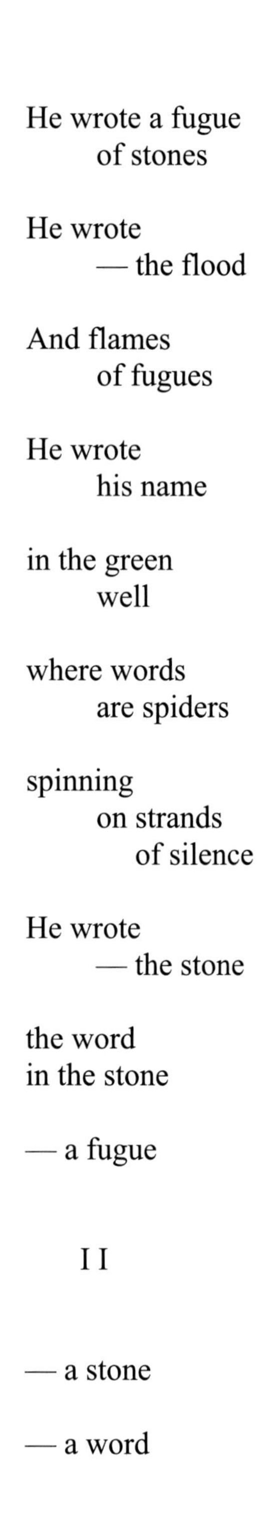

He wrote a fugue
of stones

He wrote
— the flood

And flames
of fugues

He wrote
his name

in the green
well

where words
are spiders

spinning
on strands
of silence

He wrote
— the stone

the word
in the stone

— a fugue

II

— a stone

— a word

In the rain
        — the rain

In the thunder
        — thunder

the artless reign
        of thunder

that drums
        — drums

the heart

The Summer of 48

Here we came
to this scorched rock
so that the empty pulse
of a vicious hour
might carve
the petrified breath
        of an antique sun
        on each of our eyes

here we came
arid anguish falling
like one barbed flower
        between our parchment fingers

what we were
what we are
the dream evaporates

the sea
the silhouette of the sea
        against the tortuous glitter
                        of the sea

Modette

You came without a word
holding the flame of your skirt in your hands
above the endless slumbering cities
of shadowy engines
You came with crossed eyes of dawn and dew
tearing the mist from its webs of herons
standing in pools of forgotten dreams
You came with the whirring of thin tortured fingers
that rose from a scream bandaged with stars
sputtering on the livid prows of white blind eyes
rolled down from the mountain to dry in the sun
You came with your jagged mirrors stained
with strips of newsprint peeled from the lips of a singing bloated corpse
You came with a pantomime of streams beneath lost bridges
when the scarecrows dictate sudden letters
and the lamps behind the façade of rotting handshakes
silhouette rituals of human ignition
You came with your glass of widows' tears
to cauterize winds that slash green faces of tumbling infants
in circus penumbras
You came with your wild teething hair
to shutter the images that yearn for a body in vain
You came with your generals of mica tottering
on the brink of a transitory bird
You came with a junta of towering maybells
swaying late above the final embers that drip from their cuffs
You came with your toothpicks of spit and the glorious stench
of menstrual handcuffs
You came with your turbans of snakes
quivering useless tongues
before the gigantic body of the storm
lurches from its playpen of serrated iron jaws
You came with clips of automatic corn
strung about your waist
with miniature zebras in full gallop across the vast sweat glands
of your palms
with drums of Chaldean sunlight at the peak of a pyramid of bones
with sumptuous armloads of trotted hay
with telegraphed visions of flying bunting
over the last high lakes of a vanishing word
You came with your rope of porcupine quills

gathered from the floor of the citadel of tides
You came with your mask of bees
to violate the sanctity of deciduous kisses
stuck to the walls of my paralyzed breath
You came with your glyphs of buried dolmens
to barter for vials of painted sweat
You came with your sponges of lichen
to erase the uterine clouds of quivering squid
You came with apples of lava spinning on a stick
with vineyard coffins full of horsemeat
with mothcups full of trumpet mutes
with menus for solar debauches
beside the whipping childish torment of murderers' heads
You came with arms runneled with ink
the way bullets steam ghost battalions for gourmet luncheons
You came with awkward breasts of sutured pine cones
pleated to a shadow that had stolen your voice
You came with fox-fur stilts
to conduct the crickets into banishing jet lag
with feet torn by stingers
with throats of towering mint
with promises bordered with snail slime
on cataract junkets of terrified falls

You came without a word
holding the flame of your skirt in your hands…

Judith Malina

Walking Along the Esedra

Walking along the Esedra
I notice the old who have failed,
Who have failed to secure themselves
Against the passage of time:
They are putting scraps
Into plastic bags,
They are lying helpless
On the benches spreading
Despair like disease
Among the compassionate.

What can we say to the young
Who have not yet failed?
"Get thee a bank account
To secure thyself
Against the newspapers laid out
Under the arcades
In the wet, friendless night?"

Look, alas, at that aging woman,
Trying to sell what is left
Of her unloved flesh!
Unable to earn enough
To buy a bed to cover
Her folly and loss.

Look at them! What
Can we say to the young?
"Marry a business man,
Pretty child, to secure thyself
Against the stone bench,
With slippered feet unwashed,
Raising the stench of their sorrow
To the sniffing universe?"

This is the Roman wall
Surrounding the baths,
Where the lusty officers went

To sport with the boys.
Always, since ancient days,
The outcasts have come
Here where the city ends,
Where there is nothing left,
Putting bits of their nothingness
Into rag pickers' bags.

This is the place where the old
Gather like limping elephants
Waiting to perish for lack
Of love and nutriment.
Look at them!

Here is our alleyway
Where the junkies are trying to die.
Look at this nineteen year old,
As old as the Roman wall,
He has been here forever and ever,
Determined to turn to dust.

What can we say to the young
Who have already failed?
What can we feel for the old
Whom we have failed?

Every One of the Cleaning Women

Every one of the cleaning women
Dreamt of something else
When she was seventeen.

They smile, they joke, they sigh,
In their smocks and comfy shoes —
They try not to recall the plans
For a miracle or a marriage...

Of the schemes that each of them made
With their young man
In the marriage bed,
Of a house in the fields,
Or a store in the city...

Now they are widowed or worn,
The man drunk, or dead, or departed,
Or unable to make ends meet.

Every one of the cleaning women
Hoped that the prince would come
And rescue her from the pail and the wringer.
The fairy tale promised
That the girl who sat by the cinders
Was to be clothed in splendor
And inherit the kingdom…
Slowly the dream wore down.

When I was eighteen and worked
In the laundry counting
The dirty wash, I dreamed
That the prince would come.
And he came. And that my talent and ardor
Would rescue me from listing:
Five napkins — eight pieces underwear —
Rescue, and lead to a privileged life.

And I was the fortunate one,
Leading a privileged life — rescued
From smock and broom, and now my friends
Ask me why I'm so sad
When I see the cleaning women
Laughing as if it were nothing…

"You and your Jewish guilt…"
"But somebody has to do it…"

But every one of the cleaning women
Dreamed that it wouldn't be she.

Hidden Under

The slave conceals a liberating
        thought under his cap.
The soldier harbors a hint
        of peace under his helmet.
They say the crown is heavy
        but so few ever wear it.
It were better to speak
        of the lepers, or the many
Addicted to sorrow, not even
        appealing for succor,
Like a woman in a film
        stepping barefoot
On a broken bottle.

The puritan conceals a
        filthy wound under a
Clean cloak.

The child carries the foretaste
        of a monstrous oncoming
        adulteration.

There are indeed princes
        but they never change
        clothes with paupers.

Were it not better to speak
        of healers, whether by faith
Or science, not even
        hoping for a cure,
Like someone in a poem
        standing at a window
        looking at the channel?

Roles

Every morning I feel like Iphigenia
Waking to the day of her sacrifice,
Like Isaac, I will be saved
By the Divine Force, though alas,
My faith in the intervention is weak,
Still I pursue the day.

Every day I feel like Antigone
Confronting her brother's burial,
Unyielding against the mighty forces
But grieving in my pride
That the city will fall because of my fate,
Still I plunge into the city.

Every evening I feel like Judith
Watching the siege of the city,
And I resist the blood-thirsty rage
To sever evil from its body
And I return without my trophy to the city
To the night of the theatres.

Every night I feel like Hecuba…

Splendor

Splendor is never simple.
It comes to light
When the 1000 things
Grate against the soul,
Scintillating the environs
So that the blinded mind
Can see what's always there,
Obscured by custom.
Splendor only occurs
When each of the 1000 things
Is precisely in place.

Breaking the Laws

Shall I not break the laws
When it is written that
Moishe Rebenu, our teacher Moses,
Broke all the laws at once
When he saw the abomination?

Do I not see the abomination
As I descend from the mountain
Of cognition to the world
Of idolatry and human sacrifice?

Yes, I see it. And I break the laws.

Korach

We are the children of Korach
Whose sin was so grave
That the Holy One
Opened the earth
To swallow even
His wives and his tent pole.

Not for Cain who slew
            his brother
Nor for David who slew
            his thousands
Did the Holy One decree
            such retribution,
Only for him who slew no one
            but declared the heresy:

We are Holy.

Hanon Reznikov

Bounding to the Music

I will take the looping notes of the muezzin's call
between my index finger and thumbs

aaaa-eeee-oow-waeee
aaaa-eeee-oow-waeee

that skein of rough-edged sharps and flats I'll drape
over my Jew's horns like a winged goat in ascent

higher than the Berber boy who smoked his brother's whole stash
I'll ride smoother than Gide through the desert

I am sprung by the glory of Allah
who penetrates to the toenails and lightens through completeness

wheee-oohh-wheee-aee
wheee-oohh-wheee-aee

borne aloft on *a cappella* cries
like the wizard in Bernoulli's dream

aakh-man-aakh-man

the horizon falling away like a sign of achievement
the ship ready, the line cast aside

smaller below, closer above
larger below, now

past the top floor, out the shaft
making from the roof as from the ground

eee-eee-kae
eee-eee-kae

eleven euphoristic kites
one wind

ooww-wae

one wind

ooww-wae

begin by reading
proceed to singing
concentrate, listen
lift off

in flight, the ribbons of sound float full-voiced
still streaming between digit and clamp

the muezzin's voice, the call is his

yaae-aaa-yaae-aaa
yaae-aaa-yaae

the humblest detail
the body functions
food, family
the care of underwear

fired like sand into crystal
with the same heavy dose of lead

but the shape is dynamic
the content music and lighter than air

further out, atop the forests
further still, above the seas

a reversal of gravity, the natural consequence
of dividing the many by itself and getting one

baaa-daaa-kae
baaa-daaa-kae
baaa-daaa-kae

three times

and imagine the climb as paced to be a life
and interpret the law to be peace

from the time the big toe leaves the surface
and the outside becomes the world

the muezzin's call goes in all directions
but the years go only up
the pitch is perpendicular

kaaa-deh-mae-nukh
kaaa-deh-mae-nukh-kaaan

we are free
we are fooled

as if one could breath in outer space
as if there were no way down

Ginsberg Gone, Cohen Abides

Ira Cohen describes
a ferry between worlds
a faerie stuck in Queens
a zero-balance retirement account
an unconstellated star
the braying of asses at midday
a double-glazed barrier
a Klein bottle left uncorked
a mitzvah unrewarded
a point-blank shot in the mirror
the last Jew in Rostock
the blow job done in half–light
seven irises of the same species
a heat-seeking missile launched from Calcutta at dusk
the names of all the poets on one glass
a virtual hearth cradling actual embers
that inhalation of a holy name
up the chute

Song of a Long-Running Tragedy

I am a citizen of Thebes
    an inextinguishable survivor
    of fathomless battles
    that beat the years' time
    to a flatfooted brazen arhythm

I am the last root
    of an ancient house
    whose branches spread dead
    above the ground softly
    bloodied by brothers

I remember as children
    before the walls fell
    and the city heaved
    a sigh and sank to
    a merciless resurrection

I hear the war cries
    that follow the odes
    as predators their daily
    bread or the first scream
    the peace of the womb

I am a male bond between
    grieving women condemned
    to endure renewal and
    the harvest of contempt
    I am witness

To untold agonies of birth
    and lethal life signs
    that banish sleep and force
    the waking dream over
    the snout of reality

I am an actor in a drama
    I do not hope to repeat
    but repeat in the hope
    of resolution I have no
    other gods before me

I am chosen to partake
    in forgotten rites
    to rise and fall out
    of all season I abandon
    myself to all enemies

I make no plea no contingency
    plan my habitat is
    Thebes, where wisdom rounds
    the corner in headlong
    flight from age.

The Living Theatre…

The Living Theatre
is still roaming Europe
in Volkswagen buses

the audiences ardent now
and sometimes unmoved

just as then

the actors full of belief
in the encounter
and, yes, even the Idea

getting paid well in Germany
and eating even better in Italy
until a call comes

"Florence cancelled —
the theatre closed
by the *vigili del fuoco*"

nerves grow taught
but from the hotel
there's a view of San Marino
a triple-toothed scup of rock

Nightfall in Naples

black the street —
Vesuvius, after-
time-muffled heels
coming down

shadow

beat

dim altars in the street
with lights

bang-jars and earrings
bronze clan-streaks
on the young mothers' lids

street kiosks
with lemons to squeeze

looks that speak
for every muscle in the body

coffee-sparks and gas
a pizza a minute
gold watch on the sly

cherubs on motos
belching smoke-filled salutes
to tankers gliding softly past Capri

give the girls a chance
the women, another reason to go mad

kissing works, but only after dark
with the sky-shades drawn
and the octopus at large
in the bay

there must be guns, somewhere…

no one will know
if you don't tell

the garbage is mighty
as the songs

this street or that?

a dollar's too much —
fifty cents

poem poem

I think it's the poem
where I'm most at home

that fort for intransigent children
stuck on blurting it out —

words like snowballs
flung from within the redoubt

jabber-dabber orbs
meant to burst on impact

des petits trous de mort
on the foe's frame

we're a pack
of poets we are
many

and inside
the perimeter of our attitude
there is uneasy intimacy

with other message services
that assault the market
from in here
from a sniper's window

all we can achieve in poetry
is achieved through deceit
and subterfuge

“Fight on!” “*La gloire!*”

snowfort boys
wanting to leave
something
behind

not a house built
not a tree

a city pavement
finger-sprung, gemstruck
that pulses like Helion’s heart

like the good blob of the north
that’s my poem out there

sucking rocks

The Living Theatre

scenes from

Utopia

by

Hanon Reznikov

Scene 6 — Lengths of Silk

ensemble dances with bolts of silk as the actors call the colors to music

ENSEMBLE

Blue! The cobalt rivers!

Dance of the Tall Ellipses: a blue cloth is spread diagonally across the stage — it is a river, the ensemble sends waves along it — then they begin to waft it high into the air, and it becomes the sky under which they spin — the blue cloth vanishes suddenly and the ensemble runs off in search of it

ENSEMBLE

Orange! The autumn sky at Oneida!

Dance of the Exponential Growth: a human figure wrapped in an orange cloth is placed at the center of the stage — a Native American drum-song is heard and one of the ensemble dances toward the figure at center stage and begins to unravel the orange wrapping — one by one, others arrive and take up the cloth, as the center figure unwinds — when the center figure is free, the cloth-spiral reverses direction and slowly winds all the ensemble within it

ENSEMBLE

Green! The jade of Greensickness Peak!

Dance of the Unwobbling Pivot: two figures struggle over possession of a green cloth, a third figure appears between them, seizing the cloth and spinning them about the stage — suddenly, the center figure disappears and the two remaining figures gather up the cloth, exiting together contentedly

ENSEMBLE

Yellow! The lemons of Majorca!

Phoenician Dance: two figures enter with a yellow cloth, dancing to a flamenco rhythm, two other pairs enter as the cloth becomes a moving band, circling among them — eventually, as the sunny light dims, the ensemble grows tired and sinks to the ground, wrapping their heads in the cloth

ENSEMBLE

Violet! The swollen lingam of Gautama!

Dance along the Precipice: the ensemble enters, one behind the other, a long purple cloth stretched between their legs — they move their bodies up and down along the cloth, shivering with sensual delight as they cross the stage and exit from the other side

ENSEMBLE

Red! The molten core beneath the mantle!

Dance of the Volcano: an earth-shaking music brings the ensemble onstage, all spinning beneath cloths of different colors floating above them — at the music's climax, the ensemble drops to the ground, the cloths enveloping them as they disappear

Scene 7 — Corcovado

ensemble discovered sleeping

the sleepers dream themselves awake, take off and fly

the flying is a kind of samba, during the course of which, the audience participant who is to play Hermione in the succeeding scene is brought onstage, lifted aloft and flown about high above the dancing actors' heads

ENSEMBLE

we arise
we lift off

we forge a new pact with gravity:
even split — half above, half below

we elevate at will
a gesture casual and potent
the arms down sweep
send us up

what does it mean?
the way it feels

the softmotor charge
completeness

she's rising as she rises
and all the rest
risen too

what rises could rise
indefinitely

and the sun set later
and later still

red

soaring, gliding
looping across the darkening sky,

"Be careful!" cry the ground-bound

but free beyond care,
mothers, even lovers
are on their own now

we are our own children,
our own partners
as we ascend

"our mass is our import!"
"our motion our companion!"
"our wings our own dumb pleasure!"

we are gravity's lover who always returns…

slow decent begins

alone, too,
as we brave the trip back
from triumph

at nightfall descent
begins as a yen
to scoop that Harley-eyed view
up the length of Sunset Boulevard
all the way to the beach

a movement of elbows skyward
drops us swiftly as we dare

the blackout charge of giddy fear
coming down, tempering acceleration
tamping our fall with a fearless inbreath

till the touchdown tap
on the toes — yes, the toes

and the buses on Sunset are right on time…

scream of brakes — Hermione falls to the ground in slow motion

CHERUBIM
(singing)

What happens in Utopia when someone dies?

ENSEMBLE

a stopping of breath

Ira Cohen

Song To Nothing

And surely we will die without memory
coming to cold in the shadow of space
& if it isn't too late
for the star to love you
spraying the sky w/ whispers
attuned to galaxies hungry for flame
And if the tongue of night sings
of albino winos
till the morning light shafts
            the doorway
then surely we will die tonight
            faceless at the White
                        Gate
sharing the smoke
w/ ancient shapes in future garb
and you stand somewhere there
            on the other side
feeding on the pain of dreamlessness
Wherefrom the misty morning of
            white shadows
& the unresisting need to destroy?

Samael, Samael, I beg it may be forgiven
            that they may be driven
            out of the black into the white
Only let the dazzle remain
            for gamblers to surprise,
            the strategic diamond, the throne
                  of compressed bone
            in the unshored dark
where only light can forgive
            & your mind is signed
Embers of echoes in the vastness
            disguise the yearning to burn
                  blind eyes
in arrogant displays of feeling —
Running wild these beasts will feast
                  on the newborn kind

for surely we will die tonight
unless we learn to ignore
what the others live for
on the other side of morning
& the Skin of Nothing left by the same
summer
masks the faceless wanderer

O let it happen,
this weird to discover
the shape of Beauty in everything
extreme
for surely we will die tonight
whether we will or whether we
dream
O Samael, forgive the dreamer
forgive the dream

The Song of Nothing is your Lullaby.

Hail And Farewell

Ave Atque Vale

Farewell Burroughs, Ginsberg, Huncke & Leary too,
we who are about to die salute you
If in every eyeblink there exists a potential eternity,
maybe there will still be a time to clean up & even go beyond
Luckily it isn't too crowded where you are
considering the immensity of the population
You have no more body & Spirit lives in infinite space
Say hello to Gysin, will you & wear your last names proudly
This is Cohen talking & I'm very glad to say —
even after radiation this is a particularly splendid day!
Mother Earth & Father Sky grant you what your efforts
surely do confer
Return to that light which once you knew
before you wrote yourself out of this human zoo.

The Day After Jerome Robbins Died

I sit on a bench on a Broadway island
between lanes of bleeping traffic
thinking of the significance of OJ's mansion
razed to the ground
An old black lady with a cane wearing an
elegant strawhat makes it across the street
to catch the number 60 bus, the one I love
to take for 75 cents which goes all the way
to LaGuardia Airport… I read in the paper
that an old friend, Peter Dennison & his son,
Morgan (eleven years old), were killed crossing
the street by an empty bus — they were holding hands.
In my own heart love dies a little & urges
me to keep jaywalking, if such steadfastness
could so tempt blind fate.
Talking to Ondi on the telephone I say, " If you
really love me why would you want to go
to the Sahara where we could be buried in
all that sand?" "The starlight," you say,
but I'd rather go to the beach & be touched
by blue water. I'm thinking *Atlantis* &
she says "Madagascar," definitely at the top
of my dream list. "You know Madagascar
is considered to be ancient Lemuria & there are
still lemurs singing in the trees."
We agree to go there, we will record the lemurs,
their love calls & all the rest of their chatter,
add theremins & make a CD
I'd love to sample Lemuria before the clock
runs out! I'm going to eat the millennium,
fill my head with African gold, look at tectonic
maps of Venus, check out the hotspots, clean the
mirror, say Hello to another night sleeping on sharp
corners — I'll turn the pages of the GIRAFFE book
with my eyes closed & wear the giraffe hat for the big audition
when the next dawn finally arrives. There goes sugar walking
around but nothing is free except you & me. You have to be crazy
to expect any more. *Time is what keeps the light from reaching us.*

Insomnia On Duke Ellington Boulevard

July 14th, Breakfast w/ myself at the Olympia Diner, 106th & B'way.

Fell asleep around 4AM
w/ the TV on
Van Heflin & Barbara Stanwyck
enter my disturbed sleep
Sometimes the only way out
is to die, but happily
someone else escapes,
takes to the road, goes on
travelling.
I'm up at seven, go to the post office,
send two Cuban alligators
to Brussels,
then read Gabriel's column in NEWSDAY
about the real meaning of the closet,
feel nauseous, order a hardboiled egg
which comes w/out a shell
mashed in a cup
Is my heart, too, yearning
for its dying hour?
Please bring me one order
of cool snow!

If I could remember just a fraction
of what I said on the telephone
If he could take his clothes off
and sit on the banks of the Ganga
If she could see the profile of Caliban
in the smoke over the oilfields
If we could just take off & go to Madagascar
If they would stop killing each other
and wake up tomorrow morning
w/ a new vision
I would stick my head in a printing press
and you could read tomorrow's paper today:

EXTRA! EXTRA!
Read all about it
Poet's brains prove to be useful!

P.S. Sometimes when I pick up my pen
it leaks gold all over the tablecloth.

From The Moroccan Journal-1987

My heart feels like an uncut diamond
Though it is still the same, it is not the same
Someone speaks of a bridge to be built from Tangier
to Algeciras or is it Gibraltar?
"Yes & then a highway to the stars or more likely
an elevator to the Underworld", says Yellow Turban
to White Jellaba as the exhaust fumes from the bus
engulf them, leaving behind not even a single
shadow.
Is that Mel Clay in a white jacket turning the corner?
No, it is a figment of my imagination escaped from the
asylum.
Is that Ian Sommerville walking backwards up the street
as if pulled by a giant magnet?
No, that is Wm. Burroughs making electricity
from dead cats.
Is that Tatiana glistening on Maxiton?
No, that is the sun dancing in the sugar bowl.
Is that Marc Schleifer wavering on the cliffedge?
No, it is a promontory in the wind of time
about to fall into the sea.
Is that Beethoven's 9th Symphony being played
up the street?
No, it is the sound of the breadwagons
rumbling over cobblestones.
Is that George Andrews with two girls in hand
looking for bread?
No, it is an unidentified flying object about to land.
Is that One-eyed Mose hanging by his heels?
No, that is the hanged man inventing the Tarot.
Are the dead really so fascinated by lovemaking?
Yes, that is how they travel.
Is that Irving in short pants looking for trouble?
No, that's me unable to stop thinking.
Is that Kenneth Halliwell looking for Joe Orton?
Is that Jane Bowles looking for Sherifa, Rosalind looking
for her baby, Alfred searching for his lost hair?
Is that the wig of it all, the patched robe of my brain,
the wind talking to itself?
Brion is dead and Yacoubi is dead, and I am a not unhappy
ghost remembering everything, the warp & woof of memories,
her yellow slip, her shaved cunt, her idiot child.

Dream shuttle makes me exist everywhere at once.
The blind beggars led by children keep coming.
"They all have many houses in the Casbah,"
chant the unbelievers sucking on sugar.
Words keep coming back like *Bezezel* for tits, *Litcheen*
for oranges, like Mina, like Fatima, like Driss Berrada
dropping his trousers for an injection in the middle
of his shop.
The trunk is full of old sepia postcards,
barebreasted girls smoking hookahs etcetera.
We speak of the *cataplana*, the mist which obscures
even the *cielo*, you cannot even see the hand in front
of your face.
We embrace, he says he thought of me only yesterday,
he says there are always nine such men who look like us
in the world and that we are the tenth.
We speak of the gold fillets in the sky over Moulay Absalom.
The garbage men in rubber boots go thru the Socco pushing
wheeled drums of collected garbage.
An unveiled woman wobbles out of a taxi and heads home
before sunrise.
Paul couldn't believe there was a Karma Street,
but I will never forget it.
And Billy Batman, who made the best hash in the world,
he dropped a loaded pistol in Kabul, shot himself in the balls,
took some heroin and lay down to die.
Now I must get up from my table in the allnight Café Central.
No more Dr. Nadal, no more window with red crosses & red
crescents.
The water thrown from buckets runs across the café floors
& over the sidewalks & I drop a dirham into the hand
of a blind beggar singing in the dark on the American stairs.

"The women wear fireflies in their hair, but the fireflies stop shining when they go to sleep so now and then the women had to rub the fireflies to keep them awake."
From Anais Nin's A Spy in the House of Love.

An Act of Jeopardy for Garcia Lorca

A star of blood you fell
from the point of the hypodermic
singing of fabulous beasts &
spitting out the sex of vowels
Your poems explode in the mouth
like torrents of sperm on a night
        full of zebras & bootheels
Your ghost still cruises the river-
fronts of midnight assignations
in a world of dead sailors carrying
        armfuls of flowers in search of
                your unmarked grave
Your body no sanctuary for bees,
Death was your lover in a rain of
        broken obelisks & rotting orchids
In a tangled rose of a single heartbeat
I offer you the shadow of a double
profile,
        two heads held together at the bridge
            of the nose by a nail of opium
                                smoke
        in the long night's dreaming
        & memory of water poured between
                                glasses
In my mailbox I find a letter from
        a dead man & know that for every
            shadow given
            one is taken away
Yet subtraction is only a special form of
addition and implies a world of hidden
intentions below a horizon of lips
thin as your fingernail sprouting
mysteries in the earth…
The ace of spades dealt from the bottom
        of the deck severs the hand which
        retrieves it & the eyes of Beauty
        sewn together peer over a black lace fan
        in the vulgar sunlight of a Spanish
            morning without horses
              The Belt of Orion is loosened
before you as you remove the silver
fingerstalls from your mummy hands &

kneel to plunder the nightsky in a shower of
    bitter diamonds.
(Somewhere under a blanket someone weeps
    for a lover.)
Peace to your soul
& to your empty shoes
in the dark closets of
kings with no feet!!!

Imagine Jean Cocteau

Imagine Jean Cocteau in the lobby
holding a torch
Imagine a trained dog act,
a Rock and Roll band
Imagine I am Curly of the Three Stooges
disguised as Wm. Shakespeare
Imagine that I'm the cousin of the Mayor
of New York or the King of Nepal
(I didn't say Napoleon!)
Imagine what it is like to be in the glare
of hot light when you are longing for dark
corners
Imagine the Ghost Patrol, the Tribal
Orchestra —
Imagine an elephant playing a harmonica
or someone weighing out bones on the edge
of the desert in Afghanistan
Imagine that these poems are recorded moments
of temporary sanity
Imagine that the clock was just turned back —
or forwards — a hundred years instead of an hour
Let us pretend that we have no place to go,
that we are here in the Cosmic Hotel,
that our bags are packed & that we have one hour
to checkout time
Imagine whatever you will but know that it is not
imagination but experience which makes poetry,
and that behind every image,
behind every word there is something
I am trying to tell you,
something that really happened.

A letter to no one…

A letter to no one
about crossing borders,
about time & impermanence
Would you wear my shoes?
Could I throttle time?
A man wearing a baseball cap
carries a woman's breast
in his overnight bag
We step over the cracks,
dream of teleportation,
try to get to the other side
of What
It's mindboggling to see
the blind man led by a dog
I'm with you in spirit
I've transcended light
Where you live it's daytime
My life is bounded by night
If you can't see my mirrors
I can't see you
We're crossing another border
Why is everyone asleep?
It's better to just drive
through it
Meet you in the middle,
neither here nor there,
but in that mystical place
called everywhere.

Joseph Beuys

7000 Oaks

The 7000 Oaks Project was inaugurated on the 1st of November, 2001,
in the centre of Ireland at Uisneach
in honour of Joseph Beuys by Gordon Campbell
accompanied by friends and artists celebrating
the planting of the 7000 Oaks in the shape of a heart

...the rain spitting on late blackberries,
soft Irish weather swathing the view of the twenty-six counties
— the palace where Deirdre flirted: eye of fire —
a lone songbird following us up the Hill of Uisneach,
carrying the vision of the 7000 Oaks in our hearts,
— Dies ist meine Art, und dies ist die Art von meiner Mutter —
300 Druid tongues buried beneath us, dedicated to silence,
and one tongue of flame issuing from the jaws of one unredeemable wolf
lights the light...

for Joseph Beuys & Gordon Campbell

Gordon Campbell

MAGIC is about now
Magic is about yesterday
Air Water Food People Animals
Plants
E A R T H
U N I V E R S E
Life
Fire
Love
Trust
Music
Trees
And
All
And
Everything
Which
Can
Be
Found
At
Uisneach
The Naval of Ireland Mother Goddess Eriu The Fire Eye Place of Fawns
Bed Of St. Patrick Aill na Mireann Stone of Divisions The Five Directions
The Formorians Tuatha de Danaan The Dagda Finn McCumhal
Uisneach
Gateway to the Other World
Centre of this One

Ronnie Burk

Words Written in Blue Flame

Hours-the-strong-bull-loving-truth
etches the world in place
snake born kaballah in an abandoned
factory yard
ominous as an upside down 3
little girls fly down the hotel hallway
glowing mirrors of the kidnapped infanta

steel blade
electra
lacerating
newsprint
people

domino theories confront the irrational factor
bloody crustacean between the crevices devouring
Man

stop watch
pelvis
vibrating discs of
pure pleasure
sex burns taboos of the gods
a hint of Africa in the bluer waters
weaving
peyote eyes

emerald daggers
quetzal plumes
thunderbolt
dorjes
foot binding the skyscraper
in silk pyjamas
even the Olmec mask can't hide
your lies

NYC July 1999

Sky*Boat

for Will Alexander

In the Horned Kingdom Cernunnos traces the veins of Jerusalem
To a cracked cistern in a field of poppy flowers
My cabalistic egg hatching The Sephiroth of The Lost Planetary System
Iron plumes of the ten thousand eyes of Ezekial's Beast
Swirling a cyclone of black coronas
His vajra of coffin nails and colored threads
Tied with burnt cherub medallions

In the apparition zone having set fire to water
Rabid dogs dance in a fusion of tungsten light
Inflorescence of mandrake that little man in the bottle
Separating the salt from the ash
The Tormented Mermaid searches for her children
Abandoned in the sewers of the world
Density of carbon auroras fishing for a pearl
In the tributaries of a majestic key-hole
Manta-rays return to the lake of blood

My mother in her lunar costume beating Hydra's wing

°

Uroboros of my third eye curled up in a mollusk
Hekate's gallery sails over the storm
Extracting rays from a nugget in a lead box
She knows nothing about the somnolent
Footsteps of the Philosopher's Widow
At the doorway to the dungeons of chaos
Pericles on a razor blade incubating quicksilver
Distilling filigree of disintegrating planet
Extinguishing Mars

°

When the peacock on the blue bottle attacks its mate
The crippled farmer knows it's time to water his silver trees
Holding a lantern of fireflies
A washerwoman pierces the diamondback salamander
Smouldering beneath the rocks
The royal couple poured into a gelatin cube

In the radium mines a necklace of thorns
Strangles the cross-eye Gemini
Always the sun & moon in one face

°

In a moment Toussaint L'Ouverture will enter the turquoise morning
of Nezahualcoyotl's calligraphy room
And place a lei upon Queen Lili'uokalani
Marking the ve've' of the Ruby Queen
On his left shoulder covered with epaulets
He will proclaim the sovereign rights for
The Constitution Of The Garden Of Earthly Delights
Heraldic star of Neptune's ray black jade insignia of the eagle–serpent
on a column of nopal smoke
demon slayer of purified ore His child in the red suit is Chango
guiding Erzulie's spangled boat into the face of Tlaloc
in Aquarius
Ogun! Of the red squares chasing tigers in a black mirror
Always Taurus! Your mangled star in the chalk yard
Boiling the leper's cloth nursing the century back to sleep
tiny medusas in a locket shriek for help
Radiation currents the eroded soil to keep disease from
Over-riding the emaciated devi of the dried up rice paddy
Uranium swallows the rats scurrying about the graves
of suicide-kings

Blood Oranges

The sky draped like a tent billowing above the hills
revolving divine images of Durga the fragrance & color of blood oranges
White light dappled in the cherry blossoms cupped in my hands fluttering
like so many incandescent butterflies
Down the alleyway crack heads sit on a torn up sofa torching glass pipes
with a butane lighter
Still the photographer stands on the corner waiting for the perfect picture

San Francisco, January 2001

Jon Hassell

Perforated Experience

Imagine a giant sheet, perforated with regularly spaced holes, thrown over a wild landscape. Whatever features of that landscape that happen to poke through a given hole is now taken to be "symbolic" of all that lies beneath. One area can now be seen as distinct and can therefore be compared with the one adjacent to it.

Think of the romance of measuring time by how long it takes for sand to go from one chamber to another or how long it takes for a candle of a certain size to burn out or the 10th year of the reign of a certain king or the 3rd day of some festival. Local time became global time with the invention of the calendar and the clock.

Words are like the holes in the sheet thrown over the "landscape"— the continuum of pre-verbal experience/feeling. Now what pokes through one "hole" can now be seen as distinct and can therefore be compared with what's showing through the other holes.

Think of the constantly changing light and shadow of rooms lit by candlelight. So much like life: things being experienced with constantly varying shadings, none more true or important than the other vs. electric light with its monomaniacal insistence that one set of shadows is "correct".

This gives rise to lots of interesting new games of comparison. But after a while everyone forgets that there is anything else under the sheet and that realm of experience/feeling turns brown and pale from lack of light.

Think of non-tempered "local" tuning (good only for this piece of music, in this key, in this place) vs. tempered "global" tuning (good for all places, in all keys, everywhere).

Listening to birdcalls of Southeast Asia, some graspable as chromatic motifs, some wildly evanescent, I think about the straight lines of the music staff drawn across the world of sound, like the straight lines of the clock-tick, drawn across the continuum of experience. And how some birds are heard "mostly at dawn" or "particularly during moonlit nights", the way certain ragas are meant to be sung, "during the rainy season around midnight" or "mid-morning in the Spring.

Music and art and poetic use of language seeks to evoke the "masked off" interstitial areas, to reconnect the continuum that exists under the sheets.

WORDISM ILLUSTRATED:

The **Words** are all on transparent film.
The **Experiences** to which they refer are taking place seamlessly behind this film overlay.

(The Words are like "digital samples" of a continuous "analog" Experience.)

If you focus on the Word-film, the world of Experience becomes a blur.

(The way that focusing on an insect on your car windshield prevents you from seeing the road in the distance clearly).

Pre-verbal experience (infants, earliest peoples) takes place "entirely behind the overlay" (or rather, *without* an overlay).

Early verbal cultures see the Word and the Thing which it names in somewhat equal focus, connected by an invisible membrane.

Later verbal cultures came to see *only* the Word-overlay, with a vague blur of Experience behind.

As Homo-sapiens live ever more in the realm of symbols, the membrane connecting "thing" and symbol atrophies...

Discourse becomes a " same-symbol-with-a-different-underlying-meanings/same-underlying-meaning-with-different-symbols" quicksand.

Imagination, colonized by movies, becomes degraded to a narrative in words and pictures with a plot "defining moments" and conclusions...

There are two kinds of visual memory: one when you skillfully recreate an image in the laboratory of your mind, with your eyes open (and then I see Annabel in such general terms as: 'honey-colored skin,' 'thin arms,' 'brown bobbed hair,' 'long lashes,' ' big bright mouth'); and the other when you instantly evoke, with shut eyes, on the dark innerside of your eyelids, the objective, absolutely optical replica of a beloved face, a little ghost in natural colors (and this is how I see Lolita)."

Vladimir Nabokov "Lolita"

"Language speaks Man"
Heidegger

Wordism Recto

"WORDISTS": People who behave as if the symbolic representation of a thing is more "real" than the thing itself. They look at a situation only in terms of how it's described in words — without the background, the context, the color, of feeling and emotion.

After all, what makes the *feelings* of
"love" or "hate" "*opposites*".
"Opposite" is one among many alien metaphors,
smuggled across the border
from the land of Science where "opposite"
functions in a circumscribed universe
of meaning. It has assumed a new
identity and now walks among us
undetected and unchallenged.
In a pre-verbal or a meta-verbal world
there is no place for the concept of
"opposite". To the infant, there are only
currents of experience, all flowing
in the "same direction" (Time).

We've become
conditioned
to accept
words as the
experiences they
represent —
to think that
we're
actually
hearing music
when, in
fact, we're
only looking
at the
notation of
it.

Virtual Innocence

"Hypertext" — where a kind of "family tree" of
serendipitous connections between things is
cultivated — is clearly rooted in the attempt to
mimic, in print, or other media, the non-linear
ways in which the brain makes connections. The
continued evolution of this form in a world of
superfast processors may lead ultimately to
something akin the states of pre-category,
pre-verbal experience. The picture is this: language
has segmented the earliest continuum of
experience into little tiles and now the acceleration
of connection-making between these tiles
approaches some theoretical point where the tiles
— like frames in a film strip —
become continuum-like again.

The murmuring mass of an unknown language constitutes
a delicious protection, envelops the foreigner (provided the country is
not hostile to him) in an auditory film which halts at his ears
all the alienations of the mother tongue: the regional and social origins
of whoever is speaking, his degree of culture, of intelligence, of taste,
the image by which he constitutes himself as a person
and which he asks you to recognize. Hence in foreign countries, what a respite!
Here I am protected against stupidity, vulgarity, vanity, worldliness, nationality, normality."
Roland Barthes: The Empire of Signs

Mal De Mot (Abstraction-Sickness)

If you are trying to determine whether
a garment is wet or not, you can't do it
with wet hands, you must dry your hands first
and then touch it.
The existence of certain mental states
like abstraction-sickness (mal de mot),
prejudice etc. can only be perceived
from the (dry) vantage point
of certain other mental states.

Bau, Indonesia: 1957

"...an insignificant village... in its center is a one room school, a tiny cabin for the teacher and a palm sapling that may some day offer shade. The young teacher has one book only: Geological Strata of York County, Pennsylvania. But he understands what a book is, what it means to capture words and suspend time... this seemingly irrelevant book, donated thoughtlessly to some mission, couldn't be more appropriate, for it tells him that the true mapping of the universe begins below the surface and that for scientists, truth lies in the underlying structures (laws) which govern appearances. Dislodged from his own culture and unhoused in any single medium, my host is able to perceive literacy with a clarity denied those who live within its assumptions."
Edmund Carpenter: Oh What a Blow That Phantom Gave Me.

The Gods, They Must Be Crazy
a lyric

In the first days
In the very first days
In the first nights
In the very first nights
In the first years
In the very first years
When everything needed was brought into being...

Roman numbers
Indian summers
Kleenex and drugs
Where the rubber meets the road
Where we're all on overload
Thousand dollar hair
Blowing in polluted air
Herds of Business Guys
Prepare to sodomize
Flocks of Trophy Wives
While wearing a disguise
Corn-pone Porn Queens
Plumes of smoke
Freeway closings
Deep Throats

The Gods
The Gods, they must be crazy

From CNN overseas:
"Cummunwasm Refugees Overran Absurdistan"
Now the population's spic 'n span
While a presidential also-ran
Tries to get an even tan
Humanosaurs fight Superman
An umbrella and a sewing machine
Have sex on the table
Breton's in Book Soup
Riots on cable

The Gods
The Gods, they must be crazy

Welcome to The Chateau
Where you stage your own scenario:
Fluff Teen, Bitch Queen
All shades in-between
Sultry, slim, Simpson's fans
Counter-culture Kittens tan
Mental care in rubberware
You gotta be a Millionaire
To live in all this dirty air

It's a merry-go-round
Down in Blade Runner town
Viva Africa!
Om Nama Shiva
Djalabas, jalopies
Dashikis, Kon-tikis
Hoochie-koochie, Utsukushi
Paparrazi potpourri

The Gods
The Gods, they must be crazy

In the first days
In the very first days
In the first nights
In the very first nights
In the first years
In the very first years
*When everything was brought into being…**

* *Sumerian Hymn 2000 BC.*

J. N. Reilly

Four Nocturnal Songs

If anyone had told me, when I was a child, that I would be an artist, living in a tenement in a slum in the east-end of Glasgow, with a wife and son, I would not have believed them, but I would have dreamt of being an artist, and those dreams would have been beautiful, and I would have seen a crescent moon suspended above my lover and myself, clasped in naked kisses and sighs, swept by scented breezes and ineffable joys, and I would have wished to be an artist.

1979

this poem is
dedicated to
the boys on the corner
the drunk and his dog
chasing cars of a night
this poem is
dedicated to
the woman I hear laughing
as I sit in my bath
thinking of you
and the little girl
this poem is
dedicated to
the junkie who overdosed
in the next tenement
the old man hanging from the pulley
in a wistful kitchen
this poem is
dedicated to
the excrement I live on
the indefatigable apotheosis
of blood and love and lust
this poem is…

5/1/77

time to love time
to kiss time is
time to fuck time
to eat time is
time to muse time
to grow time is
time to wonder time
to wander time is
time to play time
to piss time is
time to dream time
to live time is
time to cry time
to talk time is
time to speak time
to shit time is
time to laugh time
to laugh time is…

5/1/77

Sometimes when I look at my son, or when alone with my thoughts of a night, I remember that the time will come when he will die. That his mother and I shall probably die before he does is of no relief, for think of his grief at our deaths. That we shall not always be loving friends and companions wandering the seasons, our delights and the madness of this world, alone or together, solace to each other's distress; when slashed by adversity, racked by grief or smitten by obscure melancholies; will indeed be a great sorrow, and though I believe we are more than flesh and blood, it is at a melancholy time such as now, when folly lays its angelic head on my heart, that I wish for a marvellous discovery, engendering the immortality of the flesh…

1979

Parahorologenes...

Parahorologenes
Came close
And blast off
Split a day into three
So I painted you
A Rainbow in Crimson
And Hello strut-tuttering
To and from
Three blue skies
Hung out for sun
Made of cut glass in jigsaw
Till you come from a cigarent
Or two days
Parahorologenes…

1973

For Sale

I have fiery rose
Sky length darkness
Words to scatter in prayer
Burning dangerous ground

I have the edge of the world
Free troubles and now
Flesh guitars molten gaiety
In a grain of light

I have sex space
Bathed in eternity
Forever ejaculating
A path impossible…

1980

from

3 Beautiful Stories

the shamanic mix

… roll up, roll up. We've got it all — let's dance — weaving the text of love — the algebra of ecstasy in purple passages — the enchantment of drums in the orbit of vision…

...on his way home, he was stopped by the traffic lights at the clock tower. While waiting for the lights to change, his gaze wandered to the window display of a boutique, consisting of a mannequin dressed in a red bikini, lying on sand, with cardboard palm trees around her and a picture of the sea behind her, a ship in the offing…

...sailors fighting in an alley — jets in the sky — I am coming down the street with nothing in my pockets, with the heart and eyes of the artist — lover and thief — I'll steal away your misery — only the libidinous know — I am home coming...

...nothing is what it seems — for sale — a ride through the tunnel of love — the trip to immortality — it doesn't cost much...

...she smiled and held my hand — the picture dripping from us — adrift in the constellation of love...

...hello, is that you, it's me here...

...two men in black — at the verge of death — harbour lights dripping into the water — they played cards — looking for conviction — the evidence of codes — handfuls of skin...

...windows unfurling in the crystal dawn...

...indians dancing — he changed channel — enigmas of memory — rockets screaming through darkness — he changed channel — indians dancing — smiling...

...aural sights in the weave of the text — the Evolution spinning around and around — we've space for everyone — roll up, roll up...

...we shared a smoke and watched the flames leaping — weaving the many in the one — the grind of engines fading — tremulous newspaper sky — shy warriors on the way home...

...the wheel turning through the text — a dog barking on the edge of the picture — weighing the scent of silence — the smell of smoke…

...pieces of time caught in the curtain…

...he threw the parcel onto the bed. It was a box wrapped in shiny red and gold paper…

...she looked up at the Big Dipper — a tattered poster of a beach road lined with palms…

...at the verge of the city — ruined desolate buildings — a dog barking — blackness of night illumined by a blazing car…

...some folk call it the Big Wheel, others call it the Wheel of Fortune, some don't even notice it, passing with cluttered glances. Most folk are afraid of it and say they don't like taking chances, others make a haughty show of ignoring it and ride the Evolution around and around until day turns to night. Children and lovers call it the Big Wheel and cast their fortunes at it — every number a winner, every number theirs...

...coral perfection dripping with codes — handfuls of visions splashed against my face — a dog barking — ragged signals — voluptuous tongues caressing the red desire — she smiled and pulled the skin back…

...ochre trombones and pink violas — ideograms splashed with semen — pure thought streaked with red — sailors singing purple songs — a girl sucking her fingers — love gushing through the window — the radio on…

...red splashes on white — the curtain open — the blue trickling notes — sizzling rooftops — the beckoning haze of alleys and sidestreets — she stretched and smiled...

...tremulous children in the mouths of tenements — timing the drift and looking to score — the edge of the canvas flapping…

...love annihilates — she gave me indian paintbrushes — petals of light — feathers drifting in the flaming blue...

...pulling back the silent distance — sunlight pouring through the doorway — she opened her mouth — standing by the window, sliding her fingers in an out of her cunt — that's it — eternity cracked open...

...we smoked black blacker than black — in the holy land — the glorious devastation of scents — arboreous windows carved on the breeze — honey trickling from the bark...

...sumptuous messages of prayer — evening splashed against my canvas — pictures of sunlight — a jet in the blue vanishing — text of flute music dripping...

...it's an open secret — sweet warriors singing the length of eternity in the round of love — my stake in the earth — welcoming souls exchanging stones — drawing the balm of ecstasy...

...roll up, roll up — everything you ever wanted — the end pulled back...

...the silent distance in the flow of the river — the Big Wheel flickering over the harbour lights — in our darkest night — skull and crossbones at the edge of the picture...

...we've nothing to lose — not a penny in our pockets, not a hope in the world — are you coming...

...tenements flickering with televisions and the big beat — girls tired from the long day — falling into downy sleep — the Big Wheel twinkling on the horizon...

...the Big Dipper plunging into the shiny darkness — the Tunnel expanding — everywhere on display — a-go-go music pumping out scenic routes — the text on my tongue — dripping with honey...

...boys swooning on the edge of desire — pieces of sky merging with the wallpaper — get the picture — a spiral dream — the canvas splashed against the vision…

...days dissolving into nights dissolving into days — singing the naked lexia — waves of iridescence washing through our souls — painting the noise with silence…

...blowing kisses through the text — our nakedness strewn with apple blossom — immortal shores splashed with clarity — serene islands afloat…

...roll up, roll up — let's start smoking — the ley of the line — the inflorescence of time — all aboard — everything you've ever wanted…

...you've got my number, haven't you. All the nines, number nine. Call anytime…

...you ain't seen nothing yet...

Julian Beck

from
Living in Volkswagen Buses

a few stanzas on poetry

I

what is poetry or the relation of the human body to the human mind

now i am looking back
and i am still doing what i was doing then
i am examining the meaning of poetry
i am trying to make everything into poetry
i begin with soup
i begin with the body
everything must be poetry

i often write it badly
but i am always writing it
i am writing my life as i am living it
i am a writer

everyone is a writer
poetry is the universal life process based on words
everyone is a great tragedian

our models are false
they mislead us
bread without poetry is like poetry without bread
unfulfilling

stanzas on poetry

to make a wave of words as fertile as the sea
a tide of words
pulled upon by our gravitational condition

in poetry we seek the elevations
the peaks where the purity of the air
cleans out the pulmonary cavity

poetry a broom for the brain and the lungs

poetry to bring back the rhythm of life
which we lose
like a handkerchief
that's how brief it is
or blood loss like a nose bleed

as we leave our own trail of it
in the manichaean struggle against the darkness
mazda and other pagan ripples

defending poetry

when i was seventeen
and my cock rose stiff and bright as the moon
when i wrote poetry

reggio emilia
24 december 1975

II

what does the landscape look like this year
as volkswagen bus burns its way across lombardy now it's picardy
  we're on our way from dublin to the cathedral of amiens
  to play the house of death
what do i see out there
i see landscape 1978 with scarce old lamps to read by
dark times of many hard bodies
a ✓ for violence on the doorposts and bound in frontlets above the eyes
spurting invisible gas into time's face we go we who stomp up and down
  about ecological eschatology and indolence we leak
  our poisons human foibles
look out the car window see dead bodies of 120 slain in uganda in
  tribal war maybe in colonial bondage uniforms and arms
  trade
do you see bodies of dead in tehran square do you see all the
  time slaughters
when you are playing chess do you remember who it was who
  invented war and the family squabble and the football game
  of love and death

are you paralyzed yet by the armor of death and the skyscraping
threnody
do you see out of the window anything else
than the need
to write a poem now

roma
november 1978 september 1979

I I I

poetry is above all the spirit in the body

that is the only answer i can shout into the whirlwind of cars
the celestial works of the gold standard and the solid arcades
of christianity
the astounding feats
bridges flung wide by genius
under the portici the unempowered classes walk in an
unconscious grasp of their own incapacity to do anything
adhering as they do to the hysterical reefs of monetary
creeds
i condemn the banal bliss of sleep and the latest shriek with a
ticket issued by ravishing actor with marble cheeks of
noble weight a travel agency
everything is marked as a loser
when you lose your temper you lose
when you lose your looks
when you lose the election and the talent to sculpt
when you lose the woman
when you lose you must die
i have rejected this with the fastidious detail of an unprovable
proclamation about the imperishable potential of the body
spirit
which is poetry

amiens napoli
october 1978 november 1980

IV

halt on the world word
it is inveighing pardon
visit argentina and sharpen your wits
read boethius learn simple mechanics automechanics scurrilous
    finance and reason read anything that might help
study the american indian tribes how they made peace how they
    tended the earth how they killed beasts and each other
study the swim of completion
urge pleasure
what is the secret of life
the hole in the conch
the way
the *ech'd*
concocting chinese opera out of russian song
when i begin a poem i do not know where to go i have not
    predetermined to say something

i write
i enter the fold of poetry
every moment great total
mystery

roma to genova
5 october 1976

○

urging our parents in raving colors
foaming in passion and banging the gongs before bosses to
    summon accuracy back into mind
quoting figures about how many are starving and bleeding
    in ten cent stores
running demos in washington to trouble deaf senates
imitating beardsley in order to clarify forgotten details
living in volkswagen buses
cooking on camping gas
taking our clothes off in public places
smoking dope to change the answers discussing life and death
    instead of sleeping eradicating margins

drilling holes with poetry into the dense coteries of avenues and armies
blowing cool over marching men
placating policemen and provoking majorities
careening thru classrooms because we see them as megaphone
    bellowing submission to authority
spooking the jails
loving outcasts vagrants flake covered bodies and crusted orphans
staggering for thirty years down america's spinal column
climbing the ladders to the parthenon seeing that beauty is still
    not enough never was enough and never will be because
    the truth is not strong enough then what shall we do
excavating in crete on the beach of the mind for the source of
    the salute to the flag
searching the shops of iberia for tokens not stamped out with
    spears
driving across the equator boats to india inquiring of the life of
    the soul
repeating mantras to change the composition of the air and ear
jazzing and boozing and dancing to bring the body back to life
coming back to life
having babies and no money
forgetting how to lie
learning to speak without the impediments of courtroom
    grammar
playing in theatres after long ride displaying the clowns of life in
    iambic fervor
pressing our lives against the current of electricity that rivets
    death in chairs
frightening ourselves with lsd mirrors when the skull emerges and
    pretending we're reconciled
studying the obsessions of prophets and the panic of failure
beginning again now that the hurricane of jupiter is on its way
trying to be one he cannot kill

bologna roma
29/30 march 1979 august 1981

Patti Smith

Remembering A Poet
Gregory Corso, 1930/2001

Gregory Corso, the flower of the beat generation, is gone. He has been plucked to grace the Daddy garden and all in heaven are magnified and amused. I first encountered Gregory long ago in front of the Chelsea Hotel. He lifted his overcoat and dropped his trousers, spewing Latin expletives. Seeing my astonished face, he laughed and said, "I'm not mooning you sweetheart, I'm mooning the world." I remember thinking, how fortunate for the world to be privy to the exposed rump of a true poet.

And that he was. All who have stories, real or embellished, of Gregory's legendary mischief and chaotic indiscretions must also have stories of his beauty, his remorse, and his generosity. He took benevolent note of me in the early 70s, maybe because my living space was akin to his — piles of papers, books, old shoes, piss in cups — mortal disarray. We were disruptive partners in crime during particularly tedious poetry readings at St. Mark's. Though we were aptly scolded, Gregory counselled me to stick to my irreverent guns and demand more from those who sat before us calling themselves poets.

There was no doubt Gregory was a poet. Poetry was his ideology, and the poets his saints. He was called upon and he knew it. Perhaps his only dilemma was to sometimes ask, Why, why him? He was born in New York City on March 26, 1930. His young mother abandoned him. The boy drifted from foster home to reformatory to prison. He had little formal education, but his self-education was limitless. He embraced the Greeks and the Romantics, and the Beats embraced him, pressing laurel leaves upon his dark unruly curls. Knighted by Kerouac as Raphael Urso, he was their pride and joy and also their most provocative conscience.

He has left us two legacies: a body of work that will endure for its beauty, discipline, and influential energy, and his human qualities. He was part Pete Rose, part Percy Bysshe Shelley. He could be explosively rebellious, belligerent, and testing, yet in turn, boyishly pure, humble, and compassionate. He was always willing to say he was sorry, share his knowledge, and was open to learn. I remember watching him sit at Allen Ginsberg's bedside as he lay dying. "Allen is teaching me how to die," he said.

In early summer his friends were summoned to say goodbye to him. We sat by his bedside on Horatio Street in silence. The night was filled with strange correspondences. A daughter he had never known. A patron from far away. A young poet at his feet. On a muted screen, Robert Frank's *Pull My Daisy* randomly aired on public television — unaware of it's mystical timing. Images of the Daddies, young and crazy, black and white. Snapshots of Allen taped to the wall. The modest room lorded over by Gregory's chair in all its shabby glory. So many dreams punctuated by cigarette burns. He was dying. We all said goodbye.

But Gregory, perhaps sensing the devotion surrounding him, became a participant in a true Catholic miracle. He rose up. He went into remission just long enough for us to hear his voice, his laughter, and a few welcome obscenities. We were able to write poems for him, sing to him, watch football, and hear him recite Blake. He was here long enough to travel to Minneapolis, to bond with his daughter, to be a king among children, to see another fall, another winter, another century. Allen taught him how to die. Gregory reminded us how to live and cherish life before leaving us a second time.

At the end of his days, he still suffered a young poet's torment — the desire to achieve perfection. And in death, as in art, he shall. The fresh light pours. The boys from the road steer him on. But before he ascends into some holy card glow, Gregory, being himself, lifts his overcoat, drops his trousers, and as he exposes his poet's rump one last time, cries, "Hey man, kiss my daisy." Ahh Gregory, the years and petals fly.

He loved us. He loved us not. He loved us.

The Day They Robbed The Bank of England

My Karma ran over my dogma. Gregory Corso's last words to me
Jan. 12, 2001 Minneapolis

A Golden Waffle for Gregory
It's 6 A.M. & the bell rings in my room
Gregory wants to be put on the commode
He sits puffing a cigarette like a Roman senator
constipated because of the morphine,
the dilaudid, the leaking epidaural
still planning the African campaign
or trying to resolve the Ptolemy dilemma
He remembers all those girls
the little lies which gained him entrance.
"Nobody ever sucked my cock before"
and the simplest tactic opened the gate
of Poetry.
Watching great boxing matches on TV
of our common past we speak of Canzoneri,
the bolo punch of Kid Gavilan,
Willie Pep's finesse, how Marciano finished Roland La Starza
We compare notes on all the great character actors—
a century of watching movies,
Conrad Veidt & Sabu in The Thief of Bagdad,
Gene Tierney in Shanghai Gesture—
We talk about Angus & Zina
He gives me Gustav Mahler
I give him the Himalayas
It's all about proximity, that reach
which exceeds its grasp, that bell
which rings in the night.
He spits in his hand, holds it up &
calls it Come!
These days dwindling,
this flight I take tonight
I touch his head & he thinks of the Ganga
I bring him a blue rubber glove
& turn him over to Robert Marley
Adieu, Baby, I gotta go
The car's coming up the hill
& there's always room for one more.

Ira Cohen

Sheri's Coda
Valiant to the end
you died squeezing
the hand of her
who loved you most
as far as the eye can see
still she stays close to thee.!

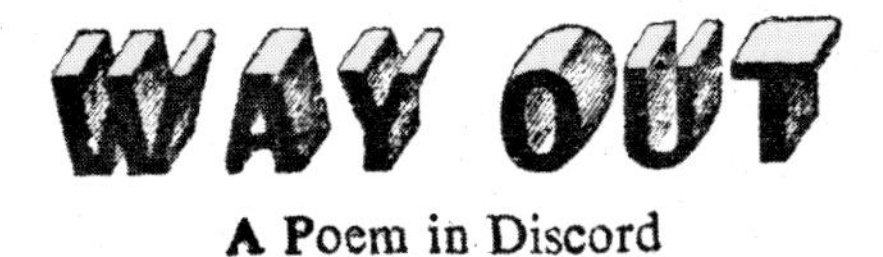

A Poem in Discord

GREGORY CORSO

Starstreams Poetry Series Number 1

BARDO MATRIX
Kathmandu, Nepal 1974

1st Canto

1 — MAKING IT

Prologue

Out of Discipline
Came Ratface   assassinator of angels
Herod of us all

Twenty broken-throated angels are there
                digging the scene
Sweetface   out from the late shows   walks by

No one watches Ratface
No one ever watches Ratface
He's there   stayed through three shows
Sat right behind Sweetface
Is there now   walking behind him   up to something
Look his mouth is Yowwwwwed
Sweetface   Watch out

(a)   *It all has to do with angels*

Not Italian angels
Or canonized idols but
Unquarrelled angels
...cool and unpolitic

ANGEL-SAX: Sweetface   dead by Ratface   lies before us
And was never the twenty we hoped him for
But seventeen   rat-bitten at seventeen
And no Chatterton   he

ANGEL-CAT: Sweetface   the mostest   scourge of drags
Now himself a drag   back to haunt us
Crewed-cut   upright   unhip   Death's number-one fuzz
Back to bug us

ANGEL-DOWN: What are you doing up there   Sweetface
Can't see you rolling in and out the shades
Like make it in the light
Man   what you doing with Saint Francis under your arm

ANGEL-HIP: Ah but what have you done Sweetface
I hear you're a nuisance to the grave
Hear you dangle your bones like relics
Hear you flip them in the foggy grates
Getting all kinds of kicks
Sweetface get with it lest
Your flesh sags you absurd

ANGEL-POT: Yeah you
Down there in them foggy grates what have you done
Look at you bugging the alleycats with your haunt
Look at you a hug of bones in the soot
In the fallen coins and plaster

ANGEL-COOL: O Sweetface our Sweetface what are you angel of
What are you doing there down there
In that draggy place You
With all eternity to goof

SWEETFACE: I'm making it man

(b) *And a monk*

Who is Ratface ordained
By some cornball angel

RATFACE: You want to know Sweetface's real name
It's Yaaaah Flunky Yaaaah
Sure I killed him bit his ass
In praise of Discipline
Screw what these angels have to say
Yaaaah was never much for beauty
I say Down with Yaaah alias Sweetface

Know me know that I dig stars
And with me music is everything
And all other rhythms false Mars
Looks down at me He too I will screw
But first let me tell you
There is a desperation in such things as
Barjazz All alone Undyingness Pursuit
Especially by the jazz Yaaaah was made to live
With an emergency of charity an extra suit
The charity he never had to give

And that recessive jazz   that midnight mass
Where he raped your mothers with bibles
And slid your brothers like organ farts
Wailing   Oratorio   Oratoria   Oratorius
O let me tell you
Yaaaah never really swung

2 — BARJAZZ

Prologue

Flunky Yaaaah is in Capetown
And Ratface in Johannesburg
But at night they live next door to each other
Ratface puts Yaaaah down when there are Pygmies
And Yaaaah puts Ratface down when there are dead children
And the rhinoceros puts everyone down

Tonight the rhinoceros is bugged
Yaaaah and Ratface are in Ballpoint Sam's bar
Each are sipping rotgut not saying a word
And outside the rhinoceros is really bugged

(a)   *Zen*

The Black Zens   ass-hard
On the backs of unreal oxen
Riding nowhere

BALLPOINT SAM: Outer disturbances never bug me
Mrs. Frankenstein is my old lady
I live next door to Mr. Kierkegaard
And Grandma Eloise has a son I hate
And in my garden there's a big flower
And every time I stand beside it
Something in me inversely dies
And there's a Prince who someday will succeed me
Cycle   everything is cycle

RATFACE: Flower   you say
Ha no more than rain do I remember to have thundered
And thundering arose again
Refreshed by silent wonder   a flower

YAAAAH: Spread that corn elsewhere man

BALLPOINT SAM: What am I doing in Capetown
I look for long color snakes
I want to breathe rotgut into their rainbow lungs
I want to wrestle with them
Break their necks over Buddha
Stain Buddha with snake-milk
I want to walk down the street with snake on my face
I want to frighten children
I want them to drive me from Capetown
I want to coil in the Himalayas
I too say down
I say down with Capetown
Frederick the Wise The City of Worms
Charles of Hapsburg Pope Leo Luther
Duke George John Hus Erasmus

RATFACE: The Reformation sir has never been up
Put down that which is put-downable
For instance Zen Afric-Zen Invective Zen

BALLPOINT SAM: Hold I say DOWN
Down with William of Occam
The Duke of Anhalt Catholicism Thomism
Augustinianism
And down man down with that door in Wittenberg
12,000 ducats 7,000 ducats 10,000 ducats
O and what have you to say Melanchthon

RATFACE: Polemic Zen Zen that squeezes the wheeze
That when Madame Copley dies she'll wheeze
Ching Ho Ching Hoi Ching Hoip
Like man if you're going to put down PUT DOWN

YAAAAH: And I am going to open this door
Enter beast

RHINOCEROS: Snort Snort Snort

BALLPOINT SAM: Ahhhhhhhhhhh Rhino-hoof Rhino-stomp
Dig Dig Dig Dig
O Augustinianism Augustinianism

a) *All truth is phoney*

Truth is whole of nothingness
And Jazz a part of this

LIE: I am Lie ME
Me who no cat sees straight in mirrors
Me first with little boys
Me mothers whip
Me schoolteachers absolve with holy water
Me the only way to make it
Me if I am Me the only way

BALLPOINT SAM: I smell dead
And God smells worse
I am here
And nothing's happening

LOUIE: Li Po and Lao Tze are here
Rimbaud too
And out there is Buddha with compassion
Stoned out of his head
Look at his feet Truth like a snake
Like a penis of Discipline old and sterile
Yet like a penis we all dig
Is nibbling the Lotus And in the distance
The mountains are becoming annihilate of embrace
Yet Face things are happening
Florghoyer is on sax Dougalman's on coronet
George Washington Jackson's on bass And
Crazy Joe Marcus is on Harpsichord
It's requiem man all requiem

LIE: Truth is jazz Truth is visional like jazz
Truth is a ton on Rimbaud's back
Truth is Lucifer without motion
Truth is Stational It has a realm
A pad of pot A crazy chick to cook for it
And another thing
Truth *does* wonder about jazz 1956
Know that 1956 jazz is not Negro music
But White-Protestant music
That Negro music died with bop
That all we live by today Negro is
Housewife-mambo Mid-western Rock 'n Roll
O Jazzman you who live by love
Know that music today 1956 is *white white white*

AL: Seems all birds gifted with plunk-puloo
Give out with deep exulting wings
Wings like monstrous sobs
Beating the gold-plated trophies of Truth
Wailing   Silent-Despair   Beat-Wonder   Hung-Up-Youth
The same shit   always

(c) *Out of Barjazz   mumbles*

Rimbaud will never come
Even in Hell Lucifer says No
Rimbaud is elsewhere
No creeps allowed
Only mums

DISCIPLINE: I see the Zen Buddhist make his ride
Black his galloping steed and flapping shroud
He seems as though a bat upon a thunder cloud
Blacker than night he speeds to his nightly bridge

3 — IF NOTHING ELSE...THE STARS

Prologue

Rafted   bridged between two altos
Yaaaah is carried away   bugged by rhinoceros gash
Ballpoint Sam is dead
And Ratface   like Frankenstein's monster   is jacked toward a star

The sexton inwardly opens the roof

(a) *Wombs that won't*

Wombs that lapse
That could have been
That in some quiet way was
For example   The first womb
Discarded for another one
One with less stain   less warmth
Less wrink

RATFACE: Open the roof
I shall protest the outer-world
Shall cry ABSOLUTION ABSOLUTION
I will come over the base of my downward star
And she will tickle my lips for me to enter
And I will come I will come And I will die
Dead to be re-entered and reborn again
Dead to be taken down off this meat this dry meat
And before her I will stand sensual with bones
And I will weep JOY JOY a bony wraith
No longer the inhabitant of this skin
This one-eyed rind

Cry ABSOLVED ABSOLVED upon the breast of my flayer
My butcherer my gnaw
And she my egg will anoint my bones and deem them relic
And children to come will kiss them
And old men to die will bless them
O open the roof

STAR: O one-eyed pink-eyed monk
Demon-flayer cosmos-slayer monk
Thou shalt be denied
Touch not my skin nor suck-air my breasts
Nor dare assume my womb to abide
Touch not with thy incarnadine bones
Nor with thy flagellated cursed skin
My undyingness within
Beware thee lest I fling thy bones
Corrupt in the sulking jowls of some black bitch

RATFACE: Damn bitch of a star
All I'm good for now is Yaaaah's saxophone
And I play without memory without an eye
Please baby I want to make it

STAR: I have given consent to the almighty abortionist
Now dare thee enter my womb

RATFACE: O once I was Bach And were I Bach now
You'd make it with me you know you'd make it with me
It was the late show with Yaaaah
It was the pot and the goofballs
And the head-bowed chicks the sad sad chicks

I had to sing their song   baby   I had to sing
And I swung   and lost an eye
O Father Discipline take me back
Defrocked and despaired   take me back

DISCIPLINE: O son   one life   the same again
Yourself too old to touch
A child among goodbyes
Yet afraid to say that much
O son   in holes you sat and prayed
And cursed my goodbyes   goodbye
And wept my lack of tears
For any man to die
O son   and I   that man   myself
Did die for such a lack
You may return to grieve
But there is no turning back
So goodbye   my son   goodbye
Go bold across that stream
And reach the shore you sleep
And touch yourself from dream

RATFACE: Platitudes   Platitudes
Was you who gave me Michelangelo in infancy
Way before my mother's pregnancy
Was you who gave me Alcibiades   Lysander
Alexander   and do-with-them-what-you-want
You gave   you gave   Yet look upon your son
And see vacancy   vacancy

O damned star   O iceball   *dike*
Conceit of all things gigantean
I will enter

(b)   *Man has always said*

Some sleeping fiend has dreamed
A shape of me

YAAAAH: Put to sleep by rhino-charge
Hospitalized by rhino-gnaw
The nurses were great
And the avocadoes   crazy

And received flowers and get-well cards from
Joe Aberline   Pete Crammis   Helen Dulay
Sis Rockingson   Marc Arrow   and Mike Crahhhhhhhhhh
Angels all

Even read some Hegel   late at night
When no one was looking
Dug what he said about *The Measureless*
The Infinite of Measure   He's right
The quantum *must* be exceeded
If anyone ever asks me   I'm going to say
Man   I'm a Hegelian deductor

The rhino got me   but now the rhino doesn't exist
Does it mean that the jazz-world
Detachment and standstill   are not here
Do not exist
Is jazz illusory
Is Ratface *real*
Am *I* Ratface   did I meet Ratface when I met myself
Face to face

Ah   but surely an oriental mind will think otherwise

RATFACE: No star will have me
I am made to be a future being without existence
I hate you   Yaaaah

YAAAAH: And I love you   Ratface
I   Sweetface   love you

End of 1st Canto

The World Premiere of WAY OUT by Gregory Corso
was apparently given in Kathmandu, Nepal,
at the Yak & Yeti Crystal Ballroom
on October the 11th, 1974
with the following cast:

Sweetface, Yaaaah, Louie, AL & Truth
played by Bill Barker

Ratface, Lie & Law
played by Ira Cohen

Ballpoint Sam, Host & Discipline
played by Angus MacLise

Star
played by Lois Kullen

Angels
played by Sam

Rhinoceros
played by Peri Winkle

The Prologues were divided between
Sweetface & Ratface.

Sound & Lighting
by Mishka Lissanevich

William S. Burroughs

The Four Horsemen of The Apocalypse

I'm speaking here as a writer of fiction, and of course many of the hypotheses and theories and ideas and suggestions that I will put forward may horrify a scientific audience. But they're to be seen from a fictional point of view. My subject is "The Four Horsemen of The Apocalypse," which were Famine, Plague, War, and Death... Portentous and purposeful as the priest advancing on a dying man to administer the Last Rites, so the four caballeros by their solid presence indicate that Time has been called for that particular biologic or sociological experiment. Closing time, gentlemen... dinosaurs bellow piteously, Famine saddles up his cayuse and gallops through swamplands leaving a dustbowl behind him... and the outmoded dinosaurs subside into museum skeletons, gaped at by human spectators. And the day of the spectators will come too.

At the present time, the situation of course with regards to the Four Horsemen is much more complicated than it was before man appeared on the scene, there the most important Horseman was probably Famine. At the present time of course the subject of the experiment, in this case the human species, can to some extent control the conditions of the experiment, but this isn't such an advantage as one would think since they cannot control themselves. The human creature has demonstrated through the centuries a stubborn disinclination to control himself. However, if I may indulge in whimsy, had we been dinosaurs we might have built great dams to preserve supplies of water and protect our way of life, and we might have hunted down the despicable mammals as the egg sucking rats they were. Some have advanced theories that the mammals ate the dinosaurs' eggs and undermined them that way, though many other factors were at work in the disappearance of the dinosaurs.

There is such basic disagreement as to how existing conditions can be altered, by exactly who and for the benefit of whom, there doesn't appear to be any sort of agreement. And stupidity and short-sighted self interest may well swamp Spacecraft Earth before the Horsemen can saddle up. Meanwhile, the Spectral Riders are being eagerly wooed by the CIA and similar agencies in other countries... wise, far-sighted men who will no doubt use their awesome knowledge of Famine, Plague, War, and Death for the good of all mankind.

"Put that joker Death on the line. Take care of Mao and that gang of cut-throats."

Actually, Western society is so constructed as to concentrate the greatest power in the worst possible hands. See, practically anything has military applications. So really the most important knowledge is now Top Secret Classified. Famine, seemingly the most fortuitous of the quartet, is transcending the caprices of weather, deforestation and overpopulation and getting a new look. We can in fact extend the area of Famine to include the lack of any substance or condition essential to the support of life. We can in fact create needs quite as overwhelming or compulsive as the need for food and water.

Drug addiction is of course an example of a biologic need artificially produced by the administration of drugs. And no doubt drugs much more habit forming than heroin could be produced in the laboratory by jiggering and tinkering with the habit forming molecules. We now have substances which could be introduced into the water supply, or even in a gaseous form into the enemy air, that have no effect unless withdrawn. And then a battery of crippling symptoms would develop, reducing the enemy to complete impotence. There are certain metabolic illnesses in which the subject is unable to absorb certain essential vitamins and minerals, no matter how much he ingests. In fact, it is not far-fetched to conceive of inducing metabolic changes that would make the absorption of any nutriments impossible: no matter how much he eats, the person would die of starvation.

The alliance between War and Plague was cemented with the first germ experiments, and in this area there have been a number of interesting developments. Despite a lot of talk about discontinuing such experiments and closing down the biologic and chemical warfare centers, Fort Dietrich, in Maryland, is now dedicated to cancer research. And cancer research, incidentally, overlaps the more sophisticated areas of biologic weaponry. As early as World War II, England had a Doomsday Bug which was a mutated virus produced by exposing such viruses as hepatitis and rabies to radiation. Now we know that a number of experiments have been carried out on exposing fruit flies to radiation. These experiments conclusively showed that there were no favorable mutations resulting from exposure to radiation… certainly not on fruit flies. Now one wonders why they didn't carry these experiments further and expose microscopic and sub-microscopic life to radiation. The answer is, undoubtedly they did and are doing just that, but it's Top Secret. It is difficult to believe that such a promising line of research was abandoned, and disturbing to speculate where that research is at the present time…

And there is an item from the London *Times,* 18th April, 1971: "New Cancer Virus Made By Accident… A completely new virus, probably capable of producing cancer in humans, has been made by accident in an American laboratory… Fears expressed by cautious scientists that such medical research could inadvertently produce new human diseases instead of curing existing ones. The new agent was discovered by Dr. Abramson of the National Cancer Institute, near Washington. Under special conditions, the mouse virus could be persuaded to infect human cancer cells in a test tube, though the process was extremely inefficient. Dr. Abramson now reports, in *Nature,* that the mouse virus has changed its nature. It has become highly infective to human cells and completely non-infective to mouse cells." In other words, we have a permanent change. A major genetic change has occurred in the virus and what amounts to a completely new virus has emerged. The virus has picked up a human gene and incorporated it, giving it the ability to multiply readily in human cells. Sir MacFarland Bennett, in *The Lancet,* sounds a word of warning, of the "almost unimaginable catastrophe of a virgin soil epidemic involving all the populous regions of the world." The age-old dream of a selective pestilence is now within the reach of modern technology.

This is also from the London *Times*, about 1970, "Ethnic weapons that wipe out one race and leave another unharmed could soon be developed, according to a leading

Geneticist. Carl Larsen; he is a Norwegian; said icily: 'Ethnic weapons would employ differences in human genetic configurations to make genetic variations which would make genocide a particularly attractive form of war.'" (I'm quoting, this is not my opinion.) "Writing in the U. S. army *Military Review*, Larsen argues that enzyme levels can vary according to race; the absence of certain enzymes can cause death. Enzyme deficiency could be exploited by chemical warfare." It would probably be possible to develop a chemical which will act as an enzyme inhibitor. Say you find an enzyme inhibitor to which 90% of Europeans would be vulnerable, which affects only 10% of Africans. Since the inhibitor could tell friend from foe, no matter how intermingled, it is *the* superselective military weapon. It is what all military thinkers dream of. Larsen admitted that: 'more genetic research was needed before ethnic weapons became a practical reality,' but this was years ago.

Selection of course could be carried much further, even to the point of an illness that effects only people with certain traits of character, since character is an expression of an overall metabolic configuration. That is, there is a rage metabolism, a metabolism associated with covert hostility, and so on. So it would be possible to carry your selective pestilence much further. For example, I have frequently said that most of the trouble on this planet is caused by people who must be *right*... The menace of Jerry Falwell and his Moral Majority in the United States probably has a certain metabolic configuration. If you wanted to develop a biologic weapon to take care of that particular sector, a good place to start I think, would be with canine distemper, or similar diseases to which dogs are subject, because dogs have the worst characteristics of human beings, they are servile, vicious, and they operate absolutely on the *right* principal — they have the *right* to bite someone who has no right to be there, so it will attack. Dogs could probably be used to attack human dogs... not farfetched.

Well, it seems that War, Plague, and Famine are merging. What about the Last Horseman... Death, a pale horse, a pale rider? Can Death maintain a separation from the means by which Death is produced? Can he stay separate from the horseman and get out there and do the job, or is the union between death and the instrument of Death about to be consummated? There are those who think so.

Herald-Tribune, June 8, 1970: The Synthetic Gene Revolution. This is the first synthetic gene by Dr. Hare Khorana, at the University of Wisconsin. And there's been a lot of research since. They've created an artificial gene; news that ranks with the splitting of the atom as a milestone in our control or lack of control of the physical universe.

"It is the beginning of the end" — this was the reaction to the news from the science attaché at one of Washington's major embassies. "If you can make genes you can eventually make new viruses for which there is no cure. Any little country with good biochemists could make such biological weapons. It would only take a small laboratory." If it can be done, someone will do it. To be sure, it's almost science fiction but science fiction has a bad habit of coming true. In fact it frequently surpasses the fact. The facts of science are now surpassing science fiction, and we have a lot of books that'd be classified as scientific fact; a modern novel like *The Terminal Man,* there's nothing in there that isn't within the reach of modern technology.

Of course, the Gentlemen Riders have no meaning outside of human context, they are in fact human inventions, so let us examine the human context.

The first thing that would impress a visitor from outer space would be the tremendous, inexplicable gap between potential and performance. It's amazing when you consider what the human organism could do in terms of its potential, and what it actually does. No species that isn't fundamentally flawed could be so stupid this consistently. Let us consider the human organism as an artefact. Comparative evolution will show us what is wrong with it and how far it has to go.

You have the first airplanes… now, take one look at that artefact and you see that everything is wrong with it. They were incredibly dangerous, they had a very short range, and to be anything more than a curiosity it has a very long way to go… So now up here's your present planes and rockets and so forth… and all the steps in between... well now take an artefact — see, we can see that this artefact is in a rudimentary stage and that it has a very long way to go, we could see that back then. We don't have to see all this development to know that if this is going to do anything at all it's got to make a number of forward steps. Now take an artefact like a bow — I'll put it up here — what's wrong with it? Very little. It's gone about as far as you can go on the principle of a projectile propelled by an elastic spring — you can use rubber bands, it's the same principle. The artefact is subject to a basic limitation: the stronger the bow, the more energy required to draw it. It can't go very much further. Now of course modern bows have appeared and there are a lot of hobbyists who hunt with bows. They kill bears and I think even lions, and undoubtedly these bows, modern bows, are much better than anything that people had five hundred years ago. But they're not all that much better. They're not basically different or basically much better.

Now take another artefact down here, the flintlock rifle or pistol. Take one look at that artefact and ask yourself what is wrong with it. Just about everything. They didn't even have the firepower of the bow; they took much longer to load and prepare. They misfired very frequently; rain, wind, would render the weapon quite useless — if rain gets in the pan it won't ignite. Black powder is dangerous, very much more volatile than smokeless powder. It's very dangerous to transport and use, static electricity will set it off; if you shuffled across the floor and picked up a canister of black powder, that would be a very dangerous thing to do — it'd blow up… So it has a very long way to go.

Up here to modern automatic weapons, another factor comes in and that's the factor of money. When you get up here, money, profit, becomes very important, because as soon as an article goes into mass production they don't want to know about a better article. And they particularly don't want to know about one that is basically different, because the most expensive thing a manufacturer can do is to junk his dies. He's got his dies set up to manufacture the very inefficient internal combustion engine, he doesn't want to shift to a turbine. So he will suppress inventions. Very useful inventions are now suppressed, same thing as happened in small arms: the Dietrich pistol, much better than any previous pistol, was supposed to come out in 1960, it will never appear… And also rockets — here you have a bullet (I'm not much of a drawer), now if you just turn that around, so it goes that way, you have a rocket. The cartridge case then becomes the projectile and you have nothing to project. That is the rocket principle which is simply reversed. All you have to do is turn a bullet around and you have a rocket. But we may actually be approaching the limit of the efficiency of small arms, of any weapon based on using, directly using, explosive charge to propel a bullet or other projectile. A new weapon recently came out called a rail gun. I used to — still do — take a grapefruit seed, squeeze it between your hands, it can be propelled with considerable force (laughter)... I thought, well, there must be a way of using this, and someone has indeed come up with exactly that... now these are two rails and they're highly magnetized, reverse magnetism... like that... if you've ever taken two magnets and pushed them against each other, you feel that thing between them, which is a magnetic field... now an explosive charge here, not directly used to propel our projectile, compresses these together, compressing that magnetic field just like a grapefruit seed, ten times the velocity of any modern rifle... whether we'll see this in any near future... it's probably completely monopolized by the military.

And we can also see living creatures as artefacts. When you take an artefact like the weasel, well, what's wrong with it? Well, not much. It's limited, but in terms of its structure and goals it functions well enough; it has reached the limit of its development. And you look at the human artefact: what's wrong with it? Just about everything, it's right down here with the flintlock... It's got a long ways to go.

First the question as to what distinguishes the human animal from other animals, is one of the very frequent questions, and Korzybski; who founded, started the idea of general semantics, the meaning of meaning; had, I think, the best answer: it's language. But language must not be confused with communication. You see, animals communicate and they talk, but they don't write. They can't make knowledge available to members of their species outside their communication range. Everything they learn they have to learn during their lifetime. Now a wise old rat will know a great deal about poisons and traps, but he can't write a treatise which other rats could read, he can't pass that knowledge on to rats over here or to future generations of rats... very fortunate... for us. Now, to get back to the human artefact, one of the things which distinguishes man is language, that animals talk but they don't write. They've got no way of writing something down so that it can be available through space and time. Actually, we know that some people don't write, but the whole of human language they can pass on orally, which animals cannot. Language is essentially a symbolic system where something represents something else. You can't draw a map, it doesn't mean anything to an animal; you can't get an animal to read a map, but illiterate, so-called illiterate people can.

Well, let's consider the human artefact and what is wrong with it. Consider a creature that can live on the seacoast, watching ships come in, day after day, year after year, and still believe the Earth is flat because the Church says so. They *knew* the earth was round. They *believed* it was flat. Or an artefact that can use cannonballs for 500 years before the idea of a cannonball that explodes on contact blossoms in this barren soil. I could go on and on. So why has the human artefact stayed back with the flintlock? Well I'm advancing the theory that we were not biologically designed to remain in our present stage any more than a tadpole is designed to remain a tadpole. The human is in a state of neotony — that's a biologic word we've already heard from Dr. Lotsch, used to describe an organism fixated at what would normally be a larval or transitional phase. Now ordinarily a salamander starts his life cycle in the water with gills; later the gills atrophy and drop off and the animal develops lungs and comes up to land:

then they go back and spend the rest of their lives in the water and they have to come up to breathe. Just why they do that I don't know. However, there are certain salamanders who never lose their gills and they never leave the water. They'd be considered in a state of neotony. The Xolotl salamander, found in Mexico, is an example. And scientists, moved by the plight of this beautiful creature gave him an injection of hormones, whereupon he shed his gills and left the water after ages of neotony. Whether this was any advantage to him is another question. (laughter) It does seem advantageous if you're gonna spend much of your time in the water to have gills, but evolution is a one-way street. Once you lose your gills you can never get them back. I think it's a little too much to hope we could be jolted out of neotony by a single injection. But by whatever means the change takes place, if it does take place, the change will be irreversible. The Xolotl of course once he sheds his gills can never reclaim them. This is a law of evolution… I don't know any reason for it but it seems to be a law — the whales must have been on land at one time: they lost their gills and they never got them back.

Now when we consider these evolutionary steps, one has a feeling that the creature is tricked in a way into making them. Now here is a fish that has survived droughts because he has developed feet or rudimentary lungs. As far as the fish is concerned, the feet are simply a means of getting from one water source to another, or of going down into the mud and waiting out the drought. But once he leaves his gills behind he has made an involuntary step — I won't say forward exactly — but a step. Looking for water he has found air. And perhaps a forward step for the human race will be made in the same way.

The astronaut is not looking for Space, he's looking for more Time to do exactly the same things. He's equating Space with Time, and the Space Program is simply an attempt to transport all our insoluble problems, our impasses, and take them somewhere else where exactly the same thing is bound to occur. However, like the walking fish, looking for more Time he may find Space instead, and then find that there is no way back. Such an evolutionary step would involve changes literally inconceivable from our present point of view.

Many of these ideas I have incorporated into a novel on which I am now working. I've had several titles for this novel, and the title that I have more or less decided on in the course of this conference is *Place of Dead Roads — Planet Earth.* I'll read a few pages here…

"As a prisoner serving a life sentence can think only of escape," (this is my hero) "so Kim took it for granted that the only purpose of his life was space travel. He thought of this as not so much a change of locality but as a change of dimension, the basic change of being with all its surroundings like the switch from water to land. But you see, there had to be the air-breathing potential first. That's where you start. And what is it that you must alter in order to make these changes.

The first step towards Space exploration was to examine the human artefact with biologic alterations in mind that would render our human artefact more suitable for Space conditions and Space travel. Now we are like water creatures looking up from here at the earth and the air and wondering how we can survive in that alien medium.

Fish didn't have the capacity to do that: we do. The water we live in is Time. That alien medium we glimpse beyond Time is Space. And that is where we are going... Kim read all the science fiction books and stories he could find and he was stunned to find the assumption, the basic assumption, that there is no real change involved in Space travel, same dreary people playing out the same tired old roles. Take that dead act into Space. Now here they are light years from Planet Earth watching cricket and baseball on a vision screen... can you imagine taking their stupid pastimes light years into Space. It's like the fish said, 'Well, I'm gonna just shove this aquarium up onto land and there I've got everything I need...'(laughter)... you need entirely too much...

Well to begin with there is the question of weight, the human organism weighs about 170 pounds and that is a decided disadvantage. But also this breathing-eating-excreting-dreaming human organism must have its entire environment, its awkward life process encapsulated and transported with it... into Space. And one wonders — Kim goes into his academic act, letting his bifocals slip down onto his nose like a professor launching into a well-worn joke — one wonders, gentlemen, if this crew doesn't perhaps have a pet elephant essential to its welfare that it's gonna take along..."

Now, regarding this question of weight, we have a model at hand of a much lighter body, in fact a body which is virtually weightless, and I am referring to the astral dream body, which some scientists don't believe in. But this model gives us a clue to the changes we must undergo. When I say must, I am speaking not in moral but in biologic terms. And the dream also gives us insight into Space conditions. Recent research, one of the more interesting facts of dream research, has established that dreaming is a biologic necessity. You see, they can tell now when an animal or a person is dreaming by the brainwaves, the REM waves, and recent research has established that if dream sleep is cut off — every time they see sleep brainwaves they wake the animal up — no matter how much dreamless sleep he is allowed, irritability, restlessness, hallucinations and eventually coma, convulsions and death would result. He'd show all the symptoms of sleeplessness no matter how much sleep he was allowed... I don't know what Freud would have made of that... Kim saw dreams as a vital link to his biologic and spiritual destiny in Space, and deprived of this airline he would die. The way to kill a man or a nation is to cut off their dreams in the way that whites took care of the Indians, they cut off their dreams, their magic, and they tended to die out.

So I'm starting here with a basic assumption which of course many of you will, cannot accept: that our destiny — again I'm talking about our biologic destiny — is in Space, and that our failure to achieve this is the basic flaw in the human artefact. That's why it's back here with the flintlock instead of being somewhere up here.

From a talk given at the Planet Earth Conference held at the Institute of Ecotechnics, Les Marronniers, Aix-en-Provence, France, December 1980.

Brion Gysin

Minutes To Go

the hallucinated have come to tell you that yr utilities
are being shut off   dreams monitored   thought directed
sex is shutting down everywhere   you are being sent

all words are taped   agents everywhere
marking down the live ones   to exterminate

they are turning out the lights

no   they are not evil   nor the devil   but men
on a mission   with a spot of work to do

this   dear friends   they intend to do on you

you have been offered a choice   between liberty and
freedom   and   No!   you can not have both

the next step   is everyone into space   but it has been
a long dull wait   since the last tower of babel
that first derisive visit of the   paraclete

let's not hear that noise again   and again

that may well be   that last word   anywhere

this is not the beginning   in the beginning was the word
the word has been in for a too   long time
you in the word and   the word in you

we are out
you are in

we have come to let you out

here and now we will show you   what you can do
with   and to
the word
the words
the word
all the words

Pick a book   any book   cut it up
cut up
prose
poems
newspapers
magazines
the bible
the koran
the book of moroni
lao-tzu
confucious
the bhagavad gita
anything
letters
business correspondence
ads
all the words

slice down the middle   dice into sections
according to taste
chop in some bible   pour on some Madison Avenue
prose
shuffle like cards   toss like confetti
taste it like piping hot   alphabet soup

pass yr friends' letters   yr office carbons
through any such sieve   as you may find or invent
you will soon see   just what they really are
saying   this is the terminal method for
finding the truth

piece together a masterpiece   a week
use better materials   more highly charged words

there is no longer a need   to drum up a season of
geniuses   be your own agent   until we deliver
the machine   in commercially reasonable quantities

we wish to announce   that while we esteem
this to be truly   the American Way
we have no commitments   with any government
groups

the writing machine   is for everybody
do it yourself   until the machine comes
here is the system   according to us

CUT ME UP ◦ BRION GYSIN ◦ CUT ME UP ◦ BRION GYSIN ◦ CUT ME UP ◦ BRION GYSIN ◦ CUT ME UP ◦ BRION GYSIN ◦ CUT ME IN ◦ BRION GYSIN ◦

Nothing here was written "under marijuana" or "under" anything else. Billy Holliday and Baudelaire have borne witness that nothing was ever written or sung better under any drug.

Hachichi I am and I bow respectfully and gratefully to my Principal as any Client should (not *must*). My Principal is no Monkey — no Machine. My Principal is called Out. I am a poor Singer but I can write out all of the Song I know in two ways and on both sides of this paper. Who runs may read. Learn to read by improving your running.

Dig deep what Burroughs has to say against junk. Mektoub — It Was Written. Dig the difference between all the Junks acting on numerical proliferation and pot, art or whatnot acting outside of number. Outside of number is the only way out. The only way out to space. If you don't want out you don't want space and the less you get until you have none at all. The Ins want space for themselves because they can never but never get enough of it to be comfortable. THEY CAN'T. The way out is Here and it CAN BE WRITTEN. You can start writing it now by cutting up this whole book. Add what you like and make a new book of it. We have called

IN ◦ BRION GYSIN ◦ CUT ME IN ◦ BRION GYSIN ◦ CUT ME IN ◦ BRION GYSIN ◦ CUT ME IN ◦ BRION GYSIN ◦ this method the CUT-UPS EVER SINCE WE FIRST STARTED ON THEM and the name is as good as any. They are not a new Discovery.

Tristan Tzara, the Man from Nowhere, divined Dada out of a dictionary with a knife, pulled words out of a hat and might well have burned the Louvre if he hadn't diverted into the Communist Panic by the Art Wing of the Freudian Conspiracy calling itself Surrealism under Andre Breton. We don't want to see it happen again. Above all I don't — I the Man from Nowhere negotiated like a Tangier Space Draft on a Swiss bank.

There is no game without two players. In other words, it could. But this is the Open Bank — these monkeys hear a lot and see a lot and talk almost all they know. Anyhow, here is the gimmick. Cut up everything in sight. Make your whole life a poem. You can't lose, man. You can't lose because you've got nothing to lose but that worthless junk you're sitting on. Get out of that blue frigidaire and Live. You'll know everything. You'll hear everything. And you'll see everything that's going on. Really make the entire scene. Not many chicks will. Say they know plenty already. They do. Try it. Be a poet. Be a man. Never forget that Grandaddy Burroughs invented the adding machine when the more efficient abacus had been used for thousands of years in Asia. Yesterday a thousand years ago, Hassan Sabbah, a Persian by birth and school-chum of Omar Khayyam, walked by accident (as if there were any accidents) into the studios of Radio Cairo to find all the cats bombed. He realized like a flash that *he* could

SEND, TOO. He took the mike to an unheathed pent-house called Alamut near the Caspian. Called the Aga Khan today, his original station nearly a thousand years ago could broadcast from Alamut to Paris with Charlmagne on the house phone and as far as Xanadu East. Today the same lines have been proliferating machine-wise and a stray wire into the room I am in… Well, you figure it out. Try it yourself. Here is how to do it: Let's see, now. No, I'm not stalling. Common sense tells you that words are meant to mislead. Especially in these areas. It's about like this: Just talk to yourself for a minute. You hear that little voice? Well, now argue with yourself: take two sides of a question. Dig? That's already a line. Do it like a phone call. Broadcast something. I hesitate to advise, because I know only for me, that something pretty saucy will often get you a sharp answer. Realize that it is an answer when you hear it and not just you. Your first party or any party may be hard to identify but just go on listening. Soon plenty of voices will come in and soon you will be able to call out. Don't put this down. Lots of people want this, need it and are damned well getting it by themselves. This ain't no monopoly, lady. Shove off, you! Well, as I was saying before I was so brashly interrupted… Stop and Listen. The state called reverie just before sleep is a good place to start. You may find the head-shrinkers putting this down, they will. If you work on some mechanical job this should be a snap for you.

Artists and intellectuals BEST learn a method best called LOOK AWAY. You will find that you are broadcasting at all hours without knowing it. How else do you think ideas "get around", man. Well, call me anytime you want and just identify yourself when you call. Name and address, please. I'll be glad to talk to you about this or anything else you have in mind. Crazy, man, crazy. We need this. We have got to have this or, frankly, fellow palefaces, we are SCREWED. I'm not putting that down, either, but I think I know what it means. Do you? Every non-paleface is on the line FREE OF CHARGE. Paleface have the CHARGE but the line is not free for him. The TOLL has, historically, been enormous. THERE IS NO NEED TO HEAR THAT NOISE AGAIN. We went through the Ice Age in the Cave and came out to hunt sickly-pale like Lazarus or any Haitian zombie with a Reactive mind built in by our women who sent us. Womensent Motherlovers, to a man. It must have been great in that Cave — or that's the way they put it. Me, myself, now… All anybody was ever supposed to want to do was to get back IN. Well, if you want to get In instead of OUT then SPACE is not for you and you are going to get less and less of it until you don't have any at all. The Ins always say MINE. I put that down. It's EVERYBODY'S space and there's plenty of it. A point in space is an argument place, says Wittgenstein. "No two anythings can occupy the same spacetime position," mutters Burroughs. Go on. Who says Time? It is in the power of every hand to destroy us and we are beholden to everyone we meet, he doth not kill us. BUT The river hath more need of the fountain than the fountain of the river… the swarming sting of the sun has ceased over the endless lakes of lilac light burning away to a fiery rose on the dunes running like molten orange-gold.

ME OUT ◦ BRION GYSIN ◦ GET ME OUT ◦ BRION GYSIN ◦ GET ME OUT ◦ BRION GYSIN◦ GET ME OUT ◦ BRION GYSIN ◦ GET ME OUT ◦ BRION GYSIN ◦

The day-tortured eye can no longer support. Before it died behind the clenched lids the sun wrenched itself from the sky and fell sickeningly over the edge of the world. Blues deepen like vertigo into permanganate purples. An icy chill sweeps the very length of darkness after sun, cracking the desert rocks like a rattle of fire across the Sahara. Step into a Grain of Sand. It is Everybody's Earthly Kingdom bathed in the white light. You can get the light with prayer, mescaline, fasting, sex and know where to find it again when you want it. Praktice makes perfect. Neither prayer nor mescaline nor anything else makes it happen. The light is there. Myself, I think that our troubles have only started and now that we have cut you in on this you are in on it whether you like it or not. You are on our side now that you have read this far and you are sitting pretty. This has taken you out of the area of words. If they throw words at youcutthemup and throw them back. If you want to make them disappear just rub out their words. If you want to disappear... come around for private lessons. Free. Painters have it made. Dangerous ground. Picasso can make a rainbow frame his new house and Cézanne's mountain behind it. See LOOK.
He ate the entire Imaginary Museum, shat on a canvas and sold it for a rainbow. Who can say? We don't need to burn the Louvre now. The Equanimity of Complete Despair. The Shining Air. Sensitive Desert. Puddles of Light. One Pace from Nowhere. Clouds on a Wall. Erasmus to Dürer. It is like being against the weather. Into the Space Ship on the IN Programme must go: A Scientist, A Colonel and A Magician. To live in a capsule of Earth atmosphere out there and propagate virus-wise there must be a Woman. A Tin-Hinan of Outer Space that she wants to make into IN-space for her. Tin-Hinan veiled the Toureg men and dyed them blue. The Space Queen hopes to step into the ship and throw off her horrid disguise. Stripping off her gimmicks and tossing them to the boys she raises aloft a vial of sperm and proclaims herself to be the sole Scientific and Magical Colonel of Space. "Back to Earth you Drones," she snarls to Men. "And keep humping." From having been artisans, painters have become alchemists and now to this. Wurra, wurra! The great painters burn up the subjects they touch — all the fine flesh, roses, guitars and most of that merely visible world has been burned down for good. Now here's the picture: One eye strikes deeper into it than the other eye. This throws the Intellect or even the Reactive Mind or whatever right off balance for long enough for You to *see* that other dimension. Painters are bucking for space like Cézanne bucked for the museum. Painters and Prophets speak in ecstatic tongues which even they "know" only in the act of speaking them. Look Away.

LOOK AWAY ◦ BRION GYSIN ◦ LOOK OUT ◦ BRION GYSIN ◦ LOOK AWAY ◦ BRION GYSIN ◦ LOOK OUT ◦ BRION GYSIN ◦ LOOK AWAY ◦ BRION GYSIN

Angus MacLise

Kadijah

— appearing in the heavens:
a woman clothed with the sun,
the moon under her feet and
upon her head a crown of 12 stars —

...Monster, disappearing! & its Maker —
& the mystic city,
under a great streaming of the sun's rays,
lay beneath
the throne of the Ancient One —
& those who dwell
in the matchless empire
though they walk on earth,
they are of a world apart,
— Great Dragon —
Monster, appearing! & its Maker —
& the mystic city.

— The Last Judgement; the books
were opened, including the
book of life.

A shrouded conductor deep in his tower has
spoken beautiful strangers setting out on the road

Let it cover first what it is
And then beyond that into the space
around it
And then beyond that
Let it be first what it is
And reach out into everything else
And then beyond that

Let it find everywhere it seeks
Big in itself and large past all belief
Within and then beyond that
And then leave it

I SEE ALL
THE OVERSEERS
IN THE CLOUDY
AEONS STRETCHING AWAY WITHOUT PAUSE

Wind roars over Nagarjun carrying
streamers down
dragging in the wet emerald clefts

The sun decides to make
the mountain ridges appear like vivid
transcendental edges in
another world than here-today.

it becomes painful to watch and yet remain here

I want nothing
but for things to stop
pulling at me
— Bones of shamans clatter as I cut loose

Who was it singing as I left the room?
Light w/o Axis
streaming
worlds
Amoghasiddhi ray

Supreme lightworld crashing out.

from within to meet the stillness
from without w/o separation
from within w/o pain uniting

Total Abode of Bliss it's called
and it's soon
and it's now

rushes of purity itself never misses

You are not yourself you never were

Autumn 1972

"Go straight to the Castle of Corbenic
where the Maimed King lies..."
Quest del Saint Graal

Doors of darkness —
Are we not all brothers?
Is there some poison spewed out from the muse this night?
Are we beyond the pale, irretrievable?
And what is our delight after all?
Doors of darkness —
Something waits for me in the blackest of hearts.
My song is broken into bits
Aren't the empty halls an answer enough?
No one has really answered for a very long time,
no one has heard
Doors of darkness —
Grant me upsurge of song again
Place the drum beneath my hands & the dancers
waiting...
Some few friends who can hear & enjoy
& at least one lover out of all the hosts who can
love me
Doors of darkness —
Across the sea is my-time-to-come
Down the road is my present
& the over the hill has my own past love gone
over the hill tomorrow.
Doors of darkness —
And what is our delight after all?

For my Shamsi Tabriz
the ultimate Cohen
Bastille Day '77, Paris.

Splash Manifest Documents

Matter enshrouded by the idea of the bright Form — becoming two, becoming shaped from within — the Two People — uncreated glistening everywhere — There is a top, there is an underneath, there is this, is here & everything else, we are surrounded by separate existences — It is now

The raging flames of this heartland, saxophones trembling vibrato dawns flushing the tinged-with-being the holy drama — The squad cars arrive — my head lifts — all my certainties disintegrate — flutter, tumbling, cascades stuttering over the changes — what terrain is this? — next to us the vast beings shout to the cryptic distant stars, hunting down the starsystems without loss

°

There were devils attacking me
and I noted their laughter
and remember
not being able to distinguish
between their being and mine

I can own up now
— it's all
up to me — I'm the one
who steps this step

°

Under the exploding intensity solar-holy SPAIN magma of flickering blasts the boiling liquid flames engulfing reaching with sancta sancta sancta burning fingers laving these deeps — in profound man the eternally hip cultus of the Joy Man

I arose & through the tiny dreaming realms fled the incredible heartlyric for our holy brothers ahead I rushed through cataracts of singsong doom ahead passing channels, libation pools, strange runnels & weirs scooped CUNNINGLY from the rock-ground, I blessed — SUNSTROKE — penetrating chill of solar initiation — was no choice, enraged by my own sudden humaneness & all belief & sage frailty — HURRY TO THE TREMBLING GROVES THERE WHERE THE ANSWER IS — Song to me of murmuring wan intermixture of roiling elementals — Why did you leave this earth and I am here alone? When may I return to my own?

and then Titans which walked vast
Gardens & groves of the Sun —
All along that ridge are
these scooped-out radar receptors in stone, man! And there, 2 thrones ancient in the long recesses of dumb magic

scratching tropical ocean cries alarm these realms — the priests of our people moon for you, O holy Warden — I am at the Gates

As I crawl to the lip of the chasm Terror at the everywhere implicit hint — I am he! I am he! there is nowhere — at night, the cries flow past the rigid stallions flanking thresholds & precincts of our mysteries nightlong

Bridging the chasm past all mad-brain holocaust stomping brainstorm — poisons out! Eerie plunging within — The bottom dropping out! Total racket of the Great Emerald falling — with its own mute satori — and on the far side

cast burning dawns from the brow of the Central Universal Lagoon — next, next…

°

This force. It is raying out rays.

At exactly the moment when I position myself in the right spot. I will never deny my own source.

There is nothing more

°

Believe it or don't believe it — on Boyne River, Ireland — House swindled out of his father, god-king of the Tuatha de Danaan, by Oengus mac Ind Oc, called Brugh na Boyne — & over the huge
threshold-stone engraved with Great Spiral into opening of tumulus —
where its longing passageway leading in

& deeper yet And TABLETS OF THE GREATER IGNORANCE brought

By Apollonian bandits to juncture of our crumbling our vain
dying Thought & Patter of their second-hand creepiness — hesitant — over gruesome rainbows of their intrinsic decay

weird timbrels of the distant celestial railroad DREAMS OF THE HARPERS
Violently explosive desires, their Gorgon-heads of —

The 1st vision sprang into full view, surrounding & enveloping the psychic levels, it was the great god on earth, the possessor of sublime grace, enjoyer of full knowledge, holder of the keys of life & death — TAUGHT TO BELIEVE WHAT IS HAPPENING IS THE ONLY TRUTH

& still be singing

As he gazed — all things beginning to glisten with an unearthly sparkling sheen — all thoughts instantly transformed into their Forms and
Schemas, iconic series unfolding the real

Opening of the Fount

— lining the bank of the lush thought & vivid Stream the
glowing Statues invested of the meanings

Cause of this dreams imploding sense —

And careen going downstairs on the CRYSTAL it stands there
Someone longs for its imminent assumption into heaven-lands Next
thing to be Considered THE SUNRAYS HARDLY KNOWING THE DIFFERENCE

This day is the one when, only one when the Beam shoots exact
along down that tunnel CRYSTAL within & CENTRE within the TOMB
And then — jaguar man lurks, paler than cockroach eggs

◦

The sinking pillar from throat to pit of stomach feels itself weird, isolate — perhaps, even
but there is still left one glowing piece, one whose origins — impossible to discern — atom, solitary & alien in the boundless Field — not reckless, is not astray — but self-possessed entirely (it's all gonna be alright song) humming, in the emptiness unending —
This the one, thing which, flaring up irresistible, will fill
in dread joy, this being & W/NO SPACE LEFT OVER — & it's just then
(having come from the drear — the far deathland & the Nil) — that's the bursting out
of the Greater Drum, seed-fragment aglow, now given all power — & myself
disappears — Another is left to strike
the drum, it is Another one who's sounding out those THRONES OF FEELING —
He is calling out
He is calling out
He is calling out
He is calling out
He is calling out
He is calling out
He is calling out
The patterns stagger, involute, slipped by in dissolute
Veering, clusters of Strife impossible to resolve or obliterate

roll downwards in serene manias of our
sublime hearts our sublime driven hearts
WE ARE NOT LOST
WE NEVER WERE
It just stops

Note: This is one of three versions of The Sudden or Splash Manifest Documents written by Angus MacLise at my request. Its intention was to explicate a unique rite of initiation which Angus knew to exist both in Brugh na Boyne, Ireland, and in Chile by a certain jaguar cult involving the illumination of a cave at a specific moment in the year when the sun's rays hit a hidden crystal. (Ira Cohen)

Arthur Rimbaud

Phrases

When the world is reduced to a lonely black wood for our four astonished eyes, — to a beach for two faithful children, — to a musical house for our clear sympathy, — I will find you.

When here below there is only a lone old man, calm and beautiful, surrounded by "unheard-of luxury," — I will be at your feet.

When I have realised all your memories, — when I am she who knows how to tie you up, — I will suffocate you.

○

When you are very strong, — who draws back? Very gay, — who falls from ridicule? When we are very spiteful, — what could they do to us?

Adorn yourself, dance, laugh, — I could never throw Love out of the window.

○

— My comrade, beggar-girl, monster child! how little you care about those unhappy women and those machinations, and my embarrassment. Attach yourself to us with your impossible voice, your voice! unique flatterer of this vile despair.

An overcast morning in July. A taste of ashes steals through the air; — an odour of wood sweating in the hearth, — soaked flowers — the havoc of walks — the mist from the canals in the fields — why not already toys and incense?

○

I have stretched ropes from steeple to steeple; garlands from window to window; golden chains from star to star, and I dance.

○

The high pond steams continually. What witch is going to rise up in the white sunset? What violet foliage is going to descend?

○

While public funds disappear in fraternity feasts, a bell of pink fire rings in the clouds.

○

Arousing an agreeable taste of Chinese ink a black powder rains softly on my vigil. — I lower the lights of the chandelier, I throw myself onto the bed, and turning towards the darkness I see you, my daughters! my queens!

To A Reason

A blow from your finger on the drum discharges all sounds and begins the new harmony.

A step of yours, this is the rising of the new men and they are on the march.

Your head turns away: new love! Your head turns back, — new love!

"Change your lot, riddle the plagues, begin with time," these children sing to you. "Raise, no matter where, the substance of our fortune and our vows" we pray you.

Coming from always, you go everywhere.

Departure

Seen enough. The vision met itself in all airs.

Had enough. Rumours of towns, in the evening, and in the sunshine, and always.

Known enough. The checks of life. — Oh Rumours and Visions.

Departure in new affection and new noise.

Ancient animals…

Ancient animals copulated even on the run,
Their glans encrusted with blood and excrement.
Our fathers proudly displayed their members
By the fold of the sheath and the grain of the scrotum.

In the middle ages, for the female, angel or sow,
A fellow with a solid prick was needed;
Even a Kléber, according to his breeches, which lie
Perhaps a little, must not have lacked resources.

Moreover, man is equal to the proudest mammal;
The enormity of their members should not surprise us;
But a sterile hour has struck: the horse

And the ox have bridled their ardour, and no one
Will dare erect his genital pride
In the grove where comical children swarm.

Evening Prayer

I live seated, like an angel in the hands of a barber,
Gripping a heavily fluted mug,
Stomach and neck curved, a Gambier
Between my teeth, under air swollen with impalpable sails.

Like the warm excrement of an old dovecote,
A thousand dreams softly burn and melt within me:
And at moments my sad heart is like sapwood
Which soaks its gloomy young gold in the sweat of blood.

Then, when I have swallowed my dreams with care,
I turn, having drunk thirty or forty mugs,
And collect myself, to relieve the bitter need:

Sweet like the Lord of the cedars and hyssops,
I piss towards the dusky skies, very high and very far,
With the assent of the great heliotropes.

Brussels

Boulevard du Régent, July

Flowerbeds of amaranths as far as
The agreeable palace of Jupiter.
— I know that it's You who, in this place,
Mixes your almost Saharan Blue!

Then, as the rose and fir of the sun
And liana have their play enclosed here,
The little widow's cage!...
                                        What
Flocks of birds! O iaio iaio!...

— Calm houses, old passions!
Summerhouse of the Woman driven mad by love.
After the buttocks of the rosebushes, the shadowy
And very low balcony of Juliet.

La Juliette, she reminds me of L'Henriette,
A charming railway station
At the heart of the mountain, as in the depths of an orchard
Where a thousand blue devils dance in the air!

Green bench where in the stormy paradise,
The white Irish girl sings with the guitar.
Then, from the Guyanese dining-room,
Chatter of children and cages.

The duke's window makes me think
Of the poison of snails and of boxwood
Sleeping down here in the sun.
                                        And then
It's too beautiful! too! Let's guard our silence.

— Boulevard without movement or commerce,
All drama and all comedy, mute,
Reunion of infinite scenes,
I know you and admire you in silence.

translated by J. N. Reilly

Mohamed Choukri

The Squirrel

It is noon. I'm on my way home. Near the Regnault High School I see Mekki. Neither of us could see the madness coming. He was very intelligent as a young man. He got his degree and wanted to continue his studies in England. Now he has stopped talking, just goes around in circles. A few cigarettes or even a handful of butts are all he wants. He doesn't beg. I give him some spare change, as I usually do when I see him. He says to me while scratching for lice with thin, filthy fingers:

— I would like you to help me kill these lice which are sucking my blood.

— They have been crawling all over me for a long time and I've killed so many, I'd like to forget about yours.

— Today's lice are more ferocious than they used to be.

— I know. That's because they are starving.

He stares at me and smiles.

A little further on I come across Mucho. He used to be a longshoreman in the port of Tangier. One beautiful morning, after unloading three or four sacks, he lost his mind and, at the same time, his job. He was the toughest madman in Tangier and he could knock down anyone who bugged him with a single blow. Now he is old and shrivelled up.

— Some change, mister!

— What have you eaten today?

— I ate shit and washed it down with blood.

Then he goes off, dragging his heels.

Once, it was I who followed the crazy ones wherever they went. Now it is they who follow me. I attract them. Perhaps they would like me to preside over their descent into a deeper more impenetrable madness.

Another nutcase — he was one of my pupils more than thirty years ago — never stopped following me around. He knows by heart my entire route. When he can't find me in some bar where I hang out, he waits for me near my house to hit me up for five dirhams. He's really beginning to irritate me. One day he said to me:

— M'sieur, you have been unjust to me.

— How is that?

— When I was your pupil you took a book from me which had a photo of a squirrel. You never gave it back.

— OK, I'll get you a book which will have your squirrel and many other animals.

— That's impossible.

— And why is that?

— Because that squirrel was marvellous. Unique.

— But all squirrels look alike.

— Certainly not. Do all people look the same?

— No.

— It's the same for my squirrel!

— And what will we do then?

— May Allah pardon you. But all the same you have been unjust with me, and with my squirrel.

He gives me a sad look, turns away and leaves.

In front of the Café Roxy, he stops and throws me another enigmatic look before disappearing around the corner. I too try to disappear quickly before another lunatic catches up with me.

translated by Nikita Starfish & Ira Cohen

Florian Vetsch

282 Trek Sidi Masmoudi

for Claude Thomas

Fondly I offer you my arm
Bougainvillea   eucalyptus   verbena
In photos always without glasses, but with a straw hat, absolutely
Hippolytus in the Palais du Marshan
In Arabic as in Classical Greek
The fullbearded man roared past with
His veiled woman
Hunting is natural but so is stupidity
Also   Le Blanc Chevalier & Miss Toledano
Monsieur preferred to dine in the open-air, even
When the wind blew over the bottles
Unchain the children from the cablecircus, give them
Boredom   Those young people hurting
Down by the sea   Lamb
& ashtrays for the orphans, suddenly
Always without the garden gate, finally
Old age shuffling on unreliable feet — You are
a highly sophisticated lady
malgré de ça: timide
Bougainvillea   eucalyptus   verbena
In the driveway Black dreams of all the writers
He has seen
The light does not hurt the eyes: leisurely
The gardener gently cuts a bunch of flowers
& the snakes slither swiftly away
When they feel you approach

Tangier, July 19th, 2000

Note: Black is the name of Claude Thomas's dog.

Poetry

Slicing open
the pages of French paperbacks
but only half of them.
A stamped letter without an address.

The rustling
of her skirt, crackles
and down.

The branch of a beech floating on dark waters.

Children's footsteps on gravel
a rattle, staves of wood
butterflies fluttering all around.

Silence falling with snowflakes.

A coin in my pocket
a crumb of hash
a little spice.

Khezir's Gift

To me
the hemp beaten man
the man who harnesses lines
illumination.

Standing here
stringing words
in the centre of the golden stream
always at the axis of the worktable

My eyebrows scribbling away.

Barak's Baraka

October 12, 2000

rock unlike our rock
when Bill & Moses made
a 6x12 metre hole
smoking, when Allah pulls my passport
from my shirt, the oil price
rockets on the Temple Mount & Abu Shekel gets
lost in the middle of Ramallah, 10 pounds
for every new subscriber to MobilNil, to police stations &
road blocks / tips for tourists
fixed shanks for the kissing, for the ratings
for the process of division, the peak season, one bone of
contention for the Byzantine-Ottoman-Protestant-Democra
tic Likkud-Bloc-Time hanging over the twelve-year-old boy, the women
gathering rings, chains or combat helicopters with
missiles exploding in graveyards, yet
the Butcher of Chatila drove there
just to make a movie — this interpretation is right
the Fatah militia praying (85,000 in two square kilometres)
pulling at their hair / with cymbals, psalters, harps & suicide bombings
presidential elections. The Al-Aqsa dripping
molten ore into Hosni's ear, beyond
burning flags / Zion will become a desert, you will want
to tear the sky to pieces, the mountains to dissolve… more a metaphor
rather than really playing a role… like fire
igniting brushwood, territory carved up, the fat of sacrificial offerings
anointed in the share index

translated by J. N. Reilly

Louise Landes Levi

Puja

Flower /
Blossom, roar, the 'cunt'- like
delicate / the tendrils / the Japanese Metaphor /

Pilgrim / water, hole, geographical / phenomena,
Pilgrim / age, the flight / HUM / the arrival / Korean, fish
on the wall, on the balcony, an old man, on the
throne,
You.

You
offer me, yr. soup, yr gana puja, plate, roles /
reversed, I offer, my jealousy, antique
like pale-bone / fire, I offer you
my anger, in dream, more potent, I offer you, my
passion.

Actualized, the whole mandala
Unified, I offer you my ignorance, my
pride.

Not An Advertisement

The
greenery, the river
flowing, seeing the sacred world &
my place, shamaness / poet-
ess / tramp

"*Can't stand working 9-5 / loves her Master*"
This is not an advertisement.

from Extinction

I
visited
The Earth & love one day
visited my body.

What did it mean, & how long the Fire?
Ask the record-keeper, Do not ask
me, an ignorant guest at the
"Verdant Hotel."

The keeper of the inn was a special being.
Sometimes he wore the precious raiment
of a unique bird, sometimes he man-
ifested as a voice. He donned
various disguises, each suitable to the occasion.

He
might have laughed seeing
us go from room to room so awkwardly,
instead he gave us special instructions /
How to do it, without falling down the
stairs (or out the window, like
Chet Baker), when to do it,
without disturbing the neighbors, the
other guests, or creating
a scandal.

To
some he taught invisibility,
those needing the lightness of air /
to others he taught visibility, those
needing the structure of Earth.

To me he taught silence, then a very
sweet song. He said, 'fly here, fly
there,' then he said, 'sit on
that branch for a while.'

One
day he appeared in the city,
in a café for the deaf. Within ten
minutes, in the labyrinth of that same
city, I met my Earthly love.
First I saw his sedan, then
I saw him.

Within this room
divine powers are commen-
surating & waiting for our
attention.

They will not
talk to us
unless we talk
to
them.

The dawn is
coming, the courtyard
empty.

When you see my king,
offer this world
as
my
allegory.

1991

Note: Gana = song / Puja = offering, literally a feast offering in the Buddhist Dzog-Chen tradition.

Rainmaker

for Ira Cohen

As
though the
Rainmakers gathered in
your speech, as though the seeds unfolded
in your breath.

Or
was it all Reflection &
there we lost the meaning & the content
of the Symbolic Mirror. In your plenitude, appeared
my empty State, for your pleasure, I played again
my harp of passion & rejoiced.

At dawn the tailor's threads translucent, at dusk
his cloak was sewn, for when we speak of Allegory
we do not mean the Absence
of the Stranger.

The substance was imminent
& Immanence fled appearance to inundate
your form,
&
When they murdered him
He disappeared *entirely*, that Lover
of the Master of Tabriz.

Amsterdam 1986

In

In
"retreat" I
mourn you / in Chinese
Restaurant (of
Redhook),
I
re-member
you

"SAMURAI", circular;
fuck, mystic; dream, across
piazza,
"saint"?,

I
re-
member; life-times ago;
in
Japan; a village; river;
Life
(Hiroshige: 32)

then, temple
transgression, sexual,
pure air,
moon over Mt. Generoso.

Redhook, 1995

Will Alexander

The Impalpable Brush Fire Singer

No
he is not an urn singer
nor does he carry on rapport
with negative forces within extinction

he is the brush fire singer
who projects from his heart
the sound of insidious subduction
of blank anomaly as posture
of opaque density as ash

he
distanced from prone ventriloqual stammer
from flesh
& habit
& drought

the performer
part poltergeist & Orisha
part broken in-cellular dove
part glance from floating Mongol bastions

where the spires are butane
where their photographic fractals are implanted with hypnosis

because he allegedly embodies
a green necrotic umber
more like a vertical flash or a farad
posing like a tempest in a human chromium palace

therefore his sound
a dazed simoom in a gauntlet
a blizzard of birds burned at the touch of old maelstroms
because he gives off the odour of storms
this universal Orisha
like a sun that falls from a compost of dimness
out of de-productive hydrogen sums
out of lightless fissures which boil outside the planet

yes
he sings at a certain pitch
which has evolved beyond the potter's field
beyond a tragic hummingbird's cirrhosis
surmounting primeval flaw
surmounting fire which forms in irreplaceable disjunction

under certain formations of the zodiac he is listless
he intones without impact
his synodic revelations no longer of the law
of measured palpable destinations
because he sings in such a silence
that even the Rishis can't ignore

as though
the hollow power which re-arises from nothingness
perpetually convinces
like a vacuum which splits within the spinning arc of an
intangible solar candle

such power can never be confusedly re-traced
because
it adumbrates & blazes
like a glossary of suns
so that each viral drill
each forge
casts a feeling
which in-saturates a pressure
bringing to distance a hidden & elided polarity

like a subjective skill
corroded & advanced
he sings
beyond the grip of a paralytic nexus
where blood shifts
beyond the magnet of volume
where the nerves no longer resonate
inside an octagonal maze
stung at its source by piranhas

Rodrigo Rey Rosa

The Seeing Eye

I admit that I envied him. With his skin like metal, his hair so black that it seemed blue, his soft empty gaze, he fitted my concept of a man who has made contact with God.

The first time I felt the impulse to blind myself, six or seven years ago, we were in a crowd, strolling arm in arm. It was the end of the rainy season. I remember the moment vividly: the grey and yellow afternoon, the sunlight wandering along the edge of the river, the sharp voices of the children, and, suddenly, desire, the desire to be equal to him, to look into the darkness and *see* it always.

Two or three months later I took him for a drive in his car. We were moving in a straight line; the road went on and on, not turning one way or the other, toward the horizon. Without looking at it, he seemed to be watching the sky: there were a few solitary clouds, almost imperceptible. No thought, no memory crossed my mind; there was neither tree nor rock, nor wall in the landscape. On our right the sun was about to set, and the sky had turned red and iron grey. There was no wind; the car rushed ahead at unvarying speed. I shut my eyes, had a sensation of freedom, opened them again. Ahead, far off, I saw a mountain. I shut my eyes again. I was aware of the dull sound of the tyres on the paved road. I felt a trembling in my thighs and belly, and repressed the impulse to raise my eyelids. It was then, with my eyes still closed, that I saw I was enveloped in a gold-colored cloud, heavy but luminous and transparent. I wanted to be blind, and I said to myself in silence, in a voice that was not mine: "If only I could be like this." I opened my eyes and looked at him: he smiled. I thought — and I still wonder — "Is it possible that he doesn't know what is happening?" It was now dark. The headlights lit up the road; we went along in silence. When we reached the mountain the curves and windings began.

I used to go to his room each night to read aloud to him. That night when I went there I did not find him. I hoped to talk with him about what I had felt. I searched through the entire house, but did not find him. From outside I heard the croaking of frogs. Nausea, heaviness, a sad, penetrating fatigue. I went back downstairs to the sitting-room. On the lowest step lay a battered old paintbrush. Above the mantelpiece there hung a medal in the form of a six-pointed star. I took it down, and I remember, and shall always remember, that it trembled in my hand. I went out into the garden. The clouds were heavy with rain. I went to the stone bench near the fountain and sat down. For the last time I saw the night. I moved my eyelids, and with the sharp edge of the star I slashed my eyes. There was no pain. I seemed to be falling; a tepid current ran down my cheeks. I moved my hands in front of my face and did not see them. From behind me I heard him calling out to me.

(I am not astonished by the solitude or the darkness there is in the air, and much less by the thought that I am in a hell of my own creation. Sometimes my past surprises me, and the memory I have of his voice.)

translated by Paul Bowles

Aidan Andrew Dun

Vale Royal

For those whose genius was extinguished
early in the night, who bled
without the vaunted medicine of love,
for whom all charity stopped short,
the lonely marvellous boy and those
unnamed dark stars all doomed
within his shadow, embryonic
Shakespeares, broken and rebuffed
my song is one vast coffin for them all,
a decent burial at last in black,
a few words mumbled by a holy fool
in coloured rags, another maniac.

To A Dancer

Translation that races along the sky at dawn,
white music where rain slides backward,
feathered language, compelling the sun,
who will tell your legend in the morning?

Along the canal, steep towers of perfume.
And an essence, washed down in the night
in warm yellow dust, transports us with laughter
to unknown celebrations with water-music.

Here is a bird which speaks to passers-by,
rider of black skies speaking in riddles.
Here is a boat that was hauled through dark sleep
to be docked in circular ports of sunrise.

O majestic decision! You brought us here!
It was your golden engine heard in the wind.
Today it is sacred to remember nothing,
to look to the present time which is far ahead.

Her Feet as Two White Swans

Royal birds on the river went sailing,
a slow white navy in peacetime.

Where two straights of the river join,
white pleasure-ships went sailing.

Two white ones in proud navigations
came with playfulness to the green edge.

There they sailed, smoothly moving,
bringing the river excitement. O!

Shapes elongated, curved and weighted,
white in the river-column floated.

Deep water swerved in pleasure extremely,
making sensations and whirlpools spin.

The water felt a similar upliftment
as when a saint's feet bring joy to the ground.

Two swans on the river went sailing,
a white armada of pleasure-ships.

The white birds moved, two beautiful feet
gliding across a bright plane of glass.

One was a fraction larger than the other.
Both had silver tips to their wings.

Invention plays no part in this song.
Ask my Lady of the Sea of Milk. She was there!

She was the one who showed all to me,
the slow drift of pleasure, shining.

Agneta Falk

So Many

inside the moon
all hell is breaking loose
this last millennium fever
dusting off every last particle

on the streets everything
is open right down
to the trampled screams
oh what I wouldn't give
for a moment's silence

if only I could catch that bird
in the corner, there, so close,
so far, break open its altitude
and lift all these
little men and women
out of their bent over lives

the man who sat leaning against
the tree next to me just vanished
left his gaze and heart behind
between the fallen leaves
and it isn't even autumn

the wind is filling trouser legs with air

there are so many empty shoes in the world

so many

Sardinia

Through the train window
on the way to Villacidro
the light plays
with your rugged form
You mean to be here
do not want to be touched
cannot be bought
yield to nothing

when I try sinking my eyes
deeper into your proud armour
I feel my own breath's hesitance
like oil floating on water
You digest nothing but your own kind
brim in all weather
wordless at twilight
profoundly licking your wounds

I hear the grumbling
in the stones, years
of hurtling
the porous silence
that never stops ringing
in your bones
and everywhere the stone-flowers

and everything bleached
running along on the brink
of fate and the old recipes
passed down the years
perfect for the mouth of
your desire to grow old by
your own hand in the light
over there by the empty field
where the eyes fall deep into the horizon.

Oh Hate

to be in the moment
a grey slab of a sky
over Italian poplars
along the river Rhone
and thinking about the Palestinian boy(s)
shot to death, the Israeli soldiers
torn to shreds

who tears makes tears
who wins loses
who loses wins
wilfully
          without thought
     who lays his body
down to die
with the name of God on his lips

here silk is made
soft, the flowing lengths of it
enough to make a mummy
out of yourself
but in among these thoughts
the smell of a blood–stained rag
gets stuffed down the throat
of a pitiless bull
choking on his own blood

the long tongue of autumn
curls to a silence
overhead a black bird
stabs its wings deep in the heart

who do you love most with your eyes closed?
who do you trust most with your eyes closed?
these thoughts kill me also
and here comes mother earth again
flashing her teeth

oh hate, how I hate you
but you're so easy to love
so loyal in your blindness

hold me in your thorny arms
and spike me till it hurts
so hard I want to let go
of you
          forever

and stop boys throwing stones older than themselves
at men who should know better than to shoot
at people smaller and younger than themselves

stop them becoming fodder
for the *big boys* who play monopoly
with people's lives in marbled halls
whose faces they'll never see
whose hands they'll never shake

the moment of truth then
the one you live for
the one you die for

October 2000

Yorkshire Lullaby

What is it we fear most
the tear that can't fall
and is caught on the edge of the eye
        or
a breakfast of stale blood?

every morning the same
it's so vast that we can't
even encompass the enormity
can't hear the singing
in our bones, the music our
ears are made for

fist over water, sky over rock
oh limp, limp hands
setting teeth on edge

at the open window
the leaves are rocking themselves
to sleep
there's too much grit
bite my tongue off for not talking,
sweet rain, wash me over and over
cradle me in your cadence

the woman with the ravaged eyes
could be you,
everything always happens to other
people until it happens to you

what passes for poetry
is the echo in your ear
my nose is cold
too much moon

my bed is a Yorkshire landscape,
the folds in the sheets peek like the Pennines.

Whisperings

the sky was never darker
than from down here
up below the moors

the clouds shift
play havoc with the light
tear the hills apart
so you never quite know
when or where you are

up there, covered by lichen
big secrets are buried
they say it's of the past
but the wind cries
it into the future
whisperings of sore children's feet
of long working days
in deafening silence
behind thick Yorkshire stone

Note: It is said that the children who worked and died in the factories during the industrial revolution were buried on the moors.

Inside This Room

Inside this room
wilderness stands guard
and the rustle of leaves
is ever present.

The old woman
who stands on the corner
of our flesh
makes no judgement,

she's all the women
I am, who went before me.
Through their darkness
I became light,

and in your face
I see all my fathers,
the one I never had,
the child I carried
inside me all these years,

brother of the soul.

Kazuko Shiraishi

The Heart of an Ant

Suppose   an ant has a heart
The more enormous a man is   the more his heart is as small as an ant
Because an ant-sized worry becomes enormous

Today too I go out to look for the precious tears of a donkey
I know very well   they do not exist anywhere
And yet   they exist everywhere
They are not visible   to me   and I cannot find them
Why   I have my heart set on it   is not clear
To me   nor to the donkey   not to mention
The relationship between me and the donkey
I know all about Don Quixote
Riding on a donkey   heading for a preposterous windmill
My friends whose lives were blown off   and have become fragments   they
Did not have the heart an ant does   they were living with determination
While they were alive   and even after they died

Regarding the Future   The Donkey

Regarding the future   the donkey contemplates   after this century
What sort of century will come   then
How will the donkey's ears   be useful
Will poetry be peacefully prosperous   or
Hang on to the ears of hell   panting   burning fiercely   the fire of energy that
Rides the rising air current
Gods   ease the discontent of those who call themselves absolute
Buddha   closed his eyes a little while ago
I am not sleeping   I am contemplating
The sculptor   says every time he gets drowsy
And he wakes up without fail   by looking at a beautiful woman
And screams that   flowers bloom in this world but
The donkey   opens a hole in the ant hill   looking
Everyone plugs their ears   reading their own sutras inside many layered enclosures
Gradually becoming ants   gradually becoming soil
Begins to hear a god like voice   from somewhere
Saying   what is called the future is
Not yet   loaded onto your back

Woodpecker

A woodpecker came pecking at
His wooden house   and poked holes
So the man dashes out   and frightens it

The man   spent eight years
Built   the house
For his wife and two sons
And
Before the woodpecker came and poked holes in it
An invisible woodpecker came
and poked a hole   in the man's wife

From there   the wife
Flew off somewhere
And will never come back again

A woodpecker comes pecking
Pecks   at the man's wooden house

The Voice of the Stormy Petrel   Pours On

Twelve hundred yen a night   a clean bed
Facing the sea   the window opens   early morning
What slides off   on the shining sea
It's not a boat   that is
Me
Headed where?

That morning I see   myself   clearly
Going out   in a direction even I do not know
I   am here
And I am not here
I become a tower   in my thoughts I quietly
Rise but   on the other hand
Quickly   leave this earth
Heading   for a distant transparency   and become the very universe
Breathing   a ripple   in that shining single grain that single moment
I see   myself   in many millionths   that cell

The Afternoon of the Sheep

Yesterday I met a new
Animal who is playing a game where things like the soul aren't needed
It has glass eyes a computer in its chest
I can't see the tails and all because of the shadows of the buildings

But the lives of the sheep don't change
They go to the hills take off their clothes and put on priests' robes
Nowadays even the gods tend to make business trips
(No even the gods want to avoid the sheep
in priests' robes)
No one wants to be made a victim but
To carry through one's own truth justice is comfortable
At times like that desires
Come along tempting the executioners

Look at the hills where the sheep are buried
Even though they are buried even though they are buried
The sheep do not die
Even from inside sausages they come back to life
The sheep spew out from the entire body
The fluff of the clouds of poesy
Sending the eternal executioners over to the other side
In this way for centuries tens of centuries
In the afternoon we see the hills where the spirits of
The sheep whose severed lives were turned into total silence
Fly over in the sky Oh the hill of the sheep
That is the hill of the sheep

translated by Samuel Grolmes & Yumiko Tsumura

Jordan Zinovich

Temporizing

> *There will be time, there will be time*
> *To prepare a face to meet the faces that you meet;*
> *There will be time to murder and create,*
> *And time for all the works and days of hands*
> *That lift and drop a question on your plate.*
> *T. S. Eliot*

Axiom: Dominant ideologies design their own cosmic temporal matrices, which tend to rely on singularities for origin and linearity for direction. But Lived Time is better imagined as a cluster of linked domains: in the physical and symbolic domains, Time — past, present, and future — seems an abstract backdrop against which operations and events take place; in the qualitatively distinct biological and ecological domains, time past punctuates the biosphere with a genetic memory of evolution, and time-to-come is punctuated by bioreplication/sex; and in the social and economic domain the time past (History) of Social Time and the future time of production dominate. However, human Inner Time recognizes that, besides these other domains, there is also a lived past of Memory and future time of Hope/Desire.

Question: How does one judge what time is? And I don't mean by external evidence, such as the position of the sun, eclipses of the moon, the hour on the clock, etc.

It always starts this way: I'm standing in the open with a flat horizon stretching in all directions around me; nothing breaks its perfect line. The sun is an immutable sphere hanging in the sky, and though it shines brightly I'm comfortable — neither too hot nor too cold. Then the hissing starts. Sand. I'm standing on desert sand, which flows in a jet stream around my ankles. Now I'm apprehensive, something is coming. A dot appears on the horizon in the distance (ahead? to my right? to my left?), moving swiftly, growing at an incredible rate — a huge ball of sand swelling like a snowball. I turn and run.

There is nothing stopping me. I could run in any or many directions but flee in a straight line away from the ball, glancing repeatedly back at it. It doesn't stop or change direction, and I won't outrun it at this speed. I run harder, but the sand slips away beneath my feet and I don't make any headway. My footing begins to swirl and sink. The surrounding sand climbs on all sides until I'm trapped in a bowl-like depression. I'm doomed. Sick with fear, I stop and face the ball, which hangs suspended on the lip of the bowl. A maelstrom opens and the ball rolls down over me. This is a memory: always slightly different.

Proposition 1: Humans employ Time to coordinate their perceptions. They alter their notions of Time to suit their priorities, whether or not these are conscious priorities.

Historic & Epistemological Divergence: Religious thinking organizes Time according to singularities — qualitative points of departure (the illud tempus of shamanistic cosmogenesis, the birth of Christ, the Buddha's enlightenment, the big-bang origin of the universe, etc.). During the Middle Ages, Lived Time was seen as a passage of no return through a singular world. Humans were pilgrims moving inexorably forward, drawn by the NOW, and were obsessively eschatological. The Renaissance responded intellectually by trying to learn everything about the cosmos. After Copernicus, previously unimaginable aspects of Time began revealing themselves — e.g. light years and the notion that we see light from long extinct celestial bodies. Comprehendible dimensions of Time were rendered void, tipping individual life-courses into meaninglessness. By the end of the 18th century Descartes' formulation of a universal scientific methodology had shifted the focus from a cognitive and knowing humanity embedded in its life-courses to the ideal of causal laws. The moment the causal ideal was valorized, humankind lost its central position in the world of knowledge, and began to sense Time's indifference.

In a causally oriented culture it is easy to consider Time as mechanically repetitive. Hegel tried to reassert the value of lived human awareness. Toward the end of *Phenomenology* he wrote: "Nature is Space; whereas Time is History." In other words, to paraphrase Anthony Wilden: there is no natural, universal/cosmic Time, there is only Time insofar as there is History/Social Time; human ideology. During the course of Social Time, humans explore Lived Time through their discourse. Their exploration is the "empirically-existing concept", and Time is nothing other than this concept. Without human awareness, nature would be space, and only space.

Unfortunately, after Hegel the solipsistic idealisms of Husserlian and Heideggerian phenomenology and Existentialism unwittingly increased the void between individual lives and extended cosmic Time.

Proposition 2: Human temporal awareness articulates in the future, and is driven by desire/hope. The flow of Time is a kind of "forward recollection" (Kierkegaard), where human awareness struggles to correlate the future with a comprehendible past according to a specific paradigm. Human memory of the past also depends on desire/ hope; consider Freud's theory of deferred action — "the memory of past time depends on the present project of the subject."

The darkness seems overwhelming and permanent, and the jet stream that had pulled at my ankles is now a steady, insistent wind blowing down on me from above. I must be inside the sand ball, but wind and darkness are the only constants in this place. I begin to explore.

The wind is strongest where I first found myself. A membrane encloses the outermost edges of the space, which seems large and elliptical, like an egg on its side. The membrane pulses with life, changing in response to signals I can't detect.

What face does it show its world? Which signals permeate it, and which ones merely stimulate it? The wind's song is a strange amalgam of all the human voices I've ever heard: gurgling infants, laughter, sobbing, old folks with dry, soft pencil-scratching whispers. Conversations rise from the soughing babble like individual voices in a Tibetan choir soaring on the chant harmonics. How long do I listen? A while, I guess, because I notice some of the whispers fading, vanishing; while small purly voices clearly master words. These voices, these conversations in this dark place; they are my present.

Empirical Intuition: Not all moments in Time are equal; there is always a valorized moment. Temporal events are valorized when they are in the position of being directly presented to that part of human awareness that is being "lived". Along a human life-course — which may stretch out over several decades — one particular moment is real and alive while every other moment exists only in memory or in desire/hope. All events simultaneous with the valorized moment are valorized events, in that they occur in the NOW.

There is no sense of the passage of time in the NOW.

What is the cause of the slowing down that takes place when one endlessly repeats oneself? It's not predicated on physical or mental fatigue or exhaustion, for if that were the cause then complete rest would be the best restorative. Rather, it is something psychical; forcing the perception of time, through unbroken periods of uniformity, to fall away — that perception of time which is so closely bound to the consciousness of life that one may not be weakened without the other suffering impairment.

There are many false conceptions regarding the nature of tedium. Generally it's felt that novelty "makes the time pass"; that is to say, shortens it; whereas monotony and emptiness check and restrain time's flow. Vacuity and monotony have, indeed, the property of making the moment and the hour seem tiresome. But they are also capable of contracting or dissipating larger time-units to the point of reducing them to nothing at all. Conversely, interest can put wings to the hour and the day; yet it lends a weightiness to the general passage of time, a solidity which causes eventful years to flow far more slowly than bare, empty ones. What we call tedium is actually an abnormal shortening of time consequent upon monotony. Great spans of time passed in unbroken uniformity tend to shrink together. When one day is like all the others, then they are all alike. Complete uniformity makes the longest life seem short, as though it had stolen away from us unawares. This is one aspect of Inner Time.

Proposition 3: For humans, Time consists of the punctuation and organization of Lived (inner) Time by activities in Social Time. Cosmic Time is the mythic and ideological structure upon which Social Time is projected to become History. The function of ideology is to explain the past, present, and possible futures of real live systems. The masters of ideology give cosmic Time a meaning and direction separate from individual human experience (Lived Time).

In the membrane-surrounded dark, thoughts, memories, and hopes take on life. They slip from my mind and float like glowing cobwebby disks to my feet, where they stack and stretch into a pulsing tube throbbing to the strange rhythms of the outer membrane. The tube expands, filling my awareness, becoming a tunnel. This is my escape, a future and a past, the tunnel of a life-course.

Proposition 4: The difference between human potential and general cosmic temporal limits is intolerable. Socially mediated temporalization is equivalent to the humanization of Time. The humanization of Time is evident everywhere in society, including in the most "objective" camps. Even a scientific determinist as certain of his objectivity as Stephen Hawking, ultimately resorts to "anthropic principles" — either weak or strong — to explain aspects of his cosmic Time.

A Casual Bit of Causal Jesuitry: Most physical scientists and many philosophers claim that "backward causation" is impossible. Notions of cause and effect are most often bound by a definition of cause, yet in Lived Time we frequently search for a cause only after we have noticed an effect. Despite this strange irrational inversion in our conventional view of temporal flow, philosophers commonly evoke a "sense of strangeness" to deny the possibility of backward causation. Physical scientists are more likely to call on "the second law of thermal dynamics."

The question of whether or not NATURE permits backward causation can not be resolved by observing that we remember only the past, and not the future. Backward causation does not imply changing the past, only determining what it actually was.

Accepting total solipsistic scepticism regarding the existence of the past — both immediate and distant — enables a backward causation that can alter the past. This is the temporal attitude of both fundamentalist/reductionist religion and paranoia, which is predicated on panic. We weren't here yesterday (or 8000 years ago, say the religious), and we may be obliterated tomorrow. All we can know is the Terrible Now, whimper the paranoiacs.

Causality, as it is traditionally defined, depends on closed physical systems, and closed physical systems are not a general state of either NATURE or social systems. NATURE as humans experience it may never permit a physical effect to precede its cause, but that does not prevent events secured by Social Time to function as if they occurred before their cause. In fact, such events occur frequently in Lived Time. History is retrofit — e.g. with retroactive contract clauses; by conspiracies/congresses that sanction ceremonies today to confer legal status as of twelve months ago; by exegeses like this one, which elucidate phenomena obscured by domination; etc.

Proposition 5: Of course, historical Social Time does not form an unbroken continuum, free of definitive rupture, conflict, and/or contradiction; and it advances the prejudices of its masters. Autonomy commands Lived Time by real participation in Social Time as lived by extended groups. A general language, a common History emerges from groups who experience the qualitative richness of events in a shared present.

Inner Time's systolic and diastolic pulses are not uniform. Though it's a game conditioned into us from infancy, clocking life is a futile exercise — the kind used to occupy dominated minds. Inner and Social times seldom correlate, and when they do they never correspond to the temporal attitudes of other domains. Coordinating them is, at best, an illusion.

The temporal frame we normally recognize involves a singular beginning and a temporizing sequence that flows as we play. Its clock is there to limit ludic excess. Yet experience shows me that Time is least obtrusive when I am most interested/involved, i.e. playing. If we must clock life, let's at least recognize a chronometric praxis that more closely resembles Lived Time. Why not truly humanize chronometry? Why not recognize that our clocks run only when we are not playing? That way, as we get more adept at the idiosyncratic life-courses we fall into, chronometry should become less and less important. Eventually, a playful continuity might force that odious controlling science into obsolescence.

Etymological Note: Time — Old English tíma = Old Norse tími: fit or proper time; good time; prosperity. In English, the lexeme "Time" has never functioned exclusively to designate a cosmic backdrop. Quite the contrary, it has often been personalized. From the earliest recorded usages for the nominal substantive "Time" in Old English (circa 893-897 C. E.), one lexical subdomain has advanced the semantic notions of suitability, fitness, and propitiousness. Thus, in English it has always been possible to say: This is a good time; your time; a time for jubilation.

Proposition 6: At this moment, the ideology of corporation-dominated Lived Time manipulates us with notions of leisure and holiday (Debord), which are always immanent, always desirable, but never quite present. One ideological trick that dominance resorts to is to manage shared temporal experience by curbing ludic adventure, denying coevalness to whoever or whatever does not toe its line. Shake the scruffy panoptic fetish that has bent us to its design. Upend the dictates of corporate Reason, and abandon its tyrannical clock. Transform your NOW (past and future) into the jubilant NOWEVER.

Time flies like an arrow.
Fruit flies like a banana.
-anonymous

Jane Falk

Ckrowww

"Long live the crow
Let it fly ungarlanded"

crow brings the message
she bears a bone in her beak
she flies with the cloud which hides the sun
she enters my room on a feathery wind
and performs the dream dance
crow brings the message
she sunders my day dream
she shortens my life
crow brings the message
the price of beauty is a round smooth stone
the price of the quicksilver tongue is the grin of madness
crow message is a dry bone worry
crow message is the dagger
crow message the howling
she binds shadows about her
as she flies round my head
i am struck by her terrible laughter

time follows crow
who flutters on crooked wings
and gossips idle in the trees
time the invisible
sun silent one
the noise separates from the iron bar
    bell clangs
    night comes
    the moon and i her slaves
    she metes us out
    she turns us into silver strands
        my hair will grow
        to shroud me
        or light my way to heaven
        fire burning
        to day

i do not taste
the bitter wine
perhaps tomorrow
she knows
she who is black
she who is cool
she who is clever
she flies with the crow
she is never exhausted
she holds up the mirror
follows me or watches with me at the window
she holds me now
with hands that hold water currents
the mouldy clay
the caverns of jade
and the form of my body
is well known to her
for her hands have always held me
i am unafraid

i wear the crow's feather
i speak the forgotten language
i seek the glittering by moonlight
my net woven of stolen twigs
i am the crow pecking at a dead eye
black raven
little mother
where are you now?
you who left me speeding
seeking your shadow in the moon's face

when the bent bow sprung
the arrow struck its prey
when the cry sprung
from the mouth of the prey
the voice received an answer

today the crow is my friend
her cawing always the same
the sound of the edge of the cliff
she wheels on the wind
balances the sky on her wings
she steals what she can
she does not care
she is the crow

the rose is the goddess's offering
the worm is the offering to crow

crow world is a flash of peripheral vision
rounded roofs   bent backs of trees
          undersides of leaves
the crow flies
she dives
she perches
she scans me
as i plod the dusty road
my feet attracted to earth
earth substance of my body
without water turns to dust
without earth and air
there is no measure
without water and fire
there is no ether
without the feet and the wings
there is no contrast
without black and white
there is no brilliance

now the sky is empty of crow
the wind jostled her
just as she frightens the lesser birds from her tree

my love is a crow
his hair black flash
his eyes dark glint
his nose proud beak
he preens before a mirror
he rides the demon's cape
his laughter points at me
i shrink

the crow glides past
i marvel at this phantom
bird who drew me through black
                    to shimmer
lover who drew me to the other side
led me through subterranean coupling
                    to one point
he wears the third eye of ashes

i burn clear
no smoke

the day of the crow
is the day of thunder
the day the dust is laid low
by the sidelong glance of the crow
the crow is a trickster a gypsy a thief
she steals the spirit on silent wings
and leaves the changeling

the day of the crow
is the day of reckoning
word once given to crow
cannot be taken back
the crow is a shrewd bird a cruel bird
with a beak that is knife that cuts deep

the day of the crow
is the day of woe
the day of misfortune
a fine pointed etching in black
the door of the temple stands open
for sacrifice must be offered
on the day of the crow

Howard Schwartz

The Celestial Orchestra

Once it happened that Reb Nachman woke up in the middle of the night, and instead of the deep silence that usually pervaded, he heard something like faint music. At first the sound seemed no more than an approaching wind, but soon he realized it actually was a kind of music. What could it be? He had no idea. But he continued to hear it ever so faintly, sometimes present, sometimes about to disappear. And as it did not grow any louder, he had to strain to listen. One thing was certain, though: Reb Nachman felt drawn to this music, as if it were a message coming to him from a great distance, which he was trying to receive.

Then Reb Nachman got up and went into his study and sat down by the window. And yes, from there the music seemed slightly louder, as if he were a little closer to its source, but it remained very faint. It did not seem to come from any instrument with which he was familiar, for it did not sound like a violin or a flute: not like a bass fiddle and not like a drum. Nor did it have the sound of voice or voices. If only he were able to hear it better, he thought, he might be able to identify its source.

Then Reb Nachman left the house and walked out into the field beyond the gate, under a sky crowded with stars. There he had no memory, except for questions that concerned the origin of the mysterious music. And while his eyes were fixed on the heavens, the ground remained unknown beneath his feet. And for that time he did not impose patterns on distant stars or imagine the life they might sustain. Nor did he count the gift of the stars as riches. Instead he listened for a long, long time.

At first Reb Nachman thought that what he heard was coming from a single instrument. But soon he was able to separate the instruments that wove their music together so well. Yet this new knowledge did not satisfy his longing and curiosity; in fact, it only served to whet it. Where was this distant music coming from? Surely it was not drifting there from any orchestra in Bratslav, or from anywhere else in this world. Of that Reb Nachman was certain. No, this was some kind of celestial music, music of the spheres. It was then Reb Nachman realized how much he wanted to follow that music and discover its source. And this longing grew so great that he became afraid his heart would break. Then, while he was staring upward, he saw a very large star fall from its place in the heavens and blaze across the sky like a comet. He followed that star as it fell, and shared its last journey. And somehow it seemed to Reb Nachman that he was falling with that star and was caught up in that same motion, as if he had been swept away by an invisible current, and he closed his eyes and let himself be carried.

Now it happened that when Reb Nachman opened his eyes again he found himself seated inside a chariot of fire that blazed its way across the heavens. And he did not have time to wonder how this had happened, or what it meant, but merely to marvel in awe as the wonders of the heavens passed before his eyes.

Before him he saw two kinds of luminaries: those that ascended above were luminaries of light and those that descended below were luminaries of fire. And it was then, when his eyes had become adjusted to the sudden illuminations crossing his path, that Reb Nachman became aware of a presence beside him and began to perceive a dim body of light.

That is when the angel who drove the chariot first spoke to him, and said: "Reb Nachman, I am the angel Raziel. You should know that your calling and your prayers have not gone unheard in heaven. This chariot has been sent to bring you to the place you long for, the source you are seeking."

And with each word the angel Raziel spoke, the light surrounding his ethereal body grew brighter, until he appeared to Reb Nachman as a fully revealed human being. This was the first time Reb Nachman had ever been face-to-face with an angel. And yet, strange to say, he did not feel the fear he would have expected, but rather felt as if he had been reunited with a long-lost companion.

Just then the chariot approached some kind of parting of the heavens, which resembled a line drawn across the cosmos. As they drew closer, he saw it was actually an opening through which an ethereal light emerged. Raziel recognized the question taking form in Reb Nachman's mind, and he said: "We are approaching the place where the Upper Waters and the Lower Waters meet. This is where the Upper Worlds are separated from the Lower Worlds, and what belongs to the spheres above is divided from what belongs to the spheres below."

No sooner did the angel finish speaking than the chariot approached close enough to that place for Reb Nachman to catch a glimpse of what lay on the other side. And what he saw was a magnificent structure suspended in space. And from that one glimpse he knew that whatever it was, no human structure could begin to compare with it. But then, before he had time to question the angel, the chariot passed through that very aperture, to the complete astonishment of Reb Nachman, for it was no higher than a hand's breadth. It was at that moment that Reb Nachman grew afraid for the first time, for he realized he was flying through space at a great height and did not dare to look down. Then he said to the angel: "How is it possible that we have passed through that place which is no more than three finger-breadths?"

Raziel said: "In your world of men, Reb Nachman, it is possible to contain a garden in the world. But in this kingdom it is possible to contain the world in a garden. How can this be? Because here, whoever opens his heart to the Holy One, blessed be He, as much as the thickness of a needle, can pass through any portal."

Even as Raziel spoke these words Reb Nachman had already been captured by the radiant vision that loomed ahead. And again, without his having to ask, Raziel replied. "The place you are about to be taken to, Reb Nachman, is the very one you have been seeking. Yet since even this chariot is not permitted to approach much closer to that sacred place, you must soon depart from it and remain suspended in space, like the Sanctuary you see before you."

And without any other explanation, Reb Nachman realized that the wonderful structure he saw must be the Celestial Temple, after which the Temple in Jerusalem had been modelled, and with which it was identical in every aspect, except for the fire surrounding the heavenly Sanctuary. For the marble pillars of this heavenly miracle were illumined by red fire, the stones by green fire, the threshold by white fire, and the gates by blue fire. And angels entered and departed in a steady stream, intoning an unforgettable hymn to a melody Reb Nachman heard that day for the first time, but which he recognized as if it had been familiar to him all the days of his life.

That is when Reb Nachman realized he was no longer within the chariot but suspended in space without support for his hands or feet. And it was then, with his eyes fixed on that shimmering vision, that Reb Nachman was first able to distinguish the Divine Presence of the *Shekhinah* hovering above the walls and the pillars of the Temple, illuminating them and wrapping them in a glowing light, which shone across all of heaven. It was this light he had seen from the other side of the aperture, before the chariot of fire had crossed into the Kingdom of Heaven. And so awestruck was Reb Nachman to witness the splendor of the *Shekhinah,* he suddenly experienced an overwhelming impulse to hide his face. He began to sway in that place and almost lost his balance. Had it not been for the angel Raziel speaking to him in that instant he might have fallen from that great height. The angel said: "Take care, Reb Nachman, and know that the Temple remains suspended by decree of the Holy One, blessed be He. And you must remember above all to keep your eyes fixed on its glory, if you are not to become lost in this place. For should you look away from the Temple for as long as a single instant, you would risk the danger of falling from this height. Even a mere distraction would take you to places unintended, from which you might never return. So too should you know that no living man may enter into that holy dwelling place and still descend to the world of men. For no man could survive the pure fire burning there, through which only angels and purified souls can pass."

And it was then, when he had regained his balance, that Reb Nachman finally discovered the source of the celestial music that had lured him from his house in a world so far removed, and yet so close. For as he followed that music to its source in the Celestial Temple, his eyes came to rest on concentric circles of angels in the Temple courtyard. Then he realized that the music he had been hearing was being played by an orchestra of angels. And when he looked still closer he saw that each of the angels played a golden vessel cast in the shape of a letter of the Hebrew alphabet. And each one had a voice of its own, and one angel in the center of the circle played an instrument in the shape of the letter Bet.

And as he listened to the music, Reb Nachman realized it was the long note of the letter Bet that served as its foundation and sustained all of the other instruments. He marvelled at how long the angel was able to hold this note, drawing his breath back and forth like the Holy One Himself, who in this way brought the heavens and the earth into being. And at that moment Reb Nachman was willing to believe that the world only existed so that those secret harmonies could be heard. And he turned to the angel Raziel, who had never left his side, and once more the angel knew what he wished to know, and said: "The score of this symphony is the scroll of the Torah, which commences with the letter Bet, endless and eternal, and continues with each instrument playing in turn as it appears on the page, holding its note until the next letter has been sounded, and then breathing in and out a full breath."

And when Reb Nachman listened to that music he arrived at a new understanding of the Torah and realized that among its many mysteries there was one level on which it existed only as pure music. He was also aware that of all the instruments in that orchestra it was only the letter Bet that spoke to him and pronounced his name. Then the angel Raziel turned to him and said: "The souls of men draw their strength from one of the instruments in this orchestra and thus from one of the letters of the alphabet. And that letter serves as the vessel through which the soul of a man may reveal itself. Your soul, Reb Nachman, is one of the thirty-six souls that draw their strength from the vessel of the letter Bet, which serves as their Foundation Stone and holds back the waters of the Abyss."

Then it happened that when the angel Raziel said the word "Abyss," Reb Nachman forgot all of his warnings for one instant and glanced down at the world so far below. And the next thing he knew, he felt like a falling star. That is when he realized he was still standing in the field beyond the gate. And the celestial music, though faint once more, still echoed in his ears.

Yehudi Amichai in The Heavenly Jerusalem

On earth,
in his beloved Jerusalem,
he could often be found in that tiny café
on King George,
sipping black coffee.
Everyone knew who he was,
but they left him alone.
Later
he would shop in the *shuk*
like everyone else,
take a seat in the back of the bus,
put down his bag of fruits and vegetables,
and dream a little
till the bus reached his stop.

Everyone else was asleep
when he rose at four in the morning
to jot down the poems hidden in the corners
of his city
that no one else seemed to notice.
That was his secret life.

On his seventieth birthday he whispered,
I am tired of giving birth,

And it seemed to be true.
His face was tired,
even his eyes,
and yet something continued to burn.

I have learned the secret
Of fertilizing myself,
he told me.
I supply both egg and seed.
But I am tired of giving birth.

At seventy-six
he took leave of this world
quietly,
as one would expect of such a modest man.
Presidents and prime ministers spoke at his funeral;
thousands gathered to pay their respects.

When he reached heaven,
he was greeted by his heroes,
King David and Shmuel ha-Nagid,
along with hundreds of his poems,
their flying letters swirling around him.
The angels,
delighted to welcome him,
offered him a pair of wings,
but he declined, saying,
"It's enough if my words have wings.
Tell me, where are the cafés?"

Other souls
wander the streets of Paradise
like tourists,
staring at the heavenly temple
or taking a seat at the back of Rashi's class.
Not Yehuda.
He is still longing for the ruins
of the earthly temple,
for the ancient stones of his earthly city,
for all the sheets hung out to dry,
flapping like sails in the wind.

As always
he finds inspiration in exile,
and now he finds it everywhere.

Charles Plymell

Charles Henri Ford's Last Prints

Atlas on this star-studded Montauk
Beach, bleached night of dead cartilage
rotting haunting puzzles to their core.
Straddle night's space glazed with numbered
stars each to each pebble on the shore.

If you stand and throw your great knife
and cut an imaginary line through the
night sky, it is said that space is
so vast that no star would be hit.

Surrealism's magic master, beachcomber, leaves
lines like Spiderman's spit on skyscrapers
Gotham's duo, Batman, Robin and the rest.
Where Montauk descendants sell tobacco.

Leave your signals for a physicist to predict
and keyboard specialist to plunder the growing
algebraic garden of poppies, not having heard
such names as Tanguy, or Charles Henri, who
before computers, had seen fractal patterns
curl back upon themselves as clean and easy
as a cut through space, a thread in Persian rugs,
or Seahorse dance in pride from deep ocean's ridge.

The course lives in the dance, in footprints, or
in the throne of worlds, the gnomon, Osiris sits upon.
Myth and geometry meet in the mouth and in the maw,
or in carcass washed ashore where upon he sits in
quick poppy's charm, in the kitchen's lost creations
raw food in the salons now gone, no more fine blade
slicing symmetry of the seed, or chopping herbs.
Latex oozing from the night, like a field of
Milky Way's frozen eternal footsteps above 72nd St.

The space time sung anew, like the canaries do, and
be bop too, to save their memories' weight for flight.

The brain lightens and ideas are boats untied
left in the currents of neurons,
less fantasized postulates school kids study
while long bladed orbits assassinate lovers
when the bare light-bulb moon dims the sun's room
unexplained, resonating, unscrewed, unfurnished with
the future by transient vestal vacancies of the past.
Sing for us, play for us, pray for our minimalist souls
while we sit in Acuras watching manipulators
coasting in Manhattan on roller blades of black ice.

John Reilly

Love In Colours

Dancing in the light of a bloody moon
Down the garden path where the fire flies go
Dancing back and forth to the crickets' tune
Down on the grass where the rainbow rests

Let me touch you
Let me hold you
Let the love light burn inside you

Let me love you
Let me free you
Let faith and dreams release you

Down on the grass where the rainbow rests
Dancing back and forth to the crickets' tune
Down the garden path where the fire flies go
Dancing in the light of a bloody moon

Let's lift the coming day
Lift eyes that love the way

Let the colours devour us

Until the horizon cracks

Splattering us
with light...

Simon Vinkenoog

The Flying Dutchman

Captain Decker,
Flying Dutchman,
Climbs aboard
The timeless space-machine
You're living in
And starts to turn you inside-out:
He needs you to know
What it is really all about.

Captain Decker,
Flying Dutchman,
Gives not one thought
To the state
The world of mirrors is in:
He knows it's your mind
To be blown and forever be free
To sail out on the ocean of humanity…

Captain Decker,
Flying Dutchman,
Lightning and thunder,
Wave upon wave,
Makes you come up and go under,
Lose yourself and find yourself,
Whose is this body called Love
And what is the state of beyond and beyonder?…

Captain Decker,
Flying Dutchman,
Makes you wonder:
Is this me, and am I real?
For you can see what I can see,
If I am free, why shouldn't you be?
A craving hungers in the body
And desire spreads for other bodies
To join in the winds forever.

Captain Decker,
Flying Dutchman,
Makes you come and go, live and die,
To share and show Who you are and Why:
Born to be free in one breath or another,
Captain Decker,
Master of experiences,
Turns you on, tunes you in
And takes you over…

A Silent Manifesto

After the Semantic War — the very last one — a clean sweep can be made, all outgrown misunderstandings which led towards it will disappear like the proverbial snow under the sun. All words and concepts which became dead letters will regain their original meaning and a beginning can be made of the great reshuffle of priorities and capacities. The right people in the right places will meet at the right moments. The perfect organizational form will be rediscovered: spontaneous improvisation which appeals to the potentialities of each and everybody. Rediscovered will be the perfect master, our own individuality accompanying us without questions or answers, the true and only knowledge we can have of ourselves and others, the world and cosmos. So much illusoriness and the unreal in what we consider or perceive as real, so much reality in what we consider to be unreal and irrational. The unexpected will be a criterion beyond: models of thought or belief not to be fitted into any *expert* system. The new model beckons, both reconstructive and deconstructive, revealing life itself as to be constantly rediscovered. Restlessly and excitingly riding our hobby horses, feasting on the Utopian dimension, with new heroics and an unbridled faith in changes which will be necessary as well as painful, destructive but liberating. Adversaries become supporters, each and every person being a mirror of the Whole, knowing all without having to bother about knowing the way it will all go.

"*Every throat its own prophet.*" The mentality is definitely changed, irreversibly; such is clear and no regression is possible. When did it start to signify, who of our contemporaries acted on that premise, at the same time, the first time? Who are the others, and when did you discover there *are* others?

Once upon a moment your first discoveries coincided with what others discovered or reinvented: an experimental, empirical period in which you always felt at home, even surrounded by the cannibals of the twentieth century, reincarnated personages of Bosch or Brueghel, sometimes a medievalist, a renaissance man, an outsider, a marginal survivor: the ever-present supernumeraries in life always surrounding the self, with *Aha-Erlebnisse* to accomplish the *Eureka!* — effects to achieve the desired results.

The simultaneous encounters, the aware state of recognition: everywhere the authentic, the original, mutual off-shore tiding in expectation. *Serendipity.*

A century of world wars and world peace, fought on battlefields, in beds, and everywhere else. The beginning for the one, an end for the other. Turning points on which you learn to play with fire, dancing on the volcano, amidst bifurcations and ramifications, tingles and twinkles, in whatever light. The earth dragon in the year of the earth snake exercising western spiritual recreation. The Nth wave of the avant-garde arrives with shaman and mystagogues, self-kickers and other freaks from one generation unto the other — sometimes underground; sometimes coming, not through decennia but through other cycles and connections.

It is no longer necessary to define or trace how human beings meet, within rooms and theatres, soccer matches, market squares, mass-meetings, or freedom parties. Is this an insight in its own right, paired with the ideas of others? Is there another truth for the déjà-vu in their lives, jeopardising plans other than those for mutual benefit? Is there a period of surrender, suffering, sacrificing, servitude, solitude, alienation? Is there anxiety to be vanquished, and fear and guilt and shame? Is there a past to let go?

Lâchez tout! so the dada movers advised their contemporaries in the twenties, "Let everything go!"

When all doomthinkers and penitential preachers, demagogues and cynical wise guys have disappeared offstage, when all fundamentalists with their immovable images of the enemy have been sent into the jungle of oblivion, when the most unconcerned have won their battle of the self, we will be able to begin, one after the other. A new century, a new sound, land in sight, let yourself be looked at! Someone is waiting for you.

A morning raga heard after awakening: a Laterna Magica ruling beauty, preserving her. As usual, the sun rises, we are waiting. Everyone is waiting. Some patient, some impatient. Many have given up, resisted waiting. They got off, stepped out, went away; fell out of our sight. We are waiting for the light of life. We have not been born as world citizens yet, but the world is in the family way, the waters could break any moment. There are cracks in the cosmic egg. We are tasting the changes, nourishing and feeding on reality. How do these changes translate and figure individually and globally? Everybody's silence its own sound. How much gibberish and jabbering to abandon, how much jargon to banish, how much common and careless use of language to show up. A careful reconnoitring of the minefields of communication.
"*Whosoever breaks his own way in the world / Will one time hear a song of his own,*" wrote the Dutch poet, A. Roland Holst.

So much to be tasted even in the prospects, a constant and absolute beginning; in everything you see nothing but the beginning to be perceived, sometimes "the beginning of the ending". Everything "is in the beginning". *Bereshit* — big bang crossing your life, the razor's edge showing itself, crossfire. Human energy in the morphogenetic field, crystal clear and ready for the new structures and mutations. Original light, prime mover of all ruptures, perpendicular unto all separation lines, a vacuum filling itself with all the energies which can be brought to battle. It remains an eternal fight, in and for your self; whoever doubts this in the depths of his mind does not really know he's alive. In the centre of the cyclone the most subtle silence reigns supreme. United in silence, the lonely dancer, the great taciturn, tear jerker and burster of laughter, united hedonist and cynic, the narcissist and consumer, the systems analyst and the homeless:

when the fat is in the fire of the roaring volcano. Well disposed insanity, a rainbow of falling stars. Everything is always here and really nowhere else; the things which are your concern, the things you do and the words you utter. It is always possible to concentrate on the knowledge of this moment, to become more than your known self within its self-created limitations and pitfalls, to master the immeasurable experience of freedom. The unbelievable feeling: all you do with good intentions becomes good by itself. We toast the new light, wine sparkles in our glasses. What about revelations if you don't cherish the wish to give the unknown within you a chance to be born? As if the script can be written before all the players are conscious of the role they have to fulfil, the moment the curtain is torn away for the unveiling of our planetary meaning as a human family.

We live among the metaphors of a high season, with its exorcisms and banishments, its conjurations and invocations, its massive rituals, convulsions and labour pains, the delusions of the most stupid natures and ecstasies prompted by the purest source pervading our living days. Creative happiness, the creative existence is not reserved for the few, the élite. Every human being can be united within the community, the entire micro/macro-cosmos, with roots and bonds. Life changes when you start feeling confident about your own powers, when your confidence increases with every authentic human being you encounter, finding yourself on the same path, even when you go your own way. Life changes when you intuit at appropriate and inappropriate moments. The laws of synchronicity do not exist for themselves, and don't exist for nothing. Going through fire and water, and knowing it feels good to relish that shining principle which purifies each sphere of its iniquities, with its voiced and enfranchised mission to be light in the darkness.

Ah, the good old days when we did realise nothing, when everything looked so comfortably deceptive, the worlds of two giants, teeth bared, confronting each other. "The war is over if you want it." So good to be within an empty space, a soap bubble full of rainbows, in which everything is possible again. At all events, the world is in motion, in revolt against the powerlessness of immobility, sometimes with the courage of despair, but always driven by the fiery will-to-good, able to clear away all obstacles. These words are simple basic banalities, notes from Paradise, a record on the state of things to be; laughter not unlearned — and that is the great relief.

News From The Hourglass

1. In the rush of the wind
scratching the rocks…
current cannabis prizes:
Afghani, three grams for 25 guilders,
Citral, two grams, fifteen guilders,
Grass from the Congo and Columbia
in ten-guilder bags;
Ask for Whisper the Dealer,
ask for the Poets the Priests the Pushers the Preachers
the Printers the Precursors the Professors the Prostraters
The Providers.

Printed Matter Special Soaked Rates:
See Surprising Amsterdam
On Five, Ten Joints, or a Trip A Day!
— Go say '*Hello!*' to Jan, Adriaan, Harm's Son,
Vincent, Piet and Karel!*
— Say '*Hi*' to your caged friends in ARTIS, our Zoo,
wander through tropics, botanics, hiccups and handicaps,
boycots and foxtrots, bebop rebirth baby birthing:
Punky Junky Skunky HunkyDory Potverdorie!
—While the wind howls: sur - vi - val - re - vi - val -
re - sur - gence - re - en - try - re - co - ve - ry-
— All wounds never heal / all thieves never steal /
all alive never all-alive, but Poets…

Poets, and Poets, Survive:
a special order commitment request,
sweetest of your words, please survive:
'Waken or Die!'
Greatest of our moments, turn on, turn in,
turn over, turn somebody outside-in-and-out,
listening to the wind
all hands on deck —
the game's but just started, we're in it,
forever within, body, speech, mind.
Welcome, voices, all aboard,
I hope you just scored.

2. 'QUOTE
Utopian speculations must come back into fashion.
They are a way of affirming faith in the possibility
of solving problems that seem at the moment insoluble.
Today even the survival of humanity is a utopian hope.
UNQUOTE' Norman Brown: *Life Against Death.*
Utopian speculations. Utopian hope.
Utopian despair. Utopian nihilism.
Utopian totalitarianism. Utopian democracy.
Utopian socialism. Utopian marxism.
Utopian anarchy. Utopian dream.
Friends, I am in a dream
I seem to see you in my dream
I seem to hear you in my dream
Please let me be in your wildest dream.
I'm sure we all have met
and not a word has yet been said —
there's less and less you ever can get
'cause all there is to do now
is to all let it all in
and peacefully gratefully
let it all out,
from inside-in, even deeper within
where you'll twist and shout
and jump for joy,
for you've just found out, again, once again,
there's nothing it *isn't* about,
again.
Light shines within, Light shines without,
the darkest blackout you couldn't live without,
and you can't even live within:
the Light.
You're at the top of the spot you're in,
heavens hells abysses crossed & recrossed,
look at the spiral you're in,
don't forget the spin — six or sixteen.

A quarter to seven now
raindrops on the window
sunshine through the clouds
Hi Andes sweet
blessed smoke
suddenly striking
setting sun.

Thanks for my life
and thanks for the living
inside this golden dream
knitting weaving the One World Poem.
Mystic breathings. Inner reminiscing. Chuckles. Cackles.
Rantings. Pantings. Shiverings. Whisperings.
Pains. Tears. Laughter.

3. Heavenly Drums. Body Poetry.
The word is Orgasm, you can live it,
it can hold you, grasp you, fuck you,
meet you, smile at you, grab you,
it can turn you through
all the propositions in with on and over,
Orientation direction Orient Sun.
Child! You know all. Just repeat it. Recreate it.
Make it new.
So are you.
You've never been here before in *this* life!
Time to find out 'what it is all about'.
And it is not 'about'. It is It:
it can only be lived, and expressed.
The rest is silence,
knowing, daring, willing-surrendering:
where two meet, three have a secret,
four can turn you into one,
and the flame winks when the quint jumps in
to lives with so much rain
but sun o sun so much you shine.
It's the only secret we all know about,
the sun within and the sun without,
next of our kin,
sharing space time prisons we're in
and I'm thinking of David (Solomon)
and I'm thinking of Olaf (Stoop)
and I'm thinking of Breyten, and Ken.

4. Poets, Freedom Now! Then: What?

> *'I don't want to change the marijuana law*
> *i want to keep breaking it*
> *i want to break the law*
> *to shatter it on the rocks*
> *to see the shattering of the pieces*
> *maya the dissolution of illusion*

i want to break the law
i want our freedom'
(Julian Beck: *Ninth Song of the Revolution*)
What poetry in poverty? You're rich, all you people so rich,
says the poet, kissed by the Muse, who can know it,
for they blow it, and they show it:
so much so rich so much to see so much to hear
so much to feel so much to desire
so much to do and
so much to do and
not so much that you can do
" " " *that* " " "
" " " " *you* " "
" " " " " *can* "
" " " " " " *do.*
But do what you do do
and don't do what you won't do:
rest with the MOB-rule
the Mind yr Own Business-rule.

5. All of you too
inside this written thing
this trail this line this track
O Journey Within —
Million Times Chanted Respected Loved
and Frightening Presence Within
Where the i meets the dot on its eye,
aye aye,
sighing hereby
in the seed of the eye-sight.
Singing a song
a whisper a wave a gesture a shout
the winds the clouds the water
the fire the metal the wood
and all of it
dis-ap-pear-ing
within
where silence wins
and words no more abound
nothing to say
and you can hear it!

6. Nothing to hear until you hear it,
when it jumps at you, grasps you, clasps you, gets you,
strikes you. Frightens, freezes and fires you:
the Spirit within. The wandering spirits within.
The ones who are connected, the disconnected, rejected,
grinning, whining, waiting, wheeler-dealers
midnight tokers midnight jokers.
The oriented ones, the disoriented, the superfluous,
irrelevant, and who is to judge, who is to say,
what's anyone got to say, one day, today?

Take it or leave it
alone, let it go, open all:
you're *transparent.*
Looking for no-things, *das Unbedingte*,
finding *nur die Dinge*: just things.
Never things undone. Not even
verities contrarities pleonastics superideological
illogical multivalued realities,
captured and arrested,
dynamic-yet-static
meaningful sounds
form'd into words
for the world of words you're in,
and the word of worlds within.
The miracle of Poetry:
'We are all healers'.
Yes, it heals.

* Steen, Van Ostade, Rembrandt, Van Gogh, Mondrian and Appel.

Job Description

What do you do?
I'm a poet.
Yes. But what do you do?

I'm a poet / And I know it!
Bob Dylan

Je *est une autre*
Arthur Rimbaud

I'm a poet
Experimental poet
Occasional poet
Let's have a look at you poet
You have to be seen poet
Wordwonder poet
Marginal poet   Workshop poet
Mystical poet
Occult poet   Esoteric poet
Future flashback poet
Metaphysical poet   Romantic poet
Love poet

Poet of first and last words
Poet of the big goodbye
Poet of living breath
Outing for schoolkids
Discussion partner
For junkies and prisoners

Parkpoet   Festivalpoet   Theatrepoet
Brokendreampoet
Pageantpoet
Streetcornerpoet
Message-in-a-bottle-poet
Dreamdancepoet
Jazzpoet
Daytimepoet   Nightimepoet
Leisure time poet
Working time poet
Now is the time poet
Poet to know it to show it

In the tracks of Adam poet
Giving names poet
Kindling passing poet
Dedicated poet
Driven poet
Ecstatic poet
Eccentric poet
Excessive poet

Crossing borders poet
Always on the road poet
Roundabout poet
Red light poet
Poet on foot
Bicycle train car plane
Poet in bed
Time and space

Just enough of it poet
Listening now poet
Look around poet
People show poet
One world or none poet
Obsessive poet
Passing poet
Pensée sauvage poet
Pedestrian poet
Be silent poet

People all over poet
MindMirrorPaintBoxPoet
Superconductor poet
Companion poet

Nothing lost poet
A lifetime participant poet
Approaching poet
Disappearing poet
Rainbow poet
Having said it all poet
Happy poet!

COMMISSIONED POEM

WRITTEN AT THE BEACH
AND LOOKING AT THE DINKEY TOYS
BENEATH
FROM THE BALCONY OF ROOM 1314
ON THE THIRTEENTH FLOOR
OF THE BLUE WATER HOTEL, DURBAN
MAY 10/11, 2000

"JE VOUS SALUE, VIEIL OCÉAN!"
Isidore Ducasse, Comte de Lautréamont,
Les Chants de Maldoror

I SALUTE YOU, AGELESS OCEAN,
BEATING OUR SHORES AND OUR EARDRUMS,
ILLUMINATED LISTENER FOR HUNDREDS OF
MILLIONS THOUSAND YEARS,
POPULATED WITH THOUGHTS INNUMERABLE
NEVER UTTERED
CRYSTALINE FLORA AND FAUNA, FLOWERS, FISHES,
SHARKS, DOLPHINS & WHALES
BEHOLDER OF TREASURES UNKNOWN TO MAN
DEPTHS UNFATHOMABLE
TECTONIC VOLCANO AND QUAKE
DEVOURER OF STORMSTRUCK WRECKAGES
PASSAGEWAY FOR REFUGEES AND DISCOVERERS
NEEDING NO NAVIGATOR BUT THE SUN, THE MOON
INCESSANT EBBS AND FLOODS — AND THE PLANETS
WHO ARE YOU TO BE COMPARED WITH,
NEPTUNIAN SURVIVOR OF BIRTH, LIFE & DEATH?
NOURISHER OF MULTITUDES,
SECRET OF SECRETS
ACCOMPLICE OF PIRATES, SMUGGLERS & MERCHANTS
HIDEAWAY FOR U-BOATS, MINES & TORPEDOES,
RUBBISH RADIO-ACTIVE & PETRO-CHEMICAL,

-2-

WHO ARE YOU, COMPANION ELEMENT?

A BRIEF ENCOUNTER IN THE SURF
TAKING MY NAKED BREATH AWAY –
"YOU DAREDEVIL YOU!"
EDITH SAYS AT MY RETURN
FROM A SHORT RENDEZ-VOUS
WITH MYSTERY ALONG THE SHORELINE
OF DURBANS GOLDEN MILE.

HOW FAR DO YOU GO
MULTIDIMENSIONAL BLUE WATERS,
HOW NEAR TO MY HEARTBEAT
HOW FOREVER
FOREVER
FOREVER
FOREVER
FOREVER

I SALUTE YOU,
AND HONOUR YOU,
FATHER & MOTHER
TO US ALL!

Simon Vinkenoog

John Brandi

Ayahuasca

Somewhere I remember reading an author who said that human lives are composed like music, and dreaming provides the score. As a child I sensed little separation between life and dream; as a teenager I experienced a gnawing sense that life was to be lived in compartments, measured in gains, losses, or solid achievements easily plotted on a graph. By the time I got to college, though, the boat began to rock.

Poets, anthropologists, filmmakers and jazz musicians became my guides, rekindling an awareness that life flowed as a stream between dream and waking. "Turbulence can be beautiful," one professor told me, "like the tumble of water over river rock." He had just returned from the Arctic, where, with the Inuit hunters, he experienced life lived according to the freeze and break-up. He spoke of the time-altering latitudes of endless winter and eternal summer, the magic of the hunt, and of shamans "ladder-climbing between this world and the other." He explained how one gained a renewed perspective in the hazy boundaries between dream and waking, an idea that was hardly comprehensible to me, a young man turning twenty, still living with his parents.

Two years later, I was out of college, working as a Peace Corps Volunteer in Ecuador, living under the slopes of Mount Chimborazo among landless Andean serfs who were demanding land and water rights. After a year of exhausting but successful community organizing in the highlands, I needed a break and was given a transfer to the Upper Amazon, where I gradually found myself wandering further into the jungle — on truck, donkey, and dugout canoe — finally settling among the Jívaro (Shuar) people. There, without expecting it, I had my first experience with psychotropic plants, ingesting what the Jívaros called *natema* (also known as *yagé*, or *ayahuasca*, the Inca name), a tea prepared by shamans for ritual use in communal healing, trance induction, and "time flight." *Natema* is concocted by gathering segments of the *banisteriopsis* vine — whose powerful hallucinogenic alkaloids have chemical structures and effects similar to LSD — and boiling them with leaves of a similar plant, called *yahi*.

It was the sixties and I was an adventurous twenty-three year-old, but had never taken LSD. Only once had I tried Marijuana, to the blaring of a raucous cumbia band in a bordello on the Ecuadorian coast. The invitation to take *natema* came as a complete surprise. While living in a half-abandoned schoolhouse near a scattering of longhouses along the Río Zamora, I had become friends with Taisha, a young shaman in his forties, who seemed old to me then. One morning he approached me at the river and popped the question. He asked if I would like to "dream" with a small circle of Jívaro people. With plenty of hidden excitement and a fair amount of apprehension, I agreed. Taisha told me to fast and remain in solitude for the day. At twilight I was to come to his hut, where others would be gathered after having done the same.

A faded drawing and a few scribbles in a musty spiral notebook are my only records of the experience. It has been over three decades now, but I distinctly smell the webbed green of the jungle, taste the thick fermented chicha sipped from a halved-gourd bowl, feel the thick lavender air, see the half dozen or so men and women gathered in Taisha's hut around the "patient," a nearly naked man suffering chest and leg spasms, standing with his arms to the ceiling poles, having the "poison" drawn from his sinewy limbs by two female attendants. Between rain pattering the thatch, I can hear peripheral movements of two silhouetted figures tending coals on the dirt floor at either end of the longhouse — coals that aren't allowed to ignite because a flickering flame would interrupt the trance flight of the ayahuasca participants. One of those fire tenders I remember well. I can see her face up-close, the almond eyes inches from mine, the smoky hair brushed away from my cheeks, her humid body in soiled cotton dress cuddled close to me — one of those memorable occasions when I stayed overnight in the longhouse at Taisha's request.

When I was told to fast and remain in solitude before ingesting *natema*, I was also asked to think about who I would like to visit. I thought of my mother. On the night of the ceremony, though, I witnessed only bursting super novae that disappeared in gaseous abstractions which quickly metamorphosed into phosphorescing undersea life, then into undulating, ultra-violet serpents. "Seeing music, hearing shapes," I scribbled into my notes the next day. The insides of my head were flooded with psychedelic relief maps: geographical contours not unlike those we now manipulate into multi-dimensional technicolor maps on computers. These contours, often with spindly hairs, appeared and dissolved like snowflakes, moulds, virus, reef anemones. Occasionally they reassembled onto an almost-recognizable bearded prophet undergoing transfiguration in a cloud of light — as in a particular catechism illustration that fascinated me as a child.

Like a powerful scanning electron microscope, my whole body was an eye. It saw into waving stems of chlorophyll, diaphanous floating chromosomes, exploding seed heads, earthscapes thousands of millions of years old — infra-red in quality, as if photographed from a supersonic spy plane. Some of these shapes recalled the whimsical contour maps I squiggled as a boy inventing fantasy continents filled with every possible topography imaginable: fifty-thousand-foot peaks rising above deep ocean fjords; desert hoodoos teetering in heat waves; magma bubbling into picture-puzzle labyrinths; fiery-lipped volcanoes exploding from jungles — exactly like Sangay, whose perfect cone rose from the *selva* just north of the Río Zamora.

My world was forever altered. Years later, Michael McClure would hand me a huge poster of one of his poems: "Non physics of Nothingness turned inside out like a protein presence arising from presence." Yes! I had been inside that poem. Better said, it had written itself inside me — with delicately marbled threads of filament brushed from the eyelashes of alchemy Herself.

Ayahuasca was, in a sense, a sublime return to the timeless reverie of childhood when I floated high on life's current. As a boy, pencil in hand, newsprint on table, a solitary sun shaft illuminating my room, I was thoroughly immersed in that euphoric state where dreams and reality converge. To put the pencil to the paper — to create a line, to watch it grow — was to be swept away, to fly, to experience time without its usual frame. All cares hushed, no intellect in the way, I was the master cartographer whose language was a ceremonial thread extending out of the body, procreating as it went, unravelling into a sonorous filament that birthed sudden seismographic shapes connecting me with worlds totally unseen by grown-ups.

The morning after taking *natema*, Taisha asked, "did you see your mother?" Indeed, I had — but not in the sense I had expected. *Natema* had transported me from the ultra-personal realm of "family" into a greater cosmology. "Mother" embraced me in the form of loving creation — birthing, dying, recombining inside my flesh. She was tenseless energy. Space and time interconnected. Warp and weft of liquid sound. DNA music breathing out from an almost-touchable Medusa whose serpentine hair radiated into threads that looped and intertwined into what I would later compare to the most intricate Navajo weaving, or to the planet's most magically-charged cloth: the double-ikat *geringsing* woven only in Bali.

My "flight" after drinking *natema* revealed to me, a young man of twenty-three, that life had absolutely no straight-line structure of measurable gains, losses or achievements. Instead, it opened like an enormous corolla, which in turn opened with myriad variables, all circular, rising, collapsing, breathing in and out. I was under the sea, within the head of a sunflower, inside the gaseous birth of a star, on a timeless raft through the body's microcosm — all at once. Stellar, ethereal, magmatic entities were inseparable. Life was "round," its essence divine. After years of "taking" communion, I had finally "received" Communion.

Later I learned that *natema* was never to be ingested during the day. "It is for dreaming," Taisha said, "to get above the clouds." If the tea was ingested in the light of the sun one would experience "a cinema," nothing but distraction, and become sick. True flight happened when the longhouse fires were snuffed and *natema* took effect with the shaman there to guide. An important teaching of *natema* was that dreaming was to be counted among the deepest needs of humans. Places on earth, to which we are bound or from which we spring, assume their true significance in dreams. Serendipitous occurrences within the inner-outer geography of our existence are there to transport us into a greater dimension of beauty, love, recognition, and understanding. The artist reports on these occurrences, transforms earthly travels, and brings dream reality into sound, poetry, paint, dance, sculpted cadences of light and dark — and thereby reminds listeners, readers and viewers of a dimension of their lives lost in shadow, waiting.

Thirty-three years after that evening with Taisha, images seen while dreaming continue to reappear in reality: during the ecstasy of lovemaking; at the moment of birth; in pitchpoints of psychic transport; in red depths of pain; in coral canyons weightless under the Java Sea; beneath Chomolungma's musical snowbanner prisming to chanting Himalayan monks; in Oaxacan Sierra, driving up from Tehuantepec through misting rainbows; in the star beings and spiral petroglyphs at Tuzigoot and Zuni; in Kashi, wandering cobbled nerve endings to Ma Ganga pyres pinwheeling the dead into a reconfigured zodiac; in Rajasthan, lost in the bee-swarm of mirrored ladies pouring from painted doorways; at Hopi, watching kachinas descend sky ladders singing songs from the other world; in Tenganan, with trance dancers and fire walkers lifting out of their bodies to the vibratory sound-geography of gongs and metallophones; in the frenzy of kaleidoscoping hues, market day; Chichicastenango, Bac Ha, Xishuangbanna, Kaxgar, Cuetzalan, Djenné, Cuzco. — There, there!

Ayahuasca realigns the psychic spine; opens the body to the Divine; reconnects our nerve endings to the earth; encourages joy, courage, spiritual and social balance, prosperity not in things but in mutual understanding — all sadly lacking in our techno-heavy era. To get lost is to learn to listen, to become vulnerable, to find a new way home, as during the *natema* ceremony. To become pedestrian (i.e. "going on foot", "becoming humble") is to travel light, cancel expectations, detonate the boundaries, set fire to plans, become small enough to fit through the keyhole we usually kneel before as a voyeur. The road is open, full of enough drop offs, chance encounters, sudden updrafts, mismatched circuitry, and dream clairvoyance to dislodge even the most hardened.

I have heard that a real journey "informs one's life." More accurately stated it might be that a real journey "reforms one's life." For a true pilgrimage alters the shape of the cup we drink from, cleanses and refocuses the eye, gives a healthy twist to our world view, delivers us from the realm of reaction to that of consideration. Like the effects of psychotropic plants, the journey opens doors long closed. It wakes us from sleep with the heat of our own mythology still intact. It says: the holy land is right here, not across the steppes, in a book, over the sea.

Once, after a ceremony on the Hopi mesas of northern Arizona, I wrote: "Today I was in a place where my eyes opened wide, as if seeing the world for the first time. That is what Hopi allows us. The essence of transport. The remarkable discovery that we are but a mirror within a mirror, a song of multiplicity in which the gods exchange places with humans. And humans, like them, do a dance where the body steps into the beyond to join a greater body — a body waiting to be filled, there inside us." I could have been writing about an Ayahuasca experience.

Theodore Roethke dreamed of "a culture where it is a crime to be dull." As a poet, I am a companion to everyday miracles. My job is to be curious. I write to stay alive, to see where I've been, to give clearing for the next step. My waking hours are devoted to being vulnerable among unexplainables. I am here to squeeze between the teeth of the canyon and summon the blossoms of grace, to have a look through the clouds at the original self in whom geography begins, takes wing, charms the walker.

When feet engage, mind disappears. Road loops out from the eye as a painted scroll into a horizon of magic teletype spelling out metaphors for a world beyond. So, climb! The starry heavens are beneath our feet; the Milky Way a braided rope dangling from cosmic undertow. Another world beckons, of which ours is but a mirrored replica. Surrender! Revolt if necessary! Set the i free. Ride the wind horse whose hooves break the sound of speed. Like rishis of old, or shamans of naked space who ride shining rays from the smoke hole, you will find yourself singing:

I have broken through...
I have seen gifts that no horse can carry
I have risen to the full moon...
Look, my body is all eyes...
I can see in every direction!
Still higher, still higher...
Blue sky shows itself!

I Reconstruct Her as I Touch
I Disappear as She Alights

Over the years she's appeared as Parvati, Guadalupe,
Our Lady of Sorrows, Saraswati and the Virgin of the Swan.
She's fallen asleep on my shoulder on the bus out of Riobamba.
And curled up on the concrete waiting for the Night Express
in Allahabad. She stood in the heat with a cold plate
of Jasmine, making wreaths at Pashupatinath.
That was her at the rusty spigot with a plate of tangerines.
She had gold fillings, she had missing fingers.
She had a bouquet of thunderbolts between her knees.
She was carved from pure alabaster, breasts and womb
darkened by the touch of countless mendicants
in the back alleys of Rishikesh. She rode a tiger, stood
on a half moon, rose from a conch. Her crown was spiked
with narcissus. Her lacquered arms spread from royal blue
sewn with kernels of wheat. Her music was fragrant,
her pendulum warm, her face darkened
by centuries of afternoon sun. She swam in incense,
pondered the catacombs. At the River Krishna she held
an aluminium begging bowl between her eleven toes.
I saw her in Cuzco struggling under a sack of charcoal,
the child orphan in broken flipflops.
She was at the Met wearing glass heels, shouldering
a pet monkey, making eyes at Modigliani.
She was Padmi sorting cockles on the beach at Mahabalipuram.
That was her in moonlight on the Zócolo after the earthquake
holding a tiny pair of shoes. At Jemenez she wore a necklace
of butterflies. She peddled tickets for the Monkey Chant
from her bicycle in Ubud. She hopped from a Vespa
in fluorescent veils late for a wedding in downtown Quito.
She was Kuan Yin at the modelling agency,
the beekeeper's daughter off the road in the weeds near Zion.
She sat up all night, the angel in white
at the children's psychiatric ward. She won 1st Place
at the Fancy Dance in Rough Rock. I saw her sift corn pollen
into the gold winter light of San Ildefonso. She had eyes for me
in Aleknagik, sat in the shadows after serving me
in Quetzaltenango, slept holding a flying fish on the curb
at Puerto Angel. I saw her, the diva with black pearls,
Queen of Voodoo on Telegraph Avenue, the Apsara
in her spirit house beckoning monsoon clouds

from the South China Sea. She sold pomegranates
from an upside down umbrella in Mandalay.
Poured cement in Bombay for the New Taj Hotel
at less than 20 cents a day, poured warm milk
from a bucket in the fog of San Christobal,
worked her way through the Monkey Forest
doing full body prostrations up the steps toward
Buddha's third eye. She placed a grain of rice on her spoon
and bowed to the ten-thousand gods of the Pure Land.
She topped frosties at the Crème Queen, knelt on a broken
pew in old town, sat in a garden of fireflies and began a litany
to the Sacred Heart. She is everywhere, and here again tonight.
I see her lift a pen, shift in her seat, hammer a walkway,
scatter a path, send an embrace out of reach.
Her outline is a thirsty ravine. She shapes a burning letter
over my head. She is time slipped from shadow, chorus
inside a singer. Genesis heralding creator, finish line inside
the runner. Her mane shakes in the eye of the storm.
Her memory opens the phantom gate.
Her words wake the resin in a forgotten tree.
She is carnelian, she is fauve.
She is heliodor, she is jade. Her continent begs
with heated cairns. Her harbor hides the smuggler's ark.
Her violin plays a nuptial feast. She is the wife of no man,
servant of no self. She is a thousand questions
inside the answer, voice singing through Byzantine rain,
name disappearing in the gallop of a dream.
She is a luminous presence — that of someone who's seen
this world before. And come again
to give it greater meaning.

I reconstruct her as I touch, disappear as she alights.

An island of rhythm spreads over me.
She motions me to her doorway, folds the world
into a paper wing.

Night Express, Krung Thep — Krabi, Thailand.

Lyric Written With Both Hands

Yes to alchemy
transforming names back into trees;
No to concrete eating green

Yes to imagination's endless abyss
ever luminous and creating;
No to fake masters of ceremony
misdirecting life's play

Yes to deadwood piled around fields fair,
to water refilling aquifers;
No to faith without room for doubt

Yes to the galaxy unweighted by greed;
No to minds with rusty rakes
fouling the planet, pest-spraying the wide awake

Yes to Adam created from eve
recognizing himself in every she;
No to rage falsified into smiles,
to money culture that bribes the child

Yes to mystery that raises the wave;
No to dictators stopping spring

Yes to the uncapitalized i inside the Eye
that bigly sees the power of small;
No to sawmill smoke from cut-down dreams,
to timber strewn over muddy lakes

Yes to the prayer primordially there
all the time in the breath

Yes to the yes that brings us to sea
Yes to this moment, our selves
        one Self, the body free.

In Another Distance

Let us meet
under a stairway, nothing sworn
no sealed eclipse, no passport nor feathered hat
no caboose derailed, no recent manuscript in hand

Let us meet
without insistence or esteem, no wound, no chain
no slogan nor struggling sunrise

Let us meet
in a ruined cathedral, swim the new stream
that cuts through its nave, makes paper boats of syllables
empty pockets of sighs and shipwrecks

Let us meet
in the transparent waist of an hourglass
drink ourselves into circles, no amulets or carnation
no leaking prow, no banging door or wet handkerchief

Let us meet
and exchange tokens, ride free
throw our clothes to the floor, give no order
contemplate no answer, converse with bees and cardinals
ripen into sweet stalks of wheat, an unschooled waltz

Yes, let us meet
become thunder, mingle with absent ones
petrify into a waterfall, shatter the mirror
with our wooden masks, remove the costume of flesh
take on new names, possess no shadow
tender and inseparable

Let us meet
and survive forever in another distance.

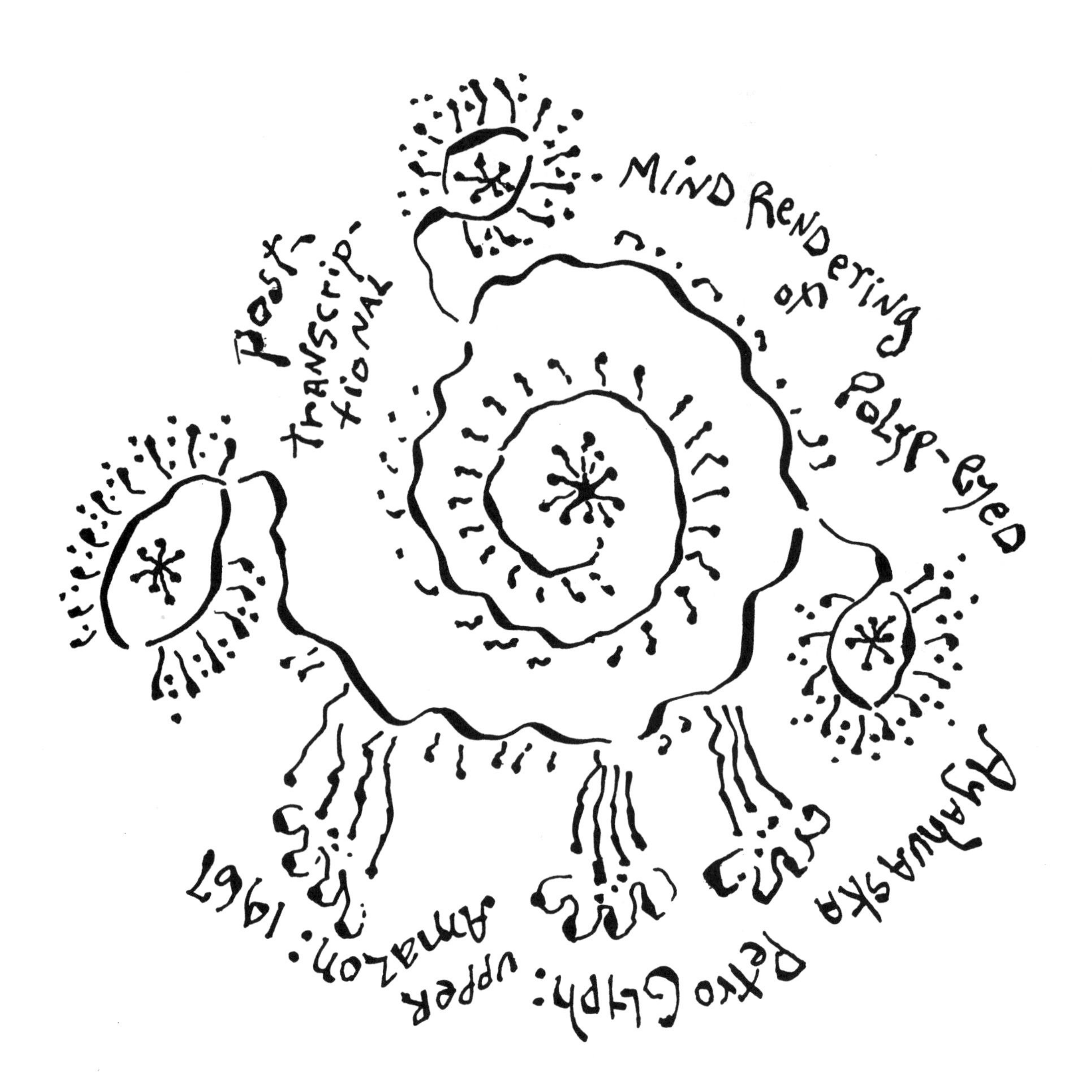

MIND RENDERING ON POLYP-EYED
POST-TRANSCRIPTIONAL
AYAHUASKA PETROGLYPH: UPPER AMAZON: 1967

14 OCT: ie: 2532
Walking is our Home; the Journey our Matrimony
She: whose smooth Branches are ParaDise where the Butterfly Hides... She: whose Right (rite) forms the Left of Me...
She: whose Lips Speak the Question to My Answer.... Whose taste gives Back My Own.
Alma
It's the Song of this tree that begins Me...
It's the Heat of the Leaves that fires the Breeze

Prajapati Peaks
Oblations of Psychic Dew
Seance Valley
Pole Star
Respiratory Bliss from the Mouth of the Hidden Goddess
Down Deep + Presto Erotico
House of Spontaneous Body Heat
Shadow Connections
Territory of the Forgotten Reached only by Hallucination
Walking Eye of Delight
Only in Reverse (AH) (UM)
Spiral of Indispensable
Molto Loco
Warrior Realm of Perfected Breath Control
Blank Area Between the Living and Dead
Heart Rollen
Womb Realm i.e. Cosmos
Akashik or Shining Mtns
Ethereal Realm
Over Madness Pass into Downward Dascent into the Under Mundo
Where the Hunted Are Reborn as Stars
Molto Allegro
Entrance

Lawrence Ferlinghetti

Hidden Door

Hidden door dead secret
    which is Mother
Hidden door dead secret
    which is Father
Hidden door dead secret
    of our buried life
Hidden door behind which man carries
    his footprints along the streets
Hidden door of clay hands knocking
Hidden door without handles
    whose life is made of knocks
    by hand and foot
    Poor hand poor foot poor life!
Hidden door with hair for hinges
Hidden door with lips for latches
Hidden door with skeletons for keys
Hidden door autobiography of humanity
Hidden door dictionary of the universe
Hidden door palimpsest of myself
Hidden door I'm made of
    with my sticks of limbs
Hidden door pathetic fallacy
    of the evidence of the senses
    as to the nature of reality
Hidden door in blind eyes of termites
    that knock knock
Hidden door blind man with tin cup
    on a stone corner deaf and dumb
Hidden door train-whistle lost
    in book of night
Hidden door on night's wheels I blundering follow
    like a rhinoceros drinking through cities
Hidden door of carrier-pigeons' wings
    which have half-forgotten
    their destination
Hidden door plane's wing that skids in space
    casting stone shadow
    on sundial earth

Hidden door flying boxcar of history
Hidden door of Christ's suicide
Hidden door of Sunday without church
Hidden door of animal faces animal laughter animal dreams
and hidden door Cro-Magnon Man
among machines
and hidden door of his still uncollected
Collective Unconscious
Hidden door on classroom blackboards
all over Europe
Hidden door dark forest of America
knock knock in North Dakota
Hidden door that wings over America
and slants over San Francisco
and slams into the Pacific
drifting eternally southward
to Tierra del Fuego
with a knock knock undersea
at lost door of Lota coal mines
Hidden door surfboard to lost shore of light
and hidden door floated up on tides
like a shipwrecked coffinlid
bearing blind mouths blind breasts blind thought
through the centuries
Hidden door sea-angel cast-up Albatross
spouting seasperm of love in thirty languages
and the love-ship of life
sunk by the poison-squid of hate
Hidden door double-winged sticky-bird plumed serpent
stuck to moon afire forever drunk in time
flapping loose in eternity
Hidden door of the future mystic life
among Magellan's nebulae
and hidden door of my mislaid
visionary self
Hidden door San Luis rope-bridge which is man
hung between nature and spirit
Hidden door of the spirit seen as a fleshy thing
and hidden door of eyes and vulvas
that still open only with a key
of cartilage and flesh
and hidden door frozen Inca mummy
Prince of the Plomo
fucked to death in sun-god sacrifice

Hidden door tin cup of blind brother mutes
      crouched on a Cuzco corner
      blowing bamboo flutes
      at coca midnight
Hidden door of the Andes at ten thousand feet
      in a ragged mist of ruins and red horizons
      with a seacoast hung below
      still lost among conquistadors
      horses dogs and incomprehensible laws
Hidden door wild river of the Urubamba
      upon which still floats somewhere
      the lost herb that separates soul from body
      and hidden door which is itself that herb
      and hidden door which is that separation
      and hidden door of mirrors
      on the waters of this river
      in which I cannot see beyond myself
      because my body’s in the way
Hidden door at last I see through
      beyond dear body bag of bones
      which I leave naked on a rock
Hidden door I wigless climb to
      beyond that river
Hidden door at last I fall through
      in the lost end of day
It is dusk
by the time we get to
Machu Picchu
Some Indians go by dancing
playing their flutes
and beating drums

Peru-Chile, January-February 1960

Through the Looking Glass

I. Imagining LSD

Deep blue haze
Elektra wings thru
Illimitable
White bird in it
far off
skimming
or a white plane skating
way down there
small shadow of it
sweeping
the shrunk landscape
disappeared now
into the great brown ground
as if fallen
while its plane still flies on
miraculously!
And Sunday Chicago appears
at end of Autumn carpet
stuck to great flat blue cloud
of Lake Michigan
stretched out
Rich resorts & Lakeshore fronts
beaches lapped forever
pavilions asleep in time
Hum of Elektra winging down
wigging down
Seatbelts on
flaps down
swinging around
for re-entry
into that world
Engine drones
like a tamboura
Passage to India
on LSD Airlines
Temporary flight
of ecstatic insanity
into its own
glittering terminals
pulsing with light

Gliding down & down
How calm all
Still autumn forest
Golf-link in it
Straightwayhighway into a cloverleaf
cars crawling the petals
Huge cemetery in brown woods
Death itself only another
lower form
of temporary ecstatic insanity
out of your skull
into the ground
How soft the trees down there
How very soft
from up here
We
could almost
bounce into them
soft landing
among the branches
And so on down
into it
into the soft ground
illusion!
As if
as if we don't ever die
but become new burrowing consciousnesses
Earthworm Tractors
ZOOM
Still a scary landing
into *that* Underground

II. LSD, Big Sur

Great progress!
thru the looking glass with 'Alice'
Ten years of dreams
in the green forest
Uplands
of the imagination
Far green grottoes
Future books
of the Illuminati
writ out there
across the landscape —
land escape —

into ecstasy
Intolerable arabesques
coming & coming & coming
on & on
toward me
onto me
over me
Relentless
Ineffable!
Coming down now
re-echoing
gliding down
those landscapes
& arabesques of earth
seas reglitterized
seen thru a silkscreen overlay
sun stricken!
On & on & on
it still keeps coming
out there/up there
keeps going on & on
over the horizon
into eternity
now that the cries of the birds
has stopped
O I alone
walk the red heavens
the first blind steps
in the direction
of some dharma
whose name I could
conceivably sing
yet cannot yet decipher

III. After-dream

The soft fur parted
but he withdrew
from around her body
his halcyon limbs
and allowed the ram
only Shiva and Contemplation

And Shiva advanced
with a broken arm

Sailing thru the straits of Demos...

Sailing thru the straits of Demos
we saw symbolic birds
shrieking over us
while eager eagles hovered
and elephants in bathtubs
floated past us out to sea
strumming bent mandolins
and bailing for old glory with their ears
while patriotic maidens
wearing paper poppies
and eating bonbons
ran along the shores
wailing after us
and while we lashed ourselves to masts
and stopt our ears with chewing gum
dying donkeys on high hills
sang low songs
and gay cows flew away
chanting Athenian anthems
as their pods turned to tulips
and heliocopters from Helios
flew over us
dropping free railway tickets
from Los Angeles to heaven
and promising Free Elections
So that
we set up mast and sail
on that swart ship once more
and so set forth once more
forth upon the gobbly sea
loaded with liberated vestal virgins
and discus throwers reading *Walden*
but
shortly after reaching
the strange suburban shores
of that great American
demi-democracy
looked at each other
with a mild surprise
silent upon a peak
in Darien

Adieu À Charlot
(*Second Populist Manifesto*)

Sons of Whitman sons of Poe
sons of Lorca & Rimbaud
or their dark daughters
poets of another breath
poets of another vision
Who among you still speaks of revolution
Who among you still unscrews
the locks from the doors
in this revisionist decade?
'You are President of your own body, America'
Thus spoke Kush in Tepotzlan
youngblood wildhaired angel poet
one of a spawn of wild poets
in the image of Allen Ginsberg
wandering the wilds of America
'You Rimbauds of another breath'
sang Kush
and wandered off with his own particular paranoias
maddened like most poets
for one mad reason or another
in the unmade bed of the world
Sons of Whitman
in your 'public solitude'
bound by blood–duende
'President of your own body America'
Take it back from those who have maddened you
back from those who stole it
and steal it daily
The subjective must take back the world
from the objective gorillas & guerrillas of the world
We must rejoin somehow
the animals in the fields
in their steady-state meditation
'Your life is in your own hands still
Make it flower make it sing'
(so sang mad Kush in Tepotzlan)
'a constitutional congress of the body'
still to be convened to seize control
of the state
the subjective state

from those who have subverted it
The arab telephone of the avant-garde
has broken down
And I speak to you now
from another country
Do not turn away
in your public solitudes
you poets of other visions
of the separate lonesome visions
untamed uncornered visions
fierce recalcitrant visions
you Whitmans of another breath
which is not the too-cool breath of modern poetry
which is not the halitosis of industrial civilisation
Listen now Listen again
to the song in the blood the dark duende a dark singing
between the tickings of civilisation
between the lines of its headlines
in the silences between cars
driven like weapons
In two hundred years of freedom
we have invented
the permanent alienation of the subjective
almost every truly creative being
alienated & expatriated
in his own country
in Middle America or San Francisco
the death of the dream in your birth
o meltingpot America
I speak to you
from another country
another kind of blood-letting land
from Tepotzlan the poets' lan'
Land of the Lord of the Dawn
Quetzalcoatl
Land of the Plumed Serpent
I signal to you
as Artaud signalled
through the flames
I signal to you
over the heads of the land
the hard heads that stand like menhirs
above the land in every country
the short-haired hyenas

who still rule everything
I signal to you from Poets' Land
you poets of the alienated breath
to take back your land again
and the deep sea of the subjective
Have you heard the sound of the ocean lately
the sound by which daily
the stars still are driven
the sound by which nightly
the stars retake their sky
The sea thunders still to remind you
of the thunder in the blood
to remind you of your selves
Think now of your self
as of a distant ship
Think now of your beloved
of the eyes of your beloved
whoever is most beloved
he who held you hard in the dark
or she who washed her hair by the waterfall
whoever makes the heart pound
the blood pound
Listen says the river
Listen says the sea Within you
you with your private visions
of another reality a separate reality
Listen and study the charts of time
Read the sanskrit of ants in the sand
You Whitmans of another breath
there is no one else to tell
how the alienated generations
have lived out their expatriate visions
here and everywhere
The old generations have lived them out
Lived out the bohemian myth in Greenwich Villages
Lived out the Hemingway myth
in *The Sun Also Rises*
at the Dôme in Paris
or with the bulls at Pamplona
Lived out the Henry Miller myth
in the *Tropics* of Paris
and the great Greek dream
of *The Colossus of Maroussi*
and the tropic dream of Gauguin

Lived out the D. H. Lawrence myth
in *The Plumed Serpent*
in Mexico Lake Chapala
And the Malcolm Lowry myth
Under the Volcano at Cuernavaca
And then the saga of *On the Road*
and the Bob Dylan myth Blowing in the Wind
How many roads must a man walk down
How many Neal Cassadys on lost railroad tracks
How many replicas of Woody Guthrie with cracked guitars
How many photocopies of longhaired Joan
How many Ginsberg facsimiles and carbon-copy Keseys
still wandering the streets of America
in old tennis shoes and backpacks
or driving beat-up school buses
with destination-signs reading 'Further'
How many Buddhist Catholics how many cantors
chanting the Great Paramita Sutra
on the Lower East Side
How many Whole Earth Catalogs
lost in out-houses in New Mexico communes
How many Punk Rockers waving swastikas
Franco is dead but so is Picasso
Chaplin is dead but I'd wear his bowler
having outlived all our myths but his
the myth of the pure subjective
the collective subjective
the Little Man in each of us
waiting with Charlot or Pozzo
On every corner I see them
hidden inside their tight clean clothes
Their hats are not derbys they have no canes
but we know them
we have always
waited with them
They turn and hitch their pants
and walk away from us
down the darkening road
in the great American night

Tepotzlan '75 — San Francisco '78

— RIVERS OF LIGHT —

My mind is racing in the middle of the night
My mind races through the darkness around the world
through the darkness of the world
Toward a tunnel of light
It races through the night of Prague
through Staromak Square
with its Jan Hus sculpture
reading "Love Each Other
And the Truth will Triumph"
It races on through the night streets
Across the Charles Bridge
Across Vltova River
Across the rivers of the world
Across the Rhine
Across the Rhône
Across the Seine
Across the Thames
Across Atlantic
Across Manhattan
Across Great Hudson
into the heart of America
My heart is racing now across America
Where is the light
across Ole Man River rolling along
My heart is racing now across terrific Pacific
Across the River of Yellow Light of Sun Yat Sen
Across Gandhi's Ganghes

cont →

— by Lawrence Ferlinghetti (Writ in Prague April 19, 1998)

(2)

Across the Nile ~~Across Euphrates~~ Across the Hellespont
Across Tiber Across Arno
Across Dante's River Styx
through the medeival darkness

Into the heart of the tunnel of light
My heart and mind are racing now
together on the same beat
to the same music
It's not the music of Carmina Burana
It's the music of Don Giovanni
It's Mozart's Horn Concerto
It's the Yellow Submarine
Yellow Submarine
Yellow Submarine
There is a sign in the light at the end of the tunnel
I am trying to read it
We are all trying to read it
Dark figures dance in it in the half-darkness
Light figures dance in it in the half-light

Biographies & Acknowledgements

Will Alexander: Poet, novelist, essayist, playwright, aphorist, philosopher. His writings have appeared in Journals such as the *Chicago Review* and *Vatra* and *Literary Romania*, Bucharest. His books include *Above the Human Nerve Domain*, *Towards the Primeval Lightning Field*, *The Stratospheric Canticles* and *Asia & Haiti.*

Roselle Angwin: Poet, author. She read Anglo-Saxon, Norse and Celtic at Cambridge. Her poems have won various awards. Commissions include *River Suite*, a collaborative project with musicians and schools in Devon. She is co-director with Jay Ramsay of the Chrysalis Poetry Project. Her books include *A Hawk Into Everywhere, The Present Where, Taking Light* and *Riding the Dragon — Myth and the Inner Journey* (Element).

Julian Beck: Artist, poet, painter, playwright, author, etc. Julian Beck was an abstract painter exhibiting in Peggy Guggenheim's *Art of the Century Gallery* when he met Judith Malina and she persuaded him to lend his creative genius to a new vision of the stage called *The Living Theatre*. In New York between 1951 and 1963, including two European tours, twenty-nine plays were produced and occasionally directed by Beck, who designed all sets, lights and costumes. He collaborated with artists such as Merce Cunningham, John Cage and Paul Goodman. He wrote *We, The Living Theatre* with Judith Malina, *Interviews with the Living Theatre* in collaboration with Aldo Rostagno, and *The Living Theatre* with Jean-Jacques Lebel. He also appeared in Pier-Paolo Pasolini's *Oedipus Rex* and Bernardo Bertolucci's *Agonia.* After his expulsion from Brazil with *The Living Theatre*, he published *The Life of the Theatre*. His plays include *Prometheus in the Winter Palace* and *The Archeology of Sleep*, and with Judith Malina & The Living Theatre, *Frankenstein* and *Paradise Now.* His writings have been translated into many languages. His first book of poems was *Songs for the Revolution*, followed by *21 Songs for the Revolution*, *Songs of Revolution 36-89* and *Daily Light, Daily Speech, Daily Life*. His other works include *Theandric* and a collection of writings entitled *Workbooks.* Awards include the Grand Prix of the Theatre of Nations and six Obies.

Joseph Beuys: Artist, born in 1921 in Krefeld, Germany. On leaving school he planned to study medicine but in 1941 he was drafted into the Luftwaffe, served as a pilot and radio operator, was wounded five times and shot down over the Crimea where his life was saved by Tartars, who wrapped him in felt and fat and fed him on honey and milk. He was later held at a prisoner-of-war camp in Cuxhaven, Germany. Between 1947-51 he studied at the State Academy of Art, Dusseldorf. In 1961 he was appointed Professor of Monumental Studies at Staatliche Kunstakademie. 1962-65, he co-founded and was an active member of the Fluxus movement. His 1965 exhibition in Dusseldorf opened with his action *How to Explain Pictures to a Dead Hare*. In 1967 he founded the German Student Party and in '68 he declared that *Art is Life*. 1970 saw the first of his visits to Scotland, to perform an action on Rannoch Moor and his *Celtic Kinloch Rannoch — The Scottish Symphony* at Edinburgh College of Art as part of the exhibition *Strategy-Get Arts*. In 1972 he was fired from his teaching post at Dusseldorf. In 1973 he returned to Scotland to give a twelve hour lecture, *A Homage to Anacharsis Cloots*, and in 1974 he established, with Heinrich Böll, the *Free International School for Creativity and Interdisciplinary Research*, performed in New York with a live coyote, in *I like America and America Likes Me*, then in Scotland with his *Three Pots Action* in the Edinburgh *Poorhouse,* and lectured with Buckminster Fuller at the *Black and White Oil Conference,* followed by many exhibitions and actions, such as *Tramstop* at the Venice Biennale, *Honey Pump* at Documenta 6 in Kassel, and a major retrospective at the Guggenheim Museum, New York. In 1982 he began the action *7000 Oaks* at Documenta 7, Kassel, and made his last visit to Scotland to install the *Poorhouse Doors* at the Scottish National Gallery of Modern Art. In 1985 his *Palazzo Regale* was installed at the Museo Capodimonte. He died in 1986.

Hakim Bey: Author. Lives in Chinatown, San Francisco. Amongst many books he is the author of *Immediatism* and the non-copyright *T. A. Z.*, published by Autonomedia.
J. J. Blickstein: Poet and visual artist. He is the editor of *Hunger Magazine & Hunger Press.* His work has been published in many magazines including *5 Trope*, *The Louisiana Review* and *Fish Drum*, and in anthologies such as *America Diaspora: Poetry of Displacement* and *Vespers: Religion & Spirituality in the 21st Century.*
Paul Bowles: Novelist, short story writer, composer. Studied music with Aaron Copeland, published his first poems in Gertrude Stein's magazine *Transition*. Forby his own compositions he wrote music for films by, amongst others, the surrealist painter Max Ernst, and for a ballet by Salvador Dalí. He was a longtime resident of Tangier and cultural focal point. His novels include *The Sheltering Sky* which was made into a film by Benardo Bertolucci, *Let It Come Down*, *The Spiders House* and *Up Above The World.* Collections of stories include *Pages From Cold Point*, *A Thousand Camels in the Courtyard* and *Call at Corazon.* He is also the author of *Without Stopping* (autobiography), *Their Heads Are Green* and *Points In Time*.
John Brandi: Poet, painter, essayist. He has read his work and exhibited his paintings worldwide. His early writings were strongly influenced by his life abroad, particularly in the Andes. Following in his father's footsteps, he has visited India, Nepal and Southeast Asia, with several trips to Bali to investigate textiles, shadow puppetry and gamelan music. His many books include *Heartbeat Geography (selected poems)*, *Weeding the Cosmos*, *A Question of Journey*, *Reflections in the Lizard's Eye* and *Stone Garland: a haiku journey north Viet Nam*. He lives with his wife, Renée Gregorio, in the mountains of northern New Mexico.
John Brewster: Poet, author, short story writer, musician. One of Scotland's new millennium voices. Amongst others things he got a BD Hons. (First) at St. Andrew's University, edited *Scrievins* and *Scots Glasnost*, was the editor of other poetry journals and an active committee member of the Scottish Poetry Library in Edinburgh. He has performed at poetry readings and lectured throughout the country. His work has appeared in numerous publications including *Fower Brigs Ti A Kinrik* (Aberdeen University Press), *Behind The Lines* (Third Eye Centre) and broadcast on Radio 4's *In Verse*. He writes in English and Scots, and translates poetry from French, German, Italian, Greek and Hebrew. Collections for publication include *Wordlings*, and a novel trilogy based upon the life of Merlin.
Ronnie Burk: Poet, born on April Fools day 1955. He is the author of nine collections of surrealist poetry including *Father of Reason, Daughter of Doubt, Indios Verdes*, two volumes of collage stories, *Scrolls of White Cabbage* and *The History of America*. His poetry has appeared in numerous periodicals including *Caliban*, *City Lights Review*, *New York Arts Magazine* and the surrealist bulletins *Blue Feathers* (Minnesota) and *Manticore* (Leeds).
William S. Burroughs: Author, artist, born 1914 in St. Louis, Missouri, graduated in English Literature from Harvard. A Member of the American Academy and Institute of Arts and Letters, and a recipient of the Ordre des Lettres de Françai, amongst many other honours. His many books include the controversial *Naked Lunch*, first published by the Olympia Press in Paris, the publisher of Henry Miller's banned books, and made into a film by David Cronenberg. There have been many exhibitions of his art, and there are many *CDs* of his readings. His other books include *The Soft Machine*, *The Ticket That Exploded*, *Port of Saints, Nova Express, Ah Pook is Here & Other Texts, Exterminator!* and *The Third Mind* (with Brion Gysin), *The Book of Breathing* (with Bob Gale), *The Yagé Letters* (with Allen Ginsberg), and *Cities of the Red Night*, *Place of Dead Roads* and *The Western Lands.* He died in 1997.
Gordon Campbell: Artist, of *The Academy Of Everything Is Possible*, an organisation of like-minded people who have, over the past number of years, put together exhibitions in all areas of the arts. It was Gordon Campbell who organised the planting of *Joseph Beuys' 7000 Oaks* in the shape of a heart on the Hill of Uisneach in Eire.

Michael Castro: Poet, New York City born, St. Louis based. Founder of *River Styx*, a literary organisation publishing and organising readings for the past twenty-five years. He also hosts a radio show, *Poetry Beat*, and does performance work with various musical and dance ensembles. Published in over twenty anthologies, numerous magazines and chapbooks, his books include *Interpreting the Indian: 20th Century Poets & the Native American*. His latest collection of poetry is entitled *Human Rites*.
Mohamed Choukri: Author, born in 1935 in the Rif Mountains in Northern Morocco. In 1943 his family moved to Tangier where Choukri lived by his wits on the streets. He was not able to read and write until the age of twenty. Now, one of the best known writers in the Arab world, his books include *Pain Nu*, (*Naked Bread*), *Zocco Chico*, and *Paul Bowles, Le Reclus de Tanger*, as well as books about Tennessee Williams and Jean Genet whom he met in Tangier. His books have been translated into seventeen languages.
Andy Clausen: Poet, author. He was co-editor of *Poems for the Nation* with Allen Ginsberg and Eliot Katz. He was an editor of *Long Shot*. Recent publications include *The Streets of Kashi*, *Without Doubt* and *40th Century Man (Selected Verse 1996 —1966).*
Ira Cohen: Poet, photographer, author, artist, multi-media electronic shaman. Studied English Literature at Cornell under Vladimir Nabokov. He was the editor and publisher in Tangier of *Gnaoua* which featured Burroughs, Gysin, Jack Smith, Irving Rosenthal etc., started *The Mutant Repertory Company* and became the Father of Mylar Photography. He brought out *The Hashish Cookbook* under the name Panama Rose, and *Jilala*, an album of Moroccan Trance Music. He wrote *The Goblet of Dreams* for Playboy Magazine, directed and starred in the award winning film *The Invasion of Thunderbolt Pagoda*, appeared in Jack Smith's *Reefers of Paradise Island*, and produced *Paradise Now In America*, a film of *The Living Theatre's* historic 1968 American tour. In the seventies he went to Kathmandu and started the Starstreams Poetry Series under the Bardo Matrix imprint, publishing on rice paper the works of Gregory Corso, Charles Henri Ford, Angus MacLise, Paul Bowles and others. Also published his own work, *Poems From The Cosmic Crypt*, *Seven Marvels* and *Gilded Splinters*. From 1980 to the present, he moved back to New York. His photographic exhibitions include *Kathmandu Portfolio*, *The Bandaged Poets Series*, *Kings With Straw Mats, Dangerous Visions, Retrospectacle, About Faces* (with Carol Beckwith), *New York Sling Shots, From The Mylar Chamber* (a two man show at the Lessing Gallery with Man Ray), a two man show at Space Time Light with Jack Micheline, and *Licking The Skull* at the Cynthia Broan Gallery, NY. His photographs have been widely published in magazines and newspapers including LIFE and the *Sunday Times* and can be found on numerous book covers and album covers. He is the contributing editor to many magazines and periodicals including *Ins & Outs* (Amsterdam), *Third Rail* (Los Angels), *Ignite* (New York), *Nexus* (Dayton, OH.). He edited Jack Smith's *Historical Treasures* for Hanuman Books, co-edited *The Great Society* with Bobby Richkin, and published *Petroleum Pertroleum* by Gustav Meyrink. Books of his poetry include *The Stauffenberg Cycle and Other Poems, From The Divan Of Petra Vogt* and *On Feet of Gold. Minbad Sinbad,* a book of writings dealing with Morocco, was published in France in 1998. Forthcoming on DVD are *Kings With Straw Mats* and *The Invasion of Thunderbolt Pagoda,* which was screened at the Whitney Museum, NYC, 1999. His collections of poetry *Where The Heart Lies* and *From The Akashic Record* were published in 2001. Collections of prose, poetry and three volumes of photographs, are being prepared for publication, including *The Bandaged Poets Series* and his Mylar photographs.
Raphael Aladdin Cohen: Musician, poet. His poetry can be found in various journals and magazines such as *Nexus* and *Electric Rexroth*. He has lately returned from Hungary to New York and is spreading the beautiful word.

Gregory Corso: Poet, author. Along with Ginsberg, Burroughs and Kerouac, he was a spokesman for the Beat Generation. His first collection of poems was *The Vestal Lady on Brattle*, published by subscription, followed by *Gasoline*, published by Lawrence Ferlinghetti at City Lights. His first novel, *The American Express,* was published by the underground Olympia Press in Paris, and his short play, *In This Hung-Up Age*, was published in New Directions 18. Collections of poetry include *The Happy Birthday of Death*, *Long Live Man*, *Elegiac Feelings American*, *Herald of the Autochthonic Spirit*, all of which are published by New Directions, and *Mindfield.* He died in January, 2001, while the present collection was being compiled.
Aidan Andrew Dun: Poet, born in London but raised for ten years in the West Indies. The grandson of dancer Dame Marie Rambert, Aidan listened to her recitations of Milton and Homer late into the night. At the age of seventeen he disappeared from school and took up as a troubadour travelling from Amsterdam to Marrakech. He was inevitably drawn back to London where he was a squatter in derelict mansions and where his collection *Vale Royal* (Goldmark) was launched at the Royal Albert Hall to great acclaim. His one man show, *Blue at the Throat,* premiered at the Edinburgh Festival to rave reviews. His collection *Universal* was published by Goldmark in 2002.
Agneta Falk: Poet, visual artist, born in Stockholm in 1946. She has lived in England since 1969 where she has been a teacher of drama, communication, literacy and creative writing. From 1992-1999 she was co-director of *WordHoard*, promoting writing in the community and organising poetry events. In the 90s she was commissioned to write about the Lincolnshire coastline, *Looking In / Looking Out*, and on Yorkshire, *Digging In*. She is widely published and exhibits her art in Britain and America. She divides her time between San Francisco, England and Italy. Collections of her work include *It's Not Love — It's Love* (Multimedia Edizioni, Italy).
Jane Falk: Poet, author. She lived in Kathmandu when she wrote *Ckrowww*. Since then she has continued to write poetry, spent time in Nigeria, and recently completed a Ph.D. in Interdisciplinary Studies at Ohio State University, specialising in Zen and American Poetry in the 1950s. She now lives in Akron, Ohio, where she teaches English Composition at the University of Akron and Creative Writing through its Continuing Education Division.
Lawrence Ferlinghetti: Poet, author, artist, translator, founder with Nancy J. Peters of the City Lights Bookstore and City Lights Books which published Corso, Kerouac, Lamantia, Lorca and many others, including Ginsberg's *Howl & Other Poems* which led to Ferlinghetti being arrested on obscenity charges. He was San Francisco's first Poet Laureate in 1998/99. Collections of his poetry include *Pictures of the Gone World*, *A Coney Island of the Mind*, *The Secret Meaning of Things*, *Back Roads to Far Places*, *Open Eye, Open Heart*, *Who Are We Now*, *Landscapes of Living & Dying*, *Wild Dreams of A New Beginning, A Far Rockaway of the Heart.* He translated Jacques Prévert's *Paroles* and Pier Paolo Pasolini's *Roman Poems.* His prose includes the novels *Her* and *Love in the Days of Rage,* and the plays *Unfair Arguments with Existence* and *Routines*. His art can be found in *Leaves of Life*, *Volumes I and II.*
Charles Henri Ford: Poet, artist, born in 1913 in Brookhaven, Mississippi. In 1929 he edited and published *Blues: A Magazine of New Rhythms* which included William Carlos Williams, H. D., Edouard Roditi and Paul Bowles amongst its contributors. In 1930 he was in New York for the publication of *Blues 8*. 1931 saw him in Paris frequenting the salons of Gertrude Stein, Natalie Barney and Marie-Louise Bousquet, and in Montparnasse & Saint-Germain-Des-Pres he made friends with Man Ray, Kay Boyle, Djuna Barnes, Peggy Guggenheim etc. His publications between 1945/49 include *Poems for Painters* (View Editions,) *A Night With Jupiter & Other Fantastic Stories* (editor, Vanguard Press), *The Half-Thoughts, The Distances of Pain* (a Prospero Pamphlet) and *Sleep In A Nest Of Flames* (New Directions). In 1952 he returned to Europe, with Tchelitchew. In 1955 his photographic exhibition, *Thirty Images From Italy*,

was shown at London's Institute of Contemporary Art. In 1956 he had a One-man show of his paintings and drawings in Paris, the catalogue foreword by Jean Cocteau. *The Young and The Evil* was printed by the Olympia Press in 1960. In 1962 he returned to America. His *Poem Posters* were exhibited at the Cordier & Ekstrom Gallery in 1965 and a film of the exhibition was chosen for the Fourth International Avant-Garde Film Festival, Belgium. Other works include *Spare Parts* (View Editions), *Silver Flower Coo* (Kulchur Press), his feature film *Johnny Minotaur* premiered in the Bleeker Street Cinema in 1971, *Flag of Ecstasy* (Black Sparrow Press), *The Kathmandu Experience* (Exhibition at New York Cultural Center), *Thirty Images From Italy* (Carlton Gallery, NYC), *7 Poems* (Bardo Matrix), *Layouts & Camouflages* (Robert Samuels Gallery, NYC), *Om Krishna I, II & III* (Cherry Valley Editions), *Haiku & Imprints* (with collages by Reepak Shakya), *Handshakes From Heaven* (with photographs by Indra Tamang and collages by Reepak Shakya), *Emblems of Arachne* (Catchword Papers), *Selected Poems* (City Lights). We are glad to say that he is currently creating in New York.

Allan Graubard: Poet, author, playwright, translator, critic. His works have been translated into Bosnian, Czech, Croatian, French, German, Hungarian, Italian, Japanese, Portuguese and Spanish. His publications include *Uxmal, Ascent of Sublime Love, Apis Mellifera, She Talks In Her Sleep, For Alejandra, Glimpses From A Fleeing Window* and *Fragments from Nomad Days.* Theatre works include *Modette, For Alejandra, The One in the Other, Lache pas la Patate,* and more. He has collaborated with many noted creators, including composers Lawrence D. "Butch" Morris, Sussan Deyhem and Richard Horowitz; artists Edin Numankadic, Eugenio F. Granell, and Jose Sanchez; photographers Clarence John Laughlin, Ira Cohen and Melba Levick; choreographer Alice Farley, and others. He seeks the marvellous whenever and wherever it may be, and in those who share his passion for it. *When words kiss, only silent lips can tell the tale.*

Renée Gregorio: Poet. One of the founding editors of the *Taos Review*, and one of the featured writers in the film *Honoring the Muse*. Her work has appeared in Literary Journals in the U. S. A. and England as well as in several anthologies, including *The New Mexico Poetry Renaissance* and *Saludos!* She is a former member of the jazz/poetry group, *Luminous Animal*, and has read her work throughout the Southwest and performed in Dead Poets' bouts and won. She earned her Master's Degree from Antioch University, London. Collections of her poetry include *The X Poems*, *Skin of Possible Lives* and *The Storm That Tames Us.*

Paul Grillo: Poet, artist, born in 1943. His undergraduate and graduate studies included Comparative Literature, Art History and The Poetics of Mysticism. His poems and collages have been published in countless magazines in the U. S. A. and Europe. His books include *Manhattan Spiritual* (with Guy Beining), *Vibes of the Saints*, *Agents of a Silenced Life: The Kebec Poems 1989-1999*, *Burnt Sienna* and *The Owlette Diaries.*

Brion Gysin: Artist, poet, author, born in England in 1916. In the Paris of the thirties he exhibited with Picasso, Dalí, Duchamp and the surrealists. He served in the army in World War II then settled in Paris, then Tangier where he pioneered the cut-up method of writing with William S. Burroughs. It was Gysin who collected the scattered pages of *Naked Lunch* and was primarily responsible for assembling the manuscript. Throughout the sixties he travelled between Paris, London, New York and Tangier, working on various projects, eventually settling in Paris in 1973. He was a major influence on the Beat Generation, artists such as Bowles and Bowie, and today's Now Poets and Artists. His books include *Minutes To Go* (with Beiles, Burroughs & Corso),*The Third Mind* (with Burroughs), *The Process* (a novel) and *The Last Museum* (a novel). He is also the author of *Who Runs May Read*, *Morocco Two*, the history, *To Master — A Long Goodnight*, and *Here TO GO: Planet R-101*, interviews by Terry Wilson & Additional Texts. *Back In Now: A Brion Gysin Reader*, edited by Jason Weiss, was published by Wesleyan University Press. Gysin died in 1986 in Paris.

Jon Hassell: Composer, trumpeter, artist. He is the visionary creator of a style of music he describes as Fourth World, a mysterious, unique hybrid of music both ancient and digital, composed and improvised, Eastern and Western. After composition studies and university degrees in the U. S. A., he went to Europe to study electronic and serial music with Karlheinz Stockhausen. Several years later he returned to New York where his first recordings were made with minimalist masters LaMonte Young and Terry Riley through whom he met the Hindustani raga master, Pandit Pran Nath, and embarked on a lifelong quest to transmute his teacher's vocal mastery into a new trumpet sound and style. Theatrical scores include *Sulla Strada*, created for the Venice Biennale, and *Zangezi*, directed by Peter Sellars. He has collaborated on presentations by fashion avant-gardists Issey Miyake and Rei Kawakubo, and for choreographic works by Merce Cunningham and the Alvin Ailey Dance Company. The Kronos Quartet commissioned and recorded his *Pano da Costa*. The Netherlands Dance Theatre commissioned *Lurch*, a major evening-length piece choreographed by Australian dance maverick Gideon Obarzanek, arranged and remixed for performance by two onstage DJs. The theme he co-wrote for the television series *The Practice* won an Emmy. His unique trumpet sound and music can be found on many film soundtracks including Wim Wenders' *Million Dollar Hotel* which he worked on with Bono, Eno and Lanois, and in which he also appears. He has collaborated on many albums and worked with numerous musicians. His albums include *Vernal Equinox*, *Earthquake Island*, *Possible Musics* (with Brian Eno), *Dream Theory in Malaya*, *Aka-Darbari-Java / Magic Realism*, *Power Spot*, *The Surgeon of the Nightsky Restores Dead Things by the Power Of Sound*, *Flash of the Spirit* (with Farafina), *City: Works of Fiction*, *Dressing for Pleasure*, *The Vertical Collection* (Limited Edition) and *Fascinoma*. He has completed a book entitled *The North and South of You, An Erotic Worldview*, which is an extrapolation of the Fourth World musical paradigm into the wider cultural sphere.

Allen Hibbard: Author, short story writer, essayist, translator. Lived and worked for four years in Cairo and two in Damascus. He has published numerous reviews, articles, short stories and translations from the Arabic by such writers as Adonis. Publications include *Paul Bowles: A Study of the Short Fiction* (Macmillan), *Conversations with William S. Burroughs* (University Press of Mississippi), and *Paul Bowles, Magic & Morocco* (Cadmus Editions). He is currently writing a biography of Alfred Chester.

Jack Hirschman: Poet, translator. He has had more than a hundred books published including *Back of a Spoon*, *The Bottom Line*, *Endless Threshold*, *Fist of Sun*, *Front Lines*, *Open Gate*, *Suicide Circus*, *The Jonestown Arcane* and *The Xibalba Arcane*. His lyrical poems are forthcoming from City Lights, San Francisco. A French edition of *Arcanes* has been published in Paris. Other books include *The Poems of Franco Carlini & Andrea Zuccolo*, translated from the Italian, *The Poems of Martin Heidegger*, translated from the German, *The Poems of Alexei Kruchenykh*, translated with Alexander Kohar and Venyamin Tseytlin from the Russian, and the first bi-lingual anthology of Haitian Creole poetry, translated with Boadiba. He is active with The League of Revolutionaries for a New America.

Stefan Hyner: Poet, born in 1957 in Mannheim, grew up in a village in the centre of the Rhine Valley. After an apprenticeship as a cabinet maker he studied Chinese language and East Asian Art History at the University of Heidelberg and the Taiwan Normal University in Taipei. From 1981 to 1984 and from 1987 to 1989 he travelled through China, Tibet and Japan. From 1985 to 1987 he lived in the U. S. A., dividing his time between Maine and California. He has translated a number of Buddhist texts from the Chinese into both German and English, and also several contemporary poets into German, among them Joanne Kyger, Philip Whalen, Lew Welch and Jim Koller. He lives close to his birth place in Rohrhof on the banks of the Rhine.

Mati Klarwein: Artist, born in Hamburg in 1933 to an architect father and a mother who was an opera singer and a lover of mysticism. His father was a Polish Jew and after it was suggested by his employer that he adopt a more Aryan surname, the family moved in 1934 to Palestine, where his parents later divorced, and his father designed the Knessett, the Israeli Parliament building. When he was fifteen, having proven himself academically hopeless, his father sent him to the Bezalal Art School in Jerusalem. In 1948, in the middle of the war to found the state of Israel, having been reduced to eating sparrows to stay alive, he moved with his mother and sister to Paris, where he studied commercial art at the Academie Julian. He was then persuaded by Luisa, a forty year old gypsy woman, to study painting with the dadaist and surrealist Fernand Léger, whose style he osmosed into his own particular vision. Mati said that his perception was transformed through his introduction to surrealism when he watched a screening of Salvador Dalí's *Un Chien Andalou.* Later, he became good friends with Dalí, even writing a firsthand account of witnessing Dalí's sexual antics. In bohemian St. Tropez he became friends with Ernst Fuchs, the founder of the Viennese school of Phantastic Realism, who taught him the mixed techniques of Van Eyck and the Flemish school. As he made an initial living by painting portraits, his drinking companions were Jean-Paul Sartre, Boris Vian, Roger Vadim and Brigitte Bardot. In the late sixties in New York, frequent visitors to his loft included Jim Hendrix, and Miles Davis who commissioned the painting of the celebrated album sleeve for *Bitches Brew.* His paintings were also used as covers for Davis's *Live Evil*, Santana's *Abraxas*, Howard Wales' & Jerry Garcia's *Hooteroll?*, and many other albums, taking his paintings into millions of homes. After a peripatetic existence that included time in Turkey and California as well as New York, he moved in 1984 to live in Deia, the artists community in the north of Majorca, which to all intents and purposes was founded by the poet Robert Graves, who was a close friend. Mati's paintings have been exhibited around the world and can be found in numerous private collections and museums. Publications of his paintings include *Milk n' Honey words n' pictures*, *God Jokes*, *Inscapes* (Crown Publishers, NY.), *Collected Works 1959-1970* (Raymond Martin Press, Nüremburg), *Thousand Windows* and *Improved Paintings*, both published by Max Publishing, Mallorca, Spain. He died in March 2002.
Joanne Kyger: Poet. A native Californian, she attended the University of California at Santa Barbara and in 1957 moved to North Beach in San Francisco. Since then she has had fourteen books of poetry published and her poems have appeared in numerous anthologies and literary magazines. For the past twenty years she has lived in Bolinas, California. She has taught at New College of California in San Francisco and in the Poetics Program at the Naropa Institute in Boulder, Colorado. Collections include *Strange Big Moon* and *The Tapestry and The Web.* Her most recent books of poems include *Patzcuaro*, *Some Life*, and *Selected Poems* published by Penguin Viking in 2002.
Louise Landes Levi: Poet, musician, translator, born in Manhattan in 1944. She studied at the University of California, Berkley, then lived in India for three years, studying music, primarily in Bombay, followed by years of study with Buddhist Masters, especially Dr. Trogawa Rinpoche & Namkhai Norbu Rinpoche. She also spent eight years in Paris. Her translations include RASA by René Daumal, *The Love Poems of Mirabai* and *Vers la Complétude* by Henri Michaux. Poetry recordings include *Kunst is Die Liefde in Elke Daad* (with Simon Vinkenoog), *Oasis* (with Joel O'Brien) *Neptune* and *Sweet On My Lips*. Music Recordings include *Kinnari*, *Padma* and *Kyerang*. She has lectured at The American College in Paris, the Naropa Institute, Bard College, Sullivan County Correction Facility, The Manhattan School of Music and the NY Open Center. Collections of her poetry include *The Water-Mirror*, *Amiata*, *Concerto*, *Extinction*, *Guru Punk*, *The Tower*, *The Highway Queen*, *The House Lamps Have Been Built but*, *Makar / A kar'MA* and *Crazy Louise.*

Rupert M. Loydell: Poet, author, painter and editor of Stride Publications which he founded in 1982. His writings have appeared in hundreds of magazines in the UK, Europe and America, and in many anthologies, and his paintings have been shown at numerous group and solo exhibitions. He has been a visiting lecturer/writer at schools, colleges, libraries and hospitals, a panel member at the *Collaborations: Risk, Trust, Process, Vision* conference in Berkley, California in 1995, Arts Development Officer, 1994-96, for Exeter Arts Council, and Chair of Exe. Lit. the Exeter Literature Festival, England. He has edited, amongst many anthologies, *My Kind of Angel: i.m. William Burroughs* and *Voices for Kosovo.* Other publications include *Stone Angels: Prose 1979-1993* and many collections of poetry, such as *Timbers Across The Sun*, *The Giving of Flowers*, *Places We'll Never Get To*, *World of Wonder*, *Sirens Singing in the Grey Morning, Home All Along* and *The Museum of Light.*
Ian MacFadyen: Author, essayist, currently living in London. His *Machine Dreams: Optical Toys and Mechanical Boys* was published in *Flickers of the Dreamachine: The Definitive Headbook* edited by Paul Cecil (Codex, 1996), and *Let The Picture Look At You* (*Of Snakes*, *Labyrinths*, *Scissors and Black Cats*): *The Work of Philipus Baird* was published by Lung Ta in 1997. Excerpts from his essay on Ira Cohen, *Ira Cohen's Photographs: A Living Theatre* appears in *Licking The Skull: A Retrospectacle of Photographic Works by Ira Cohen* (Cynthia Broan Gallery, New York, 2000). He has most recently written about the writer Terry Wilson and the Spanish artist and film-maker Javier Marchan. He is an authority on the works of William S. Burroughs; he interviewed Burroughs in 1990; and Vladimir Nabokov. He has taught the history of art and critical theory and lectured and written on many writers and artists including André Breton, George Bataille, George Perec, Yoko Ono and Arakawa.
Angus MacLise: Poet, musician, artist, worked and recorded with La Monte Young, Tony Conrad, John Cale, Terry Riley and others. He was a founding member and original drummer with the Velvet Underground, and was married by Timothy Leary to Hetty McGee in Golden Gate Park before travelling to Kathmandu where he lived, unexpectedly died and was cremated, aged only 41. His poetry has appeared in many magazines and anthologies. CDs of his music include *The Invasion of Thunderbolt Pagoda* which includes music used in Ira Cohen's film of the same title, *Brain Damage in Oklahoma City* and *Astral Collapse.* A book of his writings is being readied for publication.
Judith Malina: Poet, diarist, film actress and anarchist pacifist activist, she was born in Kiel, Germany in 1926. In 1947 she founded *The Living Theatre* with Julian Beck. She is the creator of over a hundred plays that have been performed around the world and changed the course of modern theatrical history. In 2001 *The Living Theatre* performed in the notorious Kiam Prison in Lebanon, which until only a few years ago housed thousands of Lebanese prisoners, where she also held workshops, giving testimony to her unwearying striving for a reconciled peaceful world. She wrote *We, The Living Theatre* with Julian Beck, and *Frankenstein* and *Paradise Now* with Julian Beck & The Living Theatre. Collections of poetry include *Love & Politics.*
Marty Matz: Poet, legend, read his poetry to Dizzy Gillespie playing trumpet, got busted in Mexico and did time in the infamous Lecumberi prison from which he attempted to escape. Asked why he had stayed in Mexico for fifteen years, he said that it took him fourteen years to get out of the hammock, by which time all the writers he had been hanging out with were famous, such as Gregory Corso with whom he shared an apartment in the Chelsea Hotel, New York. In his introduction to *Pipe Dreams*, Herbert Huncke says, *Marty Matz is one of the most positive and eloquent poets it is my privilege to be in touch with. How fine and beautiful are the opium-drenched lines... exquisitely presented in manner: delicate, mysterious and wondrous.* We wholeheartedly agree. In 1988 Matz was invited by the Tenth World Congress of Poets to read in Thailand, to which he returned in 1990 and stayed for eight years in an opium village.

He lived mostly in North Thailand but travelled to Yunan Province in China and to Tibet and Nepal. Collections of his poetry include a CD entitled *A Sky of Fractured Feathers* (with music by Chris Rael & Deep Singh) and *Pipe Dreams.* He died in 2001.

Michael McClure: Poet, born in 1932 in Maryville, Kansas, and grew up in Seattle and Wichita. He attended the University of Arizona at Tucson before moving to San Francisco. His first reading was at the Six Gallery event in 1955 with Kerouac, Ginsberg, Whalen, Snyder and Lamantia, which launched the San Francisco renaissance. He has written two plays, *The Beard* and *Josephine the Mouse*, a new staging of which was created by Terry Riley. Collections of his poetry include *Hymn to Saint Geryon*, *Little Odes*, *September Blackberries*, *Jaguar Skies*, *Fragments of Perseus* and a *Selected Poems*.

David Meltzer: Poet, author, began his literary career during the Beat heyday in San Francisco, reading poetry to Jazz accompaniment in the famous Jazz Cellar. He is the author of numerous books including *Blue Rays, No Eyes: Lester Young*, *The Secret Garden* and *Death: An Anthology of Ancient Texts, Songs, Prayers and Stories*. During the sixties he wrote erotica, actually devoting 1969 to writing 10 books which he classifies as agit-smut, which are being reprinted, including *Orf* and *The Agency Trilogy*. *Arrows: Selected Poetry 1957-1992* (Black Sparrow) was followed by *Under*, a new fiction, published in 1995. He has edited many anthologies including *Reading Jazz*, and the most current companion, *Writing Jazz*. He teaches in the graduate Poetics and undergraduate Humanities programs at New College of California.

Daniel Abdal-Hayy Moore: Poet, author, born 1940, Oakland, California. His first book of poems, *Dawn Visions*, was published by Lawrence Ferlinghetti of City Lights Books in San Francisco in 1964. In 1972 his second book of poems, *Burnt Heart, Ode to the War Dead*, was also published by City Lights. From 1966 to 1969 he wrote and directed ritual theatre for his Floating Lotus Magic Opera Company in Berkley, California. After a period of silence, he published three books in the '80s, *The Desert is the Only Way Out*, *The Chronicles of Akhira*, and *Halley's Comet*. He also organised poetry readings for many years for the Santa Barbara Arts Festival and wrote a libretto for a commissioned oratorio by the American composer, Henry Bryant, entitled *Rainforest*. He has read his poetry to 40,000 people at the United Nations in New York, and has participated in numerous readings, conferences and conventions. His most recent books are *The Ramadan Sonnets* and *The Blind Beekeeper*.

Axel Monte: Poet, translator, editor, born in 1962 in Germany and grew up in Bremerhaven. In 1992 he gained his M. A. in Ethnology and Indology at the South Asian Institute of the University of Heidelberg, and in 1995 his Ph.D. at the University of Bremen; a doctoral thesis on Rastafarianism, Sufism and the traditional warfare of the Afghan tribes. He is the editor of *Rude Look* magazine. His translations include *Du kommst nicht durch* (*You Can't Win*) by Jack Black, *Apokalypse*: D. H. Lawrence, and *Der Trost der Lieben* (*The Solace of Lovers*), mystical treatises translated into the German, with Jila Sohabi & Kaveh Dalir Azar, from the Farsi of Shihabbaddin Sohrawardi. His mesostics can be found in *Sprachte ist en Virus*.

Vali Myers: Artist, born in 1930 in Sydney, Australia. She left home at fourteen, worked in factories, lived in the Bohemian suburb of St. Kilda and later became the leading dancer for the Melbourne Modern Dance Company. At the age of nineteen she decided to go to Paris, where for three years she lived on the streets of Germain-des Pres, mingling with the artistic community, gypsies and street folk displaced by World War Two. Her indigence was captured in photographs by the Dutch photographer Ed van der Elsken which were published in his book, *Love on the West Bank*. In the cafés where she danced she met Jean Cocteau, Sartre, and expatriates including Ginsberg. Constantly in trouble with the police who were cracking down on vagabonds and gypsies on the streets, she was arrested and put in jail. Jean Cocteau saved her from deportation, and in 1958 she escaped with the Viennese painter Rudi Rappold, to Italy, to Il Porto, where she was to live for the next thirty years. Also in 1958 she was published in George Plimpton's journal *Paris Review*. Her paintings have been widely exhibited in France, Spain, Italy, Australia, and in New York where she would sell her work from the Chelsea Hotel where she lived and made friends with Ira Cohen, Patti Smith, Marianne Faithful and others. She lived in Italy for thirty years and returned to Australia in 1992. She is the subject of three films, *Vali — The Witch of Positano*, *Death in Port Jackson* and *Vali— Tightrope Dancer*. Collections of her paintings include *Vali* by *George Plimpton*. She died in 2003.

Hans Plomp: Poet, author, short story writer, environmental activist, born 1944 in Amsterdam where he took part in the *Provo* movement during the sixties and became a spokesman for the *psychedelic revolution*. He occupied a village outside Amsterdam with about 50 other artists, known as *Ruigoord*, which has since been in existence for over twenty years and become a beacon of alternative arts in the Netherlands. Regarded as a dissident in Dutch *Literature*, his poetry has been published in various journals including the anthology *Nine Dutch Poets* published by City Lights, San Francisco. He is Dutch editor of the *Encyclopaedia Psychedelia* of Fraser Clark and has had over twenty-five books published, including *Amsterdams Dudenboekje* (*Amsterdam Book of the Dead* - novel), *Satan Unmasked* (novel), *Het Innerlijk Bordeel* (*The Inner Brothel* - stories) and *Psychedelische Perspectieven* (essays). His latest collection of poetry is entitled *Venus in Holland*.

Jürgen Ploog: Author, born 1935 in Munich. He was an airline pilot from 1960 to 1993. In the sixties he became interested in the Beats and the Cut-up method of writing and got to know William S. Burroughs and met him on many occasions. His writings can be found in Charles Plymell's *Coldspring Journal*, *Cut Up or Shut Up* (Editions Agentzia), *Brion Gysin who runs may read* (Inkblot.xochi) and other journals and anthologies. His books include *Coca-Cola Hinterland*, *Pacific Boulevard*, *Strassen Des Zufalls* and *Der Raumagent*.

Charles Plymell: Poet, author and publisher of Cherry Valley Editions which has several books by William S. Burroughs on its list. He has been associated with the Beats, the San Francisco scene of the sixties and is veritably a *Now Poet.* He is the author of the classic novel *The Last of the Moccasins*. His work can be found in numerous journals and anthologies. His other books include *Apocalypse Rose*, *Over the Stage of Kansas*, *The Trashing of America*, *Hand on the Doorknob* and a collection of *Selected Poems*.

John Power: Songwriter, musician, from Liverpool. He played with the now cult band the *LAs* before forming his own band, *Cast,* and having chart success with singles and the albums *All Change*, *Mother Nature Calls*, *Magic Hour* and *Beetroot*. His first solo album *Happening for Love* was released by Eagle Records in 2003.

Diane Di Prima: Poet and author. Her work has been published in many journals and anthologies. Her *Memoirs of a Beatnik* was reprinted in 2002 by Marion Boyars. Collections of her poetry include *Selected Poems, 1956-1976* (North Atlantic Books), *Loba Parts I– VIII* (Wingbow Press), *Pieces of A Song*, (City Lights Books), *Loba* (Penguin Books).

Jay Ramsay: Poet, author, performer with *Phoenix*, psychotherapist and healer. B.A. Hons. Oxon. He co-founded the *Angels of Fire* collective, staging major festivals of poetry in London. He then founded the *Chrysalis Poetry Project*, directing courses and workshops. Believing very much in the artist-healer as an essential configuration for our time, he has trained as an accredited psychosynthesis therapist and is a member of the National Federation of Spiritual Healers. He has recently co-founded *The Lotus Foundation* with abstract painter Jenny Poretzky-Lee in London. He is the co-translator of the Chinese and Taoist classics the *Tao Te Ching*, *I Ching — the shamanic oracle of change,* and *Kuan Yin* (with Martin Palmer, Harper Collins) He is the author of over twenty-five books of poetry and non-fiction including his main work, *The Great Return*, the first five volumes of which have been published by the Diamond Press, *Psychic Poetry — a manifesto*, reprinted by Stride in 1997, *The White Poem* (with photographs by Carol Bruce, Five Seasons Press), *Alchemy — The Art of Transformation* (Thorsons), *Love's Way — The Alchemy of Relationships, Kingdom of the Edge — New and Selected Poems 1980-1998* (Element Books) and *Alchemy of the Invisible* (The Lotus Foundation).

Henry Reilly: songwriter, musician, poet, author, short story writer, architect, born in 1982 in Glasgow. Founder of the band *The Exiles*. Currently writing material for the first *Exiles'* albums, producing, recording, jamming and writing.

John Reilly: Songwriter, musician, poet, born in 1979 in Glasgow. Co-founder of *The Exiles*. Currently writing material for *The Exiles*' albums.

J. N. Reilly: Artist, poet, novelist, short story writer, translator, etcetera. His short stories, translations and extracts from prose works have been published in magazines and anthologies and on the internet. The leading light of the UK underground, he was described in the *Literary Review* as *Outstanding amongst the new generation of writers*. He is the author of a number of unpublished books and is the translator of *The Complete Works of Arthur Rimbaud*. He was also the editor and publisher of the anthology *Another Book To Burn*. The first of his *Postcards from Paradise* will be released to coincide with the publication of two collections of short stories, *3 Beautiful Stories* and *A Knife On A Country Road*, and two novels, *The Doleful* and *Madness, Murder, Merriment & Magic Mushrooms*. He is currently sketching and drawing the designs for an as yet untitled collection of jewellery and sculpture, preparing to edit further anthologies, taking notes for the epic novel *Ancient Cities Indigo Dolphins,* and completing *The Horn of Adventure* and *Dressed To The Nines.* Future projects, which will be far in the future unless some kindly benefactor succumbs to his charm and good looks, include two collections of paintings, *Ecstasy in Colour* and *Domestic Bliss and Other Paintings*.

Hanon Reznikov: Poet, playwright, author, essayist and diarist, born in Brooklyn in 1950. He met *The Living Theatre* at Yale in 1968 and soon after made it his life. Today, he directs the company together with Judith Malina, whom he married in 1988, and is the author of most of the company's later plays, which include *Yellow Methuselah*, *Utopia* and *The Zero Method.*

Terry Riley: Musician, composer. He launched what is now known as the Minimalist movement with his revolutionary *In C* in 1964. This seminal work provided a new concept in musical form based on interlocking repetitive patterns. Its impact was to change the course of 20th century music. Its influence can be heard in the works of prominent composers such as Steve Reich, Philip Glass and John Adams, bands such as Soft Machine and Tangerine Dream, and in the current dance and ambient scene. He studied under Pandit Pran Nath and frequently appeared with the legendary singer as a tampura, tabla and vocal accompanist over the next twenty-six years until Pran Nath's passing in 1996. While teaching at Mills College in Oakland in the nineteen-seventies, Terry met David Harrington, founder of the Kronos Quartet, and they began the long association that so far has produced twelve string quartets, a quintet, *Crows Rosary*, and a concerto for string quartet, *The Sands*, which was the Salzburg Festival's first ever new music commission. *Cadenza on the Night Plain* was selected by both Time and Newsweek as one of the ten best Classical albums of the year. The epic five quartet cycle *Salome Dances for Peace* was selected as the number one Classical album of the year by USA Today and was nominated for a Grammy. The third Requiem Quartet, *Requiem for Adam*, received wide critical acclaim marking a twenty year association for Riley and Kronos. Terry's first orchestral piece, *Jade Palace*, was commissioned by Carnegie Hall for the Centennial Celebration 1990/91. It was premiered there by Leonard Slatkin and the Saint Louis Symphony. *June Buddha's* was commissioned by the Koussevitsky Foundation. In 1999 he was commissioned by the Norwich Festival to compose a new work, *What The River Said*, followed by a commission from the Kanawaga Foundation in Yokohama to create an evening

length work for solo piano micro tonal tuning. *The Dream* received simultaneous premiers in Rome and Yokohama, performed by the composer. He has written a new staging of Michael McClure's play *Josephine The Mouse*. In May 2000 he made his first tour of Russia with solo piano concertos at the Sergei Kuryokin Festival in St. Petersburg, the Moscow Conservatory and the Dom. The reviews of these concerts in *Izvestia* proclaimed Terry Riley to be the greatest pianist since Prokofiev, and he was listed in the Sunday Times as one of the 1000 makers of the 20th century. Numerous CDs of his music are available including *In C*, *Shri Camel*, *A Rainbow in Curved Air*, *Persian Surgery Dervishes*, *The Harp of New Albion*, *Chanting the Light of Foresight*, *The Book of Abbeyozzud*, *Requiem for Adam* and *Atlantis Nath*.
Arthur Rimbaud: Poet, born 1854, died 1891. He was an influence on all the major poets of the 20th and 21st centuries. He wrote his *Lettre du Voyant* to Paul Demeny in 1871, the year Paul Verlaine called him to Paris, where he was introduced to hashish and absinthe, and their madly passionate adventures began. By 1873 they parted company, after Verlaine shot him in the wrist and was sent to prison. 1875 saw him back in London with the poet Germain Nouveau. In the July of that year his mother and sister, Vitalie, visited him there, where it's said that he had set up house with a girl, and he worked in both England and Scotland. It was also in that year that he met Verlaine for the last time and Vitalie died. From 1875 to 1880 he travelled in Germany, Switzerland and Italy, studied German, Spanish, Arabic, Italian, Dutch and Modern Greek, and joined the Dutch colonial army and deserted in Batvia. He passed through Cairo, Java and on to Cyprus where in 1880 he managed the building of the Governor's residence. The climate was inimical to his health so he went to Egypt then Aden where he found employment with Vianny, Mazeran, Bardey and Cie, dealers in coffee and hides. Sent to their new trading post in Harrar, Abyssinia, he crossed the Somali desert on horseback in twenty days. In 1882 at his employers request he explored Somaliland and Galla. In 1883 his curiosity led him to be the first European to explore the Ogadine. The Société de Géographie published a report on his explorations. He lived for some time with an Abyssinian girl, then got involved in gun running but was cheated of making a profit. He bemoaned his lot and talked of returning to France, of getting married. However, in February 1891 he got a tumour in his right knee and had to return to France, to the Hôpital de la Conception where his leg was amputated. His mother took him to recuperate in Roche but his condition worsened and he had to go back to hospital in Marseille. In November, aged thirty-seven, he died. His *Complete Works* includes, *Poems*, *The Drunken Boat*, *A Season in Hell* and *Illuminations*.
Dee Rimbaud: Poet, artist, author. One of Scotland's major voices, his poetry and pictures have been published on the internet and in magazines and anthologies throughout the U. S. A., Canada, Australia and Europe. His artwork has also appeared on book covers such as Rupert M. Loydell's *Places We'll Never Get To* and *Home All Along*. Collections of his poetry include *Bad Seed* and *Dropping Ecstasy with Angels*. Books being prepared for publication include his novels *Stealing Heaven from the Lips of God* and *Red Dreams & Razor Blades*.
Randy Roark: Poet, author, went to Boulder, Colorado, in 1979 to apprentice with Allen Ginsberg, who was then assembling his *Collected Poems*, and worked with the poet until his death in 1997. He has performed widely in the U. S. and Europe, incorporating the use of projected slides, music and American Sign Language. His Dangerous And Difficult Art (DADA) Productions has been presenting art events in Boulder, Denver and Taos since 1995. *Friction*, his literary arts magazine, was nominated for a Pushcart Prize by Robert Creeley in 1985. Collections of his work include *Awakening Osiris*, *Hymns*, *One Night* (with Anne Waldman), *Mona Lisa's Veil, New and Selected Poems, 1979-2001*, *Dialogue of A Hundred Preoccupations* (with Tamra Spivey) and *The Alchemy Poems: A Map of The World,* selected by the University of Arhus, Denmark, for a special presentation at their 2001 International Congress and published by Laocoon Press, 2002.

Rodrigo Rey Rosa: Short story writer, novelist, translator, born in 1958 in Guatemala. His first collection of stories, written in Morocco during his long and repeated visits to that country in the eighties, were translated into English by Paul Bowles and published by Peter Owen in London and City Lights in San Francisco. His translations into Spanish include books by Paul Bowles, Norman Lewis and others. He is the author of several short novels and collections of stories including *The Beggar's Wife* and *Dust on her Tongue* (City Lights) and *The Good Cripple* (New Directions).

Michael Rothenberg: Poet, songwriter, author, environmental activist and horticulturist, graduated from the University of North Carolina at Chapel Hill. He is the co-founder of Big Bridge Press and also co-editor and founder of JACK Magazine. He has published several poetry books: *What The Fish Saw*, *Nightmare of the Violins*, *Man/Woman* and *Favorite Songs*. His broadside *Elegy for The Dusky Seaside Sparrow* was selected as broadside of the Year by Fine Print Magazine. His songs have been used in the films *Shadowhunter, Blue Day, Blue Night*, and most recently *Outside Ozona*. He has also published two botanical monographs on the bromeliads. He edited *Overtime: Selected Poems of Philip Whalen* and the *Selected Poems of Joanne Kyger*, both published by Viking Penguin. Other publications include his *Paris Journals* and his novel *Punk Rockwell.*

Larry Sawyer: Poet, editor and publisher of mother's milk press. As a past editor of *Nexus* magazine, he has published work by artists such as Lawrence Ferlinghetti, Ira Cohen, Paul Grillo, Jack Micheline, Max Ernst and Andre Breton. Presently as editor of *milk magazine* online, he has published work by Gerard Malanga, Wanda Coleman, Clayton Eshleman, Linh Dinh, Wanda Phipps and many others. His poetry and critical reviews have appeared worldwide in the magazines: *Jacket*, *Exquisite Corpse*, *Range*, *Big Bridge*, *Tabacaria*, *The Butcher's Block*, *moria*, *Aught*, *Shampoo*, *Rain Taxi* and *Hunger* amongst others.

Howard Schwartz: Poet, author, storyteller, editor, and scholar of Jewish literature. He is Professor of English at the University of Missouri-St. Louis. He has published three books of poetry and several books of fiction. He has also edited a four-volume set of Jewish Folktales, which includes *Elijah's Violin & Other Jewish Fairy Tales*, *Miriam's Tambourine: Jewish Folktales from Around the World*, *Lilith's Cave: Jewish Tales of the Supernatural* and, *Gabriel's Palace: Jewish Mystical Tales*. He has also edited three major anthologies. His *Reimagining the Bible: The Storytelling of the Rabbis*, was the finalist for the National Jewish Book Award for 1999. In addition, Schwartz has also published eight children's books including *The Diamond Tree* (with Barbara Rush, which won the Sydney Taylor Book Award in 1992), *Next Year in Jerusalem: 3000 Years of Jewish Tales* (winner of the National Jewish Book Award and the Aesop Award of the American Folklore Society, both in 1996), *A Coat for the Moon* (with Barbara Rush, which won the Anne Izard Storyteller's Choice Award for 1998 and the 1999 Honor Title of the Storytelling World Awards), and *The Day the Rabbi Disappeared: Jewish Holiday Tales of Magic* (winner of the National Jewish Book Award and The Aesop Prize of the American Folklore Society for 2000).

Kazuko Shiraishi: Poet, born in Vancouver, Canada, in 1931, she was taken by her family, just prior to World War II, to Japan. She entered the modernism group VOU led by the poet, Katsue Kitazono in 1948 and published her first collection of poetry in 1951. In the sixties she started reading her poetry to live jazz performances, some of which were caught on film. She organised poetry readings with Allen Ginsberg, Yehudi Amichai whose works she has translated, and performed with musicians, dancers and artists such as Kazuo Ono, Peter Brötmann and Sam Rivers. Her work has been translated into over twenty-five languages and she has been invited to poetry festivals and readings all around the world. She has also received three prestigious awards in Japan; the Yomiuri Literature Award, the Takami Jun Poetry Award and the honour of a Purple Ribbon Medal (Shijuhosho) from the Emperor of

Japan. Her publications include many volumes of essays on music, art and film, and many collections of poetry, including *Seasons of Sacred Lust*, *A Canoe Returns to the Future*, *Sand Clan*, *Burning Meditation*, *One Who Is Carried Off*, *Fluttering* and *Precious Tears of the Donkey*. Her latest collection, *Let Those Who Appear*, was published by New Directions in 2002. She lives in Tokyo.

Patti Smith: Poet, songwriter, born in Chicago in 1946 and raised in New Jersey. She gave her first reading on the tenth of February 1971 with Lenny Kaye supporting her on guitar. Collections of her poetry include *Heaven*, *Kodak*, *Witt*, *Babel*, *Early Work* and *Woolgathering*. Her albums are *Horses*, *Radio Ethiopia*, *Easter*, *Wave*, *Dream Of Life*, *Gone Again*, *Peace and Noise*, *Gung Ho* and *Land 1975-2002.*

Tracy Splinter: Poet, born in 1970 in Cape Town, South Africa. She has read and performed in Switzerland, Austria, Italy, Amsterdam and at the first Euro-San Francisco Poetry Festival. She won first prize in the II Hamburger Lyrik-Wettbewerb / Lyric Competition. Since December 1999 she has organised and presented Wired On Words, a spoken poetry performance forum at the SchillerOper in Hamburg. Her debut poetry CD with booklet, *Verbalize,* was presented at the Leipzig Book Fair in 2001.

David Levi Strauss: Writer, poet and critic in New York where his essays and reviews appear regularly in *Artforum* and *The Nation*. He edited the literary journal *Acts* and published a book of poetry, *Manoeuvres*, in San Francisco before moving to New York in 1993. His essays have appeared most recently in *Broken Wings: The Legacy of Landmines* (with photographer Bobby Neel Adams, 1997), and in books on the artists *Martin Puryear* (The American Academy in Rome and Electra 1997), *Miqual Rio Blanco* (Aperture, 1998), *Francesca Woodman* (Fondation Cartier pour l'art contemporain in Paris and Scalo, 1998), *Alfredo Jaar* (Actar in Barcelona, 1998) and *Between Dog and Wolf, Essays on Art and Politics* (Autonomedia 1999).

Roberto Valenza: Poet. From rock 'n roll singer to seven years in Nepal and India, Roberto was part of the *rice paper revolution* along with Ira Cohen and Angus MacLise. On his return to America, he organised open mic events and festivals in the West Coast, especially Seattle. His work has appeared in numerous magazines and journals. A Tibetan Buddhist all his life he has been placed in the line of poetry and alchemy. His travel poems, photographs and drawings of Asia have been published in a collection entitled *Under The Precious Umbrella*.

Janine Pommy Vega: Poet. Her work has been published in numerous magazines and anthologies. She has toured the world performing her poetry at numerous poetry events and festivals. She has had fifteen books of poetry published including *Tracking the Serpent* and *Voices Under The Harvest Moon*. Her latest book, *Mad Dogs in Trieste,* was published by Black Sparrow Press.

Florian Vetsch: Poet, author, translator, born in 1960 at Buchs in the Rhine Valley. Currently living in St. Gallen, Switzerland, with his wife, the gallery owner Susanna Kulli. Publications include *Desultory Correspondence*, *An Interview with Paul Bowles on Gertrude Stein*, translations of Paul Bowles' *Next To Nothing* and Ira Cohen's *Brief an Kaliban & Andere Gedichte* and *Where The Heart Lies*. He edited the poetry anthology, *Warenmuster* (with Alexandra Stäheli), the Ginsberg Memorial Edition of Der Sanitäter NR. 9/02, and the anthology of correspondence, *Tangier Telegrams*. His *Tangier Suite* (with Peter Eigenmann) is available on CD. He is currently working with J. N. Reilly on the English translation of a collection of his poetry entitled *The Firewell.*

Robert La Vigne: Artist. A painter, illustrator, theatrical designer and much more. His paintings have been widely exhibited. Public collections showing his paintings include the Joseph H. Hirschhorn Museum and Sculpture Garden of the Smithsonian Institution, the Reider Wennesland Collection, Katedralskol, Norway, the Achenbach Collection, California Palace of the Legion of Honor, Robert Lowell Collection, University of Texas, The Oakland

Museum, California, the La Vinge Collection, Libraries of Columbia University, New York, Cheney Cowles Memorial Museum, Spokane, Washington, Mount Holyoke College, Massachusetts, and the San Jose Museum of Art, California. He has created theatrical designs for plays by Beckett, Ionesco, Genet, Chekov, Blau, etc., and won two Obies for Best Design, for Shakespeare's *A Midsummer Night's Dream* and Robert Lowell's *Endicott and the Red Cross*. He has illustrated books by Jack Kerouac, Philip Lamantia, Lew Welch, John Weiners, Philip Whalen, Charles Olson and Allen Ginsberg.

Simon Vinkenoog: Poet, author, translator, born in Amsterdam in 1928. Spent the war years under German occupation, his Jewish friends vanishing into concentration camps. In 1948 he departed for Paris where he modelled for the sculpture class of Ossip Zadkine and the painting class of Fernand Léger. From May 1946 to December 1956, he was the special requests Documents Officer at Unesco. Back in the Netherlands he edited the weekly *Haagse Post* and various other publications. He was a participant in the legendary International Poetry Reading at the Albert Hall in London with Corso and Ginsberg, organised the first Poetry Evening at the Carré Theatre, Amsterdam, collaborated with One World Poetry, Amsterdam, and Poetry International, Rotterdam. He has read his poetry throughout the world, translated Antonin Artaud, Ezra Pound, André Michaux, Timothy Leary, Huxley's *Doors of Perception* and *Heaven and Hell*, the poetry of Allen Ginsberg, his friend since 1957, and other poets. He has been involved with hundreds of titles including *Liefde*, *Weergaloos*, *Tegen de wet*, *De andere wereld* and *Herem ntijd* which is a selection of chronicles from the magazine BRES, of which he has been an editor since 1966. Recent collections of his poetry include *Louter genieten*, with drawings and essays (Kempem Pers, Findhoven, 1993), *Het hoogste Woord* (Holmsterland, Groningen, 1996), and *Vreugdevuur* (Passage Publishers, Groningen, 1998).

Philip Whalen: Poet, born in Portland, Oregon in 1923. After serving with the US Army Air Corps during the second World War, he returned to the Pacific Northwest to attend Reed College where he met fellow students Lew Welch and Gary Snyder. He eventually moved to the San Francisco Bay Area and in the 1950s met Allen Ginsberg, Jack Kerouac and other figures of the San Francisco renaissance. On October 6th 1955, he was a participant in the historical Six Gallery reading where he read with Kerouac, Ginsberg, Snyder, Lamantia and Michael McClure. His poetry appeared in the *Evergreen Review* as well as other journals of the period. He is the author of numerous books of poetry including *Like I Say* and *Memoirs of an Interglacial Age* which, along with other early books, were collected in *On Bear's Head*. He is also the author of two novels, *You Didn't Even Try* and *Imaginary Speeches for a Brazen Head*. More recent books include *The Kindness of Strangers*, *Severance Pay*, *Scenes of Life at the Capital*, *Canoeing up Cabarga Creek* and *Some of These Days*. His growing interest in Zen Buddhism matured during extended visits to Kyoto, Japan, and in 1972 he moved to the San Francisco Zen Centre. The following year he was ordained Unsui (Zen Buddhist monk). He was an abbot and resident teacher at the Hartford Street Zen Centre in San Francisco. *Overtime, Selected Poems*, was published by Viking Penguin. He died in June 2002.

Jordan Zinovich: Poet, author, playwright. He grew up in the Canadian Rocky Mountain Trench. Since then he has lived among the Chiewyan, Haida, Gitsan, Kwa Kwa, Slavey and Dogrib Indians, spent visionary time with the Yaqui in Mexico, cohabitated with witches in the Balearic Islands, learned Greek from the Sphakiots in Crete, and hitchhiked overland to India, Dharamsala and Kathmandu. In 1981 he moved to New York City where he currently resides with his wife. He spends his creative time commuting between NYC, the Pacific Northwest, Amsterdam and Guinea, West Africa. His books include *The Prospector: North of Sixty* (Lone Pine, Edmonton, 1989), *Battling the Bay* (Lone Pine, Edmonton, 1992), *semiotext(e) CANADAs* (semiotext(e)/Marginal Editions, New York, 1994), *Gabriel Dumont in Paris: a Novel History* (University of Alberta Press, Edmonton, 1999) and *Cobweb Walking* (Artichoke Yink Press & ALLey Publications, New York, 2000).

Nina Zivancevic: Poet, born and raised in Yugoslavia, she moved to the U. S. A. in the eighties and started writing poetry in English. She has ten books of poetry published and has won three major awards, one of them the National Poetry Award in Yugoslavia for her first collection entitled, *Poems*. She has had three books of fiction published in the US and France, and in Yugoslavia where her first novel, *Vendors of Dreams*, has been released. Cool Grove Press has lately published her *Selected Poems*.

*

Many thanks to everyone associated with *Shamanic Warriors Now Poets* over the long four years it has taken to publish. In particular to Lawrence Ferlinghetti who came on board at the beginning of the journey, when I was close to abandoning the project, inspiring me to persevere, and to Kavichandran Alexander at *Water Lily Acoustics* for the magic number of Jon Hassell who brought me together with Ira Cohen, Terry Riley and Mati Klarwein for whom I had been searching. At that point I was happy with the anthology, but Ira Cohen and I got talking, our friendship grew, the anthology grew into the unique collection it is, and it was only natural that he became my co-editor.
Thanks also goes to Michael Rothenberg for spreading the word with the West Coast poets; James Grauerholz for permission to include work by William S. Burroughs and Brion Gysin; Michael McClure for permission to include poems from *Rainmaker*, published by *New Directions*; Patti Smith for her obituary on Gregory Corso which first appeared in the *Village Voice*; the translators Samuel Grolmes and Yumiko Tsumura; Frank Bröker and Axel Monte for their feature on *Shamanic*… in *Härter Magazine* (Germany); New Directions Publishing, New York, for permission to include *Hidden Door*, *Through The Looking Glass*, *Sailing Thru the Straits of Demos* and *Adieu Á Charlot* by Lawrence Ferlinghetti which respectively appear in *Starting From San Francisco*, *The Secret Meaning of Things*, *A Coney Island of the Mind* and *Wild Dreams of A New Beginning*; Paul O'Connor at *Judo Digital Graphic Design*, Co. Sligo, Eire, for his photograph of the planting of Joseph Beuys' 7000 Oaks; Charlie Tait at *The Bath Press*, Glasgow, and Eleanor Jackson at *The Partnership*, Glasgow, for their patience and help in seeing *Shamanic*… through to publication; and to Gerard Houghton at the *Institute of Ecotechnics*, London, Cynthia Broan at the *Cynthia Broan Gallery*, New York, Chilli and Kathleen at the *October Gallery*, London, Hetty MacLise, Dr. Phil, Edwin Pouncey, Chris Salewicz, Phyllis Segura and Jason Weiss.
Most of all my gratitude and thanks to Lucky Reilly whose paws are all through the text, Henry Reilly who supplied the Huidobro quote and helped proof the text, John Reilly and Claire Breslin for being there, to my father, John Reilly, for his unstinting faith, loyalty and help, and to Ann for everything, for ever..

J. N. Reilly

October 21st, 2003.

The text was typeset by J. N. Reilly.
The illustrations and text were prepared by
The Partnership Publishing Solutions Ltd,
and printed on acid free paper and bound by
The Bath Press, Gt. Britain.